BRITISH
LEYLAND
MINIS

BRITISH LEYLAND
MINIS

Maintenance
Tuning and
Modification

THIRD EDITION

DAVID MARSHALL
AND
IAN FRASER

First published as *BMC Minis* May 1965
Reprinted August 1965
Revised Edition April 1968
Third Edition as *British Leyland Minis* September 1973
Reprinted November 1976

© DAVID MARSHALL
and IAN FRAZER
1965, 1968, 1973 and 1976

ISBN 0 85429 156 3

A FOULIS Motoring Book
published by
Haynes Publishing Group
Sparkford, Yeovil, Somerset BA22 7JJ
England

CONTENTS

v

APPENDICES

LIST OF PLATES

ACKNOWLEDGEMENTS

The Authors are grateful to the British Leyland Motor Corporation for their assistance and for permission to publish information and line illustrations from their official publications. Their thanks are also due to the following companies for assistance:

Champion Spark Plug Company.

Dunlop Rubber Company.

Ferodo Ltd.

Joseph Lucas Ltd.

CHAPTER 1

A SHORT HISTORY OF THE MINI

When the Mini was first introduced to the public at the 1959 Motor
Show, few people would have dreamed that production figures would
have topped the million mark by February 1965, two million by June of
1969 and three million by October 1972.

After a hesitant start, the sales figures rose rapidly when it became
apparent that apart from the Mini's practical virtues of roominess,
economy and safety, it was great fun to drive. Its transverse engine,
front-wheel-drive layout together with all-independent rubber suspension
endowed it with a degree of roadholding no other family saloon could
match.

The power unit was derived from the 948cc B M C A-type engine
as fitted to the Austin A35 and Morris Minor 1000 with the capacity
reduced to 848cc by shortening the stroke from 76mm to 68·2mm. Drive
was taken from the clutch, mounted back-to-front on an extended
crankshaft, via transfer gears, to the gearbox housed in a cast aluminium
sump. The four-speed gearbox had constant-load synchromesh on 2nd,
3rd and top gear but this system proved rather ineffective and later
models were fitted with the much more satisfactory baulk-ring type
synchromesh now in use.

An automatic gearbox became available as an optional extra and
this, like the Mini, incorporated many unusual features. It was controlled
through a floor-mounted lever moving in a simple fore-and-aft gate. One
position of the lever giving fully automatic operation, as with a normal
automatic gearbox, but other positions enabling it to be used as a very
fast-changing, clutchless, four-speed manual gearbox.

On both gearboxes, the differential is contained in a cast-aluminium
housing bolted to the back of the sump and driven by helical gears.
Drive is taken from the differential by universally-jointed shafts. The
Hooke type joints at their inner ends have either needle-roller or
rubber-bushed spiders and at the outer end of the shafts Rzeppa-type
constant-velocity universal joints are used, in which drive is transmitted
through six hardened steel balls running in curved grooves.

The Mini's all-independent suspension was originally sprung on
rubber 'doughnuts'. These, apart from being virtually indestructible, give
a very progressive spring rate which allows for large variations in load
without excessive spring travel. In 1964, the suspension of all the Minis,
except on vans and estate cars, was changed to the hydrolastic system

1

developed for the B M C 1100 series. The hydrolastic suspension units, which are interconnected front to rear, simply replace the rubber springs used on earlier models. With this system the ride is improved by the elimination of pitching which can be a problem with short-wheelbase cars. However it is debatable whether the extra cost of the hydrolastic system is really worthwhile on a vehicle as small as the Mini and British Leyland have since reverted to the cheaper 'dry' suspension on all their Mini models.

Although the Mini was originally introduced as the 'Morris Mini Minor', it was soon joined by an Austin version called, for a brief period, the 'Austin Seven'. It was not long, however, before both cars became universally known, simply, as a 'Mini' and the name stuck. It became its official title when in 1969 the Austin and Morris tags were dropped.

In 1960, a 5 cwt van appeared, with a wheelbase four inches longer than the saloon, and from this, later the same year, a miniature 'Estate' car was evolved as the 'Austin Countryman' and 'Morris Traveller'.

A year later, in 1961, a rather cosy little two-seater body appeared with an extra large rear window, an open 'pick-up' rear and drop-down tailboard; and at the same time two more variations on the basic saloon theme bearing 'Wolseley' and 'Riley' badges on their dummy radiator grilles. On both these models the luggage space was increased by extending the boot, though the wheelbase remained the same, and each carried more elaborate instrumentation and was generally more lavishly trimmed; both were given the 998cc engine and better brakes in 1963. Further refinements during their production run eventually made them rather desirable little cars, the choice being mainly a question of 'Marque' loyalty, though the Riley always carried a slightly higher price-tag.

Also in 1963, came the Mini 'Moke', an agricultural-cum-military type open model of somewhat austere design which nevertheless has its devotees.

The engine of the Mini is very amenable to tuning and it was not long before the racing fraternity and tuning specialists began to modify it. Racing success at first was quite good, the excellent handling qualities making up for the small engine size. It was obvious however that there was a large demand for a sporting version of the cars and so in 1961 the Mini-Cooper was introduced. This car was developed by B M C in conjunction with the Cooper Car Company of Surbiton, whose racing cars at that time were achieving considerable success. John Cooper and his colleagues gained much experience when racing B M C A-type engines in Formula Junior racing cars. Many of the lessons learned by them have been incorporated in the engine of the Mini-Cooper.

The first Mini-Cooper differed from the original Mini in several ways. Its engine had a longer stroke and fractionally smaller bore which together resulted in a capacity of 997cc. Twin carburetters were fitted, also a special cylinder head and camshaft; disc front brakes and many other improvements were added in the interests of reliability. The competition successes of the Mini-Cooper are numerous, especially in the fields of rallies and saloon car racing. Many improvements have been made to the Mini-Cooper since its inception, these culminating in the 'S' types. The engines of the 'S' type Coopers were developed from the 1100cc B M C Formula Junior racing engine, and were produced in three sizes, 970cc, 1071cc and 1275cc; all had identical bore size, much bigger than the normal Mini-Cooper, but the stroke was altered to vary the capacity.

Apart from having bigger bores and short strokes, the 'S' engines incorporated many other features which enabled them to produce high power outputs reliably.

The crankshafts were especially strong, 2in. diameter main bearings were fitted and a special cylinder head with larger valves and two extra retaining studs was fitted.

The cars were fitted with disc front brakes of an improved type and vacuum servo assistance was provided as standard fitment, as were special wheels and braced-tread tyres.

The 'S' type Coopers have been extremely successful in all branches of motoring sport. Probably the best-known achievements have been in the field of tough international rallying in which the B M C works teams have scored an enviable record of success so ably described by Peter Browning in his book *The Works Minis*.

Apart from those modifications already mentioned, many other detail changes have been made to the Mini's specification. Among these are the improvements to the interior trim, heating arrangements and braking system.

In September 1967, further changes were made and for the first time the exterior appearance of the car was slightly altered. The 998cc single carburetter engine, first used in the Mk II Riley Elfs and Wolseley Hornets, was fitted to the de-luxe 'Minis' while retaining the 850cc engine for the basic models. The revised front grille and tail-lights, together with a larger rear window, distinguish these Mk II Minis from the earlier cars but all the best features of the design remain.

The Wolseley Hornet and Riley Elf were phased out with the introduction in October 1969 of the Mini Clubman, a new looking, square-fronted Mini with fresh-air ventilation and further improved trim. An estate version of the Clubman was also produced, using the same 998cc single-carburetter engine and drum brakes. At the same time a sporting version was introduced offering rather less performance than the Cooper S but somewhat cheaper. This car has the Clubman body with the single carburetter 1275cc engine from the Austin 1300 and the large disc brakes from the Cooper S and is proving to be a very popular model.

The early Minis had many small faults most of which have been eliminated in the current models but even so any Mini, if properly maintained and cared for, can provide enjoyable and economical, if somewhat basic, transport. Much of the fun to be had from driving a Mini stems from its roadholding capabilities. It can be driven round corners at much higher speeds than most other cars in complete safety and even when a bend is entered too fast, taking one's foot off the accelerator will save the situation. This is useful as it is a natural reaction, especially for the novice. Taking the power off in the middle of a bend reduces the degree of understeer and the car tightens its line round the corner. Many people feel, and rightly so, that a car as safe as a Mini could easily accept greater power and, as the engine can well be tuned for greater output, have carried out various modifications to achieve this. A lot of conversion kits, bolt-on accessories and many special parts are available for all the Minis and Coopers, in fact some firms have virtually built up an accessory business round the Mini, so great is the demand.

The Authors have been intimately involved with the Mini since its inception. Their experience, built up over more than 12 years involvement, covers much private motoring in Minis of all types, tuning both privately and commercially, the building, development and racing of their own Minis and years of commercial servicing, repair and overhaul of customers' Minis.

They have done their best to separate their special knowledge and experience in this book so as to make it useful to two distinct classes of reader. On the one hand, in the early chapters they have set out to make routine servicing and overhaul as manageable and painless as possible to the average practical owner. There has been no holding back on trade secrets; the reader is shown the short cuts and is warned of dangers and difficulties as far as possible. It is hoped that readers may also benefit from the Authors' knowledge of what is most likely to be a source of trouble.

The latter half of the book, on the other hand, is unashamedly devoted to those who for fun on the road or serious saloon-car racing want their Mini to go. Here too there has been no holding back and the tuning and modification chapters have been completely rewritten for this edition to bring them up to date.

CHAPTER 2

ROUTINE MAINTENANCE

With the improvements in lubricants, design and materials used in modern motor cars, British Leyland, in line with most other manufacturers, have reviewed their servicing recommendations and now suggest an optional inspection check at 3,000 miles with a change of oil at 6,000. If however, a car is either continuously driven hard or is constantly used for short stop/start journeys, then the Authors consider it well worth while carrying out oil and filter changes at the 3,000 mile service; this is essential with the automatic transmission models.

The detailed maintenance instructions, as recommended by the manufacturers, are given in Appendix V. The following notes have been compiled to assist in implementing those instructions.

LUBRICATION

The following points should be given 3–4 strokes with a grease gun filled with Castrolease LM or equivalent (See Appendix VIII) but before attempting to grease them, the car should be jacked up and any mud removed from the nipples. If no grease can be forced in it may be that the joint already contains sufficient, but it is wise to check that the nipple is not blocked with rust or dirt.

Steering swivels
Grease nipples are fitted to the upper and lower steering swivel knuckles (see fig. 2:1) on each front wheel.

Front suspension arm pivots
A nipple is situated at the inner end of each arm.

Rear radius arm pivot
The lubricating nipples are situated just ahead of each rear wheel, and on some models are covered by large rubber plugs.

A grease gun should be applied until a small quantity exudes from the inner bush.

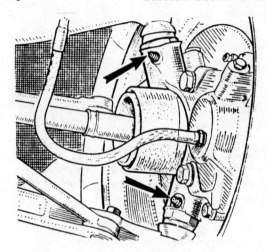

Fig. 2:1. The arrow shows the grease nipples for the top and bottom steering swivel knuckles.

The handbrake cable

Guide channels, situated in the centre of the car at the end of the exhaust pipe tunnel and, on the early models, the cable guide tube sectors, mounted on the underside of the rear radius-arm pivot points, should be greased liberally. On later models, the guide tube sectors have been replaced by pressed steel swivels, the pivot point of these should be lubricated with engine oil.

Water pump

During normal service, the water pump will require little or no lubrication; since over-lubrication can easily damage the carbon sealing ring, many pumps are no longer fitted with a greasing point. Lubrication is effected by removing, when fitted, the slot-headed plug from the pump casing just behind the pulley and inserting a very little grease (LM or equivalent).

Generator bearing lubrication

One or two drops of SAE 20 grade oil should be inserted into the lubrication hole in the centre of the rear bearing plate of the generator. This must be done sparingly and is usually only necessary at about 9,000 mile intervals.

Distributor lubrication

The lubrication of the distributor is important since, if this is neglected, corrosive moisture from the crankcase can rust up the cam spindle when it usually remains stuck in the fully advanced position causing a baffling occurrence of pinking. It is however, equally important to avoid over lubrication, as oil and grease must not be allowed to reach the contact points. Lubrication therefore must be done very sparingly but at regular intervals.

Remove the rotor arm and add a few drops of clean engine oil to the cam bearing and advance mechanism. This should be dropped through the gap around the cam spindle (see fig. 2:2). At the same time the cam lobes and contact-breaker pivot point may be lightly smeared with grease.

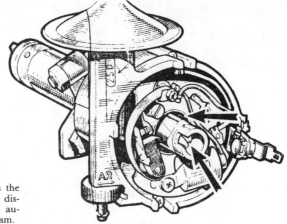

Fig. 2:2. The arrow shows the lubrication points for the distributor cam bearing and automatic advance mechanism.

Speedometer cable lubrication

Disconnect the cable from the speedometer head and withdraw the cable from the outer casing. Lubricate this cable sparingly with light grease, taking care not to over lubricate as this may damage the speedometer head. Wipe the excess grease from the top six inches of cable and thread it back into its casing until the gearbox end engages and the cable may be pushed home so that the square drive stands out approximately $\frac{3}{8}$in. from the outer casing. Reconnect to the speedometer head, taking care to engage the square drive correctly in the instrument.

Draining the transmission casing

It should be remembered that in a transverse power unit, as fitted to the Mini, the engine oil serves the threefold purpose of lubricating the engine, the gearbox and the final drive gears; in the automatic transmission models it also acts as the transmission fluid and so it must be kept clean by regular oil and filter changes.

The drain plug is on the offside of the transmission casing, towards the front corner. It will be easier to drain the oil if the engine has been run for a short period prior to draining and the oil is warm, as it will flow more freely. The sump holds one gallon of oil (the automatic version will

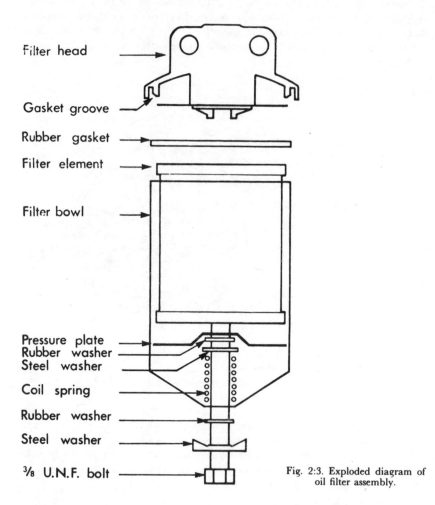

Filter head

Gasket groove

Rubber gasket

Filter element

Filter bowl

Pressure plate
Rubber washer
Steel washer

Coil spring

Rubber washer

Steel washer

⅜ U.N.F. bolt

Fig. 2:3. Exploded diagram of
oil filter assembly.

drain 10 pints) and therefore a shallow receiver should be at hand to contain this amount at least. The oil should be allowed to drain for 10 minutes before replacing the drain plug in the casing. It will be noticed that the drain plug is fitted with a copper sealing washer and contains a permanent magnet to remove particles of iron and steel from the oil, this should be wiped clean before replacing. Ensure that this plug is tightened before filling up with fresh oil.

Replacing the oil filter element

The oil filter, which is of the full-flow type, is contained in a unit on the forward side of the engine just below the generator. On manual transmission models this is mounted vertically but on automatic transmissions it is fitted horizontally and it may be easier to get at if the front grille is removed first. The filter element is removed by unscrewing the central bolt from the filter bowl and carefully lowering the bowl which, when mounted vertically, remains full of oil; a ⁷⁄₁₆in. AF socket, on a short extension, greatly simplifies this task. The old element may then be removed from the bowl which, together with the other components, should be washed thoroughly in petrol, ready for replacing. The rubber gasket between the bowl rim and the filter head should be removed from its seating in the filter head and replaced by a new one. This gasket becomes hard and sometimes adheres to the filter head making it difficult to remove. In this case it should be levered from the seating with a sharp pointed instrument, taking care not to damage the seating.

A new gasket must then be inserted in the groove and a smear of grease on the new rubber will hold it in position while refitting the bowl. The external sealing washer between the bolt head and the bottom of the filter bowl should be checked and if damaged or hardened with age, replaced with a new one. The filter bowl assembly should now be re-assembled as shown in fig. 2:3. The retaining bolt is fitted through the external metal washer and rubber sealing washer, then through the filter bowl, the pressure spring is followed by a steel washer, a rubber sealing washer, which should be in good condition, a pressure plate (the correct way up, see fig. 2:3) and, in some types of assembly, a circlip before the new filter element. Only a paper-element filter should be used for automatic transmission. The Unipart number for the standard oil filter is GFE 103, and GFE 106 for the automatic transmission version.

The filter assembly must now be replaced on the filter head, making sure that the rim of the bowl is correctly seating against the gasket (late model engines have four lugs to assist centralization). The central bolt should be tightened carefully, remembering that the bowl rim seats on a rubber gasket; overtightening can easily damage the filter head. Immediately the engine is started, the filter bowl should be checked for signs of leakage, as a lot of oil can be lost very quickly if the bowl is not seating properly. When a new filter element has been fitted, 9 pints of oil will be needed to fill the engine, since the filter bowl holds approximately a pint. The automatic transmission version needs 10 pints normally and 14 pints to fill a completely empty engine.

Whenever oil is added, the dip stick must be checked (one pint of oil will raise the level from minimum to maximum on the dipstick) and on no account should the engine be run with the oil level above the maximum mark as this may cause leakage through the flywheel-housing oil seal on to the clutch assembly.

Remember to re-check the oil level in the automatic transmission casing after the engine has been run and top up as necessary, some oil will have been displaced into the filter and torque converter.

GENERAL MAINTENANCE

Air cleaner maintenance

The air cleaner element should give satisfactory service up to 12,000 miles, except when the car is used in very dusty conditions. Unless it is thought to be causing trouble, the element need not be disturbed during these periods.

Paper element air filters are now fitted to all B L. Minis, although the filter housings differ from model to model. Twin carburetter models have two elements in a siamesed container, automatic and 1275 G T models have a single larger element. To remove any of these filters, first remove the wing nuts from the top cover, disconnect the breather hose, slacken the retaining clip on the air intake pipe (if fitted) and remove the container from the car. Remove the cover from the container and take out the element. Thoroughly clean the inside of the container, fit a new element and replace the cover, refit the unit to the carburetters.

On early Cooper models, oil-impregnated gauze filters were fitted. These should be removed periodically and the wire gauzes washed in petrol, dried and lightly oiled with SAE 20 grade oil before being replaced.

It should be remembered that replacing an old air cleaner element with a new one may affect the air/fuel mixture and it is worth while checking this, as indicated in the following section.

The positive crankcase ventilation system

The positive crankcase ventilation systems fitted to some models incorporated a valve, mounted on the inlet manifold, which connected the rocker cover breather pipe to the induction system. This valve should only require servicing at 12,000 mile intervals when it should be tested and inspected.

When a PCV system is fitted, the oil filler cap, which acts as an air intake, incorporates an air filter and a new cap should be fitted before testing the control valve. With the engine at normal operating temperature, and running at idle speed, remove the filler cap. If the valve is functioning correctly, the engine speed will increase by approximately 200 rev/min as the cap is removed; the change in speed should be easily noticeable. If no change in speed occurs the valve is not functioning correctly and should be stripped and cleaned.

Remove the spring clip from the top, lift out the cap and dismantle the valve. All the metal components should be cleaned in paraffin or petrol but the rubber diaphragm is best washed in detergent or methylated spirits to avoid damage. Renew any parts which are damaged and reassemble the valve, checking that the metering needle is located in the central guides. When complete, re-check the valve operation by removing the oil filler cap as detailed previously. If the valve still fails to function correctly, check that the rubber hose connections in the system are not blocked or perished and clean or replace as necessary.

On recent models the PCV 'system has been simplified and the valve used previously has been eliminated. The crankcase fumes are now led directly to a connection on the body of the carburetter, here a pipe feeds the vapours into the constant depression area between the choke and the throttle butterfly. This position in the induction system was chosen because the additional hydrocarbon vapour has little effect on the operation of the carburetter. However if the pipe is left off or develops leaks the slow running of the engine will be affected and it is best to inspect the pipe before attempting to tune the carburetter.

Carburetter maintenance

The carburetters fitted to the Mini range, as standard equipment, are all SUs, although two sizes are used. The HS2 fitted to most of the range has a 1¼in. diameter bore while the HS4 fitted to automatic transmission models and 1275 GTs has a 1½in. bore. Both types are normally fitted with a 0·090in. jet but different needles are used. SU carburetters differ from fixed choke carburetters, such as the Zenith and the Solex, by having an automatically expanding choke and single fuel jet to serve the complete throttle range.

The cross sectional area of the choke and the effective size of the jet is controlled by the variation of the depression in the choke, which is dependent on the engine speed and throttle opening. This is achieved (see fig. 2:4) by a cylindrical slide (a) formed on to the bottom of the piston (b) in a 'suction' chamber (c); the 'suction' chamber is connected to the engine side of the carburetter choke (d) by an air passage (e) and hence the pressure difference between the atmospheric side and the manifold side causes the piston to move. When the manifold side is at a lower pressure (when the throttle (f) is open) the piston moves up thus increasing the area of the choke; when both sides are at the same pressure (when the throttle butterfly is shut) the piston drops and reduces the choke area. The effect of the variation in choke area is to maintain a reasonably constant depression above the fuel jet irrespective of the volume of air being drawn into the engine. The effective size of the jet is controlled by a tapered needle (g) attached to the bottom of the choke slide; this moves in the jet, which consists of a simple metal tube, and regulates the volume of fuel mixing with the air as it enters the engine.

Fuel is fed directly from the bottom of the float chamber via a small bore flexible tube. Enrichment of the mixture for starting is achieved by a lever lowering the complete jet assembly so that the jet orifice is level with a thinner portion of the needle, allowing more fuel to be drawn through.

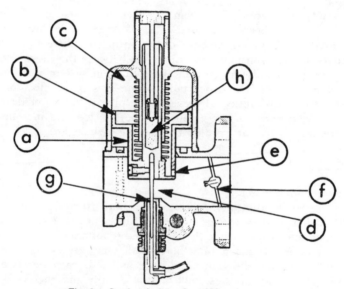

Fig. 2:4. Sectional view of an SU carburetter.

(a) cylindrical slide.   (e) air passage.
(b) piston.   (f) throttle butterfly.
(c) suction chamber.   (g) needle.
(d) carburetter choke.   (h) oil filled damper.

An added refinement on the SU carburetter is an oil filled damper (h), acting on the suction piston. This damper prevents sudden movement of the piston and the otherwise inevitable weakening of the mixture when the throttle is quickly opened.

Carburetter needles

The carburetter needles fitted to the various models are listed in Table 2:I, together with the colour code of the spring which should be used with them. If it is necessary to change the carburetter needles, this should be done as follows: Mark the base of the suction chamber and an adjacent part of the carburetter body to assist in reassembling the parts in their original positions.

Remove the screws securing the suction chamber and carefully remove this chamber complete with piston and spring.

Slacken the needle clamping screw and remove the needle, check the identification number stamped on the thick shoulder. Fit the new needle, checking that the shoulder is flush with the piston base and tighten the clamping screw. Refit the assembly to the carburetter body in its original position. Keep the number away from the clamping screw or it will be defaced.

TABLE 2:I

CARBURETTER NEEDLES AND SPRINGS

Model		Needle		Spring
	Standard	Rich	Weak	Colour
850 Manual	EB	M	GG	Red
850 Automatic	AN	H6	EB	Red
997 Cooper	GZ	AHZ	EB	Red
998 Cooper	GY	M	GG	Blue
998 Wolseley, Riley and Clubman	GX	M	GG	Red
970 Cooper S	AN	H6	EB	Red
1071 Cooper S	H6	3	EB	Red
1275 Cooper S	M	AHZ	EB	Red
1275 GT	DZ	BQ	CF	Red

Carburetter piston damper

To top up the piston damper, unscrew the knurled cap from the top of the suction chamber and pour in enough SAE 20 grade oil just to fill the internal well (fig. 2:5); replace the cap. If there is no oil in the piston damper, the choke will be allowed to open too quickly and the acceleration performance will be poor. However, acceleration will not be improved by using too heavy a grade of oil. The carburetter linkages should be lubricated, when servicing, with the same grade of oil.

Carburetter slow running adjustment

The slow running adjustment is materially affected by the mixture strength which, if satisfactory results are to be obtained, should be checked and if necessary corrected as described in the following section. When servicing the carburetter, remember that bad slow running is not always due to the carburetter settings but may also be due to badly adjusted contact-breaker points, faulty plugs, incorrect valve clearances, faulty valves and springs or exhaust leaks, and these should be checked before making any adjustments to the carburetters. Too fast an idling speed may be caused by an air leak weakening the mixture. This can occur through a faulty manifold gasket, a loose carburetter or, on engines fitted with 'positive crankcase ventilation', by the oil filler cap on the rocker cover being left off.

Before making adjustments to the carburetter, be sure that the engine has reached normal running temperature.

To adjust the slow running, the throttle adjusting screw is turned clockwise to give a fast idling speed, then unscrewed a fraction of a turn at a time until the desired slow running has been achieved; check that

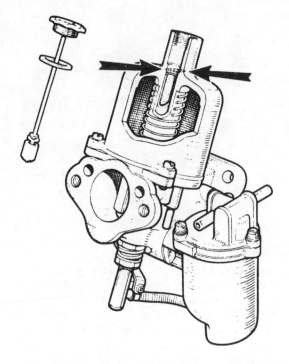

Fig. 2:5. Correct level of oil in carburetter piston damper.

the 'fast idle' adjustment screw, which works in conjunction with the 'choke' control, is clear of its actuating cam by approximately $\frac{1}{16}$in.

When adjusting the carburetter, on an engine with automatic transmission, be sure to engage 'N' and to set the handbrake; once the engine is warm and preferably with the help of a tachometer, set the slow running to 650 rev/min and the fast idle, with the 'choke' control pulled out about $\frac{1}{4}$in. (far enough to operate the fast idle cam but not the jet linkage), to 1,050 rev/min.

Carburetter jet adjustment

Uneven running of the engine, at idling speed, may indicate a faulty mixture. An uneven beat with an irregular type of misfire and colourless exhaust gas indicates a weak mixture. Uneven firing of the rhythmical or regular type, coupled with a blackish exhaust gas is due to too rich a mixture. Before attempting to correct the mixture adjustment, the air filter should be inspected and a new one fitted if necessary, as a dirty,

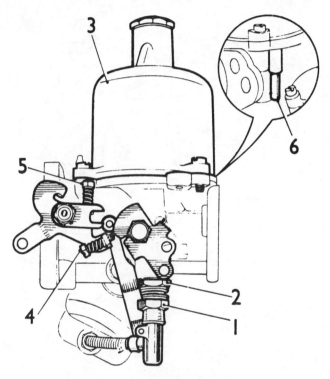

Fig. 2:6. The HS2 SU carburetter.

1. jet adjusting nut.   4. fast-idle adjusting screw.
2. jet locking nut.   5. throttle adjusting screw.
3. suction chamber.   6. piston lifting pin.

blocked filter will upset the mixture by restricting the air-flow. Before adjusting the jet position, the engine should be run until it attains a normal running temperature. The throttle stop adjusting screw should then be turned clockwise to set the throttle to a fast idling speed (approx. 1,000 rev/min).

With the engine running and according to the symptoms noted, screw the jet adjusting nut, only one 'flat' of the hexagon at a time, either upwards for weakening or downwards for enriching, so that a

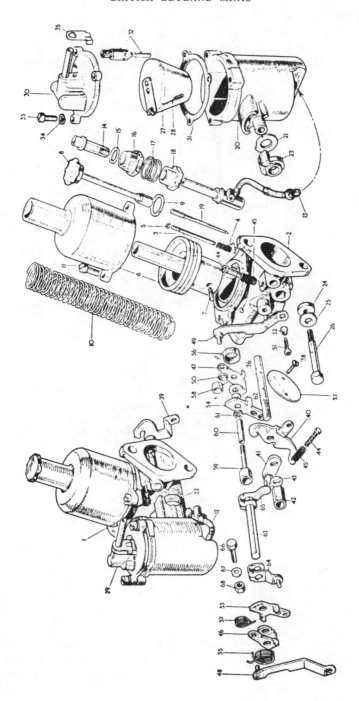

1. Carburetter body (left).
2. Carburetter body (right).
3. Piston lifting pin.
4. Spring.
5. Circlip.
6. Piston chamber assembly.
7. Screw.
8. Cap and damper assembly.
9. Fibre washer.
10. Piston spring.
11. Screw.
12. Jet assembly (left carburetter).
13. Jet assembly (right carburetter).
14. Bearing.
15. Washer.
16. Screw.
17. Spring.
18. Screw.
19. Needle.
20. Float-chamber.
21. Support washer.
22. Rubber grommet (left carburetter).
23. Rubber grommet (right carburetter).

24. Washer (rubber).
25. Washer (steel).
26. Bolt.
27. Float assembly.
28. Lever pin.
29. Float-chamber lid (left carburetter).
30. Float-chamber lid (right carburetter).
31. Washer.
32. Needle and seat assembly.
33. Screw.
34. Spring washer.
35. Baffle plate.
36. Throttle spring.
37. Throttle disc.
38. Screw.
39. Throttle return lever (left carburetter).
40. Throttle return lever (right carburetter).
41. Lost motion lever.
42. Nut.
43. Tab washer.
44. Throttle screw stop.
45. Spring.
46. Pick-up lever (left carburetter).

47. Pick-up lever (right carburetter).
48. Link (left carburetter).
49. Link (right carburetter).
50. Washer.
51. Screw.
52. Bush.
53. Cam lever (left carburetter).
54. Cam lever (right carburetter).
55. Pick-up lever spring (left carburetter).
56. Pick-up lever spring (right carburetter).
57. Cam lever spring (left carburetter).
58. Cam lever spring (right carburetter).
59. Bolt.
60. Tube.
61. Spring washer.
62. Distance washer.
63. Jet rod.
64. Lever and pin assembly (left carburetter).
65. Lever and pin assembly (right carburetter).
66. Bolt.
67. Washer.
68. Nut.

Fig. 2:7. Exploded diagram of Twin SU carburetters.

mixture strength is obtained which will give the best running speed for this particular throttle opening, taking care that the jet head is in firm contact with the adjusting nut the whole time. In no circumstances should the jet locking nut be slackened as this will cause misalignment of the jet, resulting in the jamming of the piston.

To complete the fine adjustment of the mixture: with the engine still running, raise the carburetter piston about $\frac{1}{16}$ in. by means of the piston lifting button to be found under the suction chamber. If the engine tends (1) to stall, the mixture is too weak, (2) to remain at the same speed, the mixture is only just too weak, (3) to speed up slightly when raised $\frac{1}{16}$ in. but also to slow down if raised further, the mixture is correct, (4) to speed up and continue to increase in speed if the piston is raised further, the mixture is too rich. The adjusting nut is therefore turned fractionally in the appropriate direction until the correct mixture is obtained. After adjustment, the throttle stop screw should be reset to give the correct idling speed.

Synchronization of twin SU carburetters

First remove the air cleaner assembly from the mouths of the carburetters. Before attempting to adjust the mixture, the interconnecting linkage between the carburetters must be adjusted so that both throttles are operating in the same position. To do this, slacken the actuating arms on the throttle spindles; close both throttles fully by unscrewing the throttle stop screws, then re-open each throttle slightly by turning each throttle-stop screw again one complete turn. Remove the suction chambers and pistons from both carburetters. Then screw the jet-adjusting nuts up until both jets are nearly at the top of their adjustment and then check inside the body of the carburetter that the top of each jet is in exactly the same position relative to the jet housing. Replace the pistons and suction chamber assemblies, check the oil level in the piston dampers and check that both pistons operate freely. Then turn each jet adjusting nut down two complete turns. Both jets must be moved the same amount.

Start the engine and, by turning each throttle adjusting screw the same amount, set the idling speed to approximately 1,000 rev/min. If the engine is cold it may be necessary to operate the mixture control ('choke') in order to start the engine but once the engine is warm this should be released and both jets returned to contact the adjusting nuts. Listen to the hiss of air in the intakes through a piece of flexible tubing and by fine adjustment of the throttle screws obtain the same intensity of noise from each intake. This will ensure that the throttles are synchronized. Retighten the actuating arms on to the throttle spindles and refit the air cleaner assembly. The mixture in the two carburetters may now be adjusted. Using the piston lifting button (see previous section), raise the piston of one carburetter about $\frac{1}{16}$ in. but no more. This may cause the engine to misfire or even stall. The same should be found to occur with the other carburetter when its piston is lifted. Returning to the first carburetter, screw the jet nut down about half a turn and repeat the piston lifting technique as above, this time the engine may not misfire. (See previous section for details.) The other carburetter jet is adjusted the same amount and tested likewise.

The jets on both carburetters should be adjusted as for single carburetters, until lifting the piston on either of them $\frac{1}{16}$in. results in a slight increase in engine speed. Final adjustment is by fractional movement of the jet-adjusting nuts until the same increase in engine speed is achieved from each carburetter when tested. Always adjust each jet in turn or the original balance may be lost and the procedure must be started again. After adjustment of the mixture, the throttle adjusting screws should be returned to the correct position for idling.

Adjustment of valve rocker clearances

To maintain the best performance from an engine, it is important that the valve clearances are regularly checked and corrected where necessary. Remove the two rocker-cover securing nuts and the rocker cover; be careful not to lose the two cupped steel washers and their rubber seals which may drop off if the cover is turned over. It is always preferable to fit a new cork gasket when the rocker cover is disturbed from its seating for any reason so get one if possible before starting the job. If no new gasket is available, great care must be taken not to damage the original one as correct seating is essential to prevent oil leakage. The clearance gap between the rocker arms and the end of the valve stems may now be measured with a feeler gauge. Checking, and adjustment where necessary, must be carried out with the tappet on the back of the cam, i.e. with maximum clearance between rocker and valve stem. The correct position for checking the clearance is easily found by observing the movement of other valves whose fully open position coincides with the closed position of the valve to be checked and this may be done in pairs. Proceed as follows:

With the ignition switched off, engage top gear and release the hand-brake. Pull the car forwards to turn the engine; it will move more easily if the spark plugs are taken out but this is not really necessary. Turn the engine, by this means, until valves 1 and 3 (numbering from 1 at the radiator end) have moved down into the fully open position when valves 6 and 8 will be right for checking and adjusting if necessary. Pull the car forward again and when valves 2 and 5 are fully open, check 4 and 7. Move it again to open 6 and 8 and check numbers 1 and 3. Pull forward once more and when 4 and 7 go down, valves 2 and 5 may be checked. The correct rocker clearance should be 0·012in. when the engine is cold or 0·011in. when hot. Set the Cooper S to 0·015in. (cold) for better performance. To adjust the clearance slacken the $\frac{7}{16}$in. AF lock-nut and rotate the slot-headed screw clockwise to reduce the clearance and anti-clockwise to increase it. The clearance is correct when very slight resistance is felt on the feeler gauge as it is withdrawn. When the correct clearance has been obtained, tighten the lock-nut, holding the adjusting screw with a screwdriver to prevent further movement. Re-check the clearance.

When fitting the new cork gasket to the rocker cover, wipe the rim of the cover free from oil and stick the new gasket on to the cover with a slight smear of adhesive such as clear Bostik. This helps to maintain its correct alignment and prolong its life.

When carrying out adjustments on an engine with automatic transmission, it is not possible to turn the engine by moving the car even when a 'drive' position is selected. In these circumstances the engine may either be turned by careful use of the starter motor (use the solenoid button and avoid turning on the ignition) or else by removing the spark plugs and turning the engine by hand with the fan belt.

Adjustment of plugs and points

To maintain the optimum performance and ease of starting, it is essential that the ignition system is kept in good condition. Provided that the carburetter is set correctly, misfiring at idling speeds or poor starting is probably due to dirty or incorrectly adjusted spark plugs or contact-breaker points.

The plugs normally fitted to the 850 and 998 engines are $\frac{3}{4}$in. reach, 14mm Champion N5 or equivalent; those fitted to the 'S' type Coopers are the extended nose type, Champion N9Y or equivalent. The gap between the electrodes should be set to 0·025in. and checked with a feeler gauge.

While the plugs are removed for adjustment, have a look at the electrodes; the appearance of these often gives an indication of the condition of the engine and the petrol/air mixture provided by the carburetter. (See plate I).

Under normal running conditions, the end of the plug and insulator may range in colour from brown to grey with a fine powdery deposit. Very white or yellow powdery deposits with heavy build-up are usually due to prolonged periods of constant speed and whilst not harmful it should be cleaned off. If the plugs have a light brown to white powdery deposit, the petrol/air mixture may be slightly weak and should be checked as previously described (page 15). Plugs having a white, burned appearance and badly eroded electrodes are overheating; this may be due to faulty ignition timing, a leak in the inlet manifold or sustained high speeds. When the electrodes are coloured dark grey or black, but dry, the petrol/air mixture is probably too rich and combustion is incomplete. Excessive use of the choke will also result in this appearance.

If the black deposits are wet and very thick, the engine is burning oil. This may get into the combustion chamber via worn valve guides, piston rings or cylinder bores. In most cases the only cure will be an engine overhaul. Plug cleaning is easily carried out at a garage equipped with an air-blast plug service unit but careful use of a wire brush and a sharp-pointed file is almost as effective. The electrodes should be cleaned carefully and the gap set by bending the side electrode and checked with a suitable feeler gauge. If either electrode is badly eroded, the plugs should be discarded and new ones fitted.

Servicing the distributor

During servicing, the contact-breaker points should be inspected and the gap between them checked as follows:

With the ignition turned off, engage top gear and release the handbrake, remove the distributor cap and, by gently rocking the car forward, turn the engine until the contacts are fully opened. Inspect the contacts for signs of burning, blackening or pitting.

If they are clean and flat, the gap should be checked with a 0·015in. feeler gauge which should be a sliding fit. If the points are blackened, they may be cleaned with a fine carborundum stone or fine emery cloth. After removing any dust, check the gap as above. If the fixed contact is pitted, the moving one will have a build-up or 'pip' which should be carefully flattened with a carborundum stone.

When the distributor requires servicing, it is often more convenient to remove it from the engine, this may be simply achieved as follows: Disconnect the vacuum pipe (if fitted) from the unit and remove the l t spade connector from the side of the distributor body. Mark the clamp and the base of the distributor, so that it may be replaced in exactly the same position, then slacken off the clamping bolt and withdraw the distributor from the block. The clamp assembly must be left bolted to the engine. The contacts may now be easily removed for servicing.

Remove the rotor arm from the top of the spindle; if very tight it may be necessary to use a small screwdriver to lever it off. If two-piece contacts are fitted, remove the nut and washer from the moving-contact anchor pin and withdraw the insulating nylon bush from the condenser and low-tension lead connectors, noting the order in which they are fitted. Lift the moving contact from the anchor pin and remove the large insulating washers from both the anchor pin and the pivot pin. Remove the screw, spring and flat washers securing the fixed-contact plate and remove the plate. If Quikafit contacts are fitted, these are simply removed, after disconnecting the l t leads, by withdrawing the one retaining screw. If the contacts are too badly pitted for renovation they should be renewed. Before a new contact set is fitted, the protective coating must be wiped from the contact faces.

The contacts are reassembled by reversing the above instructions.

Place a very small amount of grease on the pivot of the moving contact, but on no account allow any oil or grease to get on to the contact faces. Care must be taken to replace the insulating bush, washers and wires on

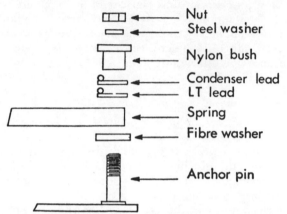

Nut
Steel washer
Nylon bush
Condenser lead
LT lead
Spring
Fibre washer

Anchor pin

Fig. 2:8. Correct order of assembly of contact breaker parts.

the anchor pin in the correct sequence (see fig. 2:8). The terminals from the condenser and the l t connector should contact on the spring of the moving contact but must be insulated from the anchor pin on the arm of the fixed contact by a nylon bush. Incorrect fitting will result in the absence of sparks at the plugs. When the contacts have been assembled,

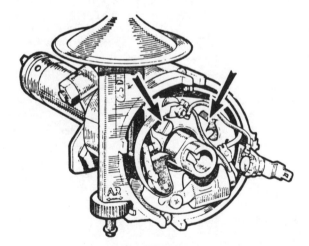

Fig. 2:9. The arrows show the contact plate securing screw and the screwdriver notched adjusting slot.

the gap should be adjusted, with the heel of the moving contact on the peak of the cam. The gap should be 0·015in. and to adjust this, slacken the fixed contact plate securing screw and by inserting a screwdriver in the notched hole at the end of the plate (fig. 2:9) and twisting clockwise to decrease or anti-clockwise to increase, adjust the gap to the correct settings; when correct, tighten the securing screw and re-check. Lightly smear the cam with a small amount of grease or clean oil. Lubricate the cam bearing beneath the rotor arm with a few drops of clean oil and replace the arm. If removed, replace the distributor in its housing on the engine, turning the drive shaft by the rotor arm until the offset driving-key engages correctly in its slot. Turn the body of the distributor to the original position in the clamp and retighten the clamp bolt; wipe the inside and outside of the cap with a clean dry cloth, cleaning between the terminals. Replace the l t lead spade-connection and replace the distributor cap and securing clips.

Timing the ignition

To time the ignition from scratch, proceed as follows:

Remove the distributor unit from the cylinder block. Take off the valve rocker cover and engage top gear; by moving the car forward, turn the engine until the exhaust valve of No. 4 cylinder is just closing and the inlet is just opening. No. 1 piston is now approximately at t d c on its compression stroke. Remove the inspection

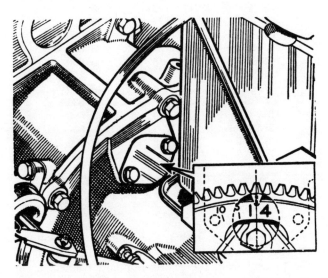

Fig. 2:10. After removing the inspection plate on the clutch cover, the timing marks on the flywheel may be seen with the aid of a mirror.

plate at the top of the clutch housing so that the timing marks on the flywheel may be seen (fig. 2:10) with the aid of a small hand mirror. Move the engine slowly backwards or forwards until the 1/4 mark on the flywheel is exactly in line with the pointer in the inspection hole; No. 1 piston is now accurately at t d c.

Marks on the flywheel indicate t d c, 5 degrees before t d c and 10 degrees before t d c. Turn the engine back from the t d c position until the pointer indicates the correct amount of advance. The correct setting for the various models is given in Table 2:II. Adjust the contact breaker points as described on page 23. Turn the distributor until the rotor points towards the electrode, inside the cap, for No. 1 plug, and then insert the unit into the block, engaging the driving dog lug correctly in the slotted driving spindle. If the gear drive has been removed it must be re-positioned as described in chapter 4, page 111.

Loosely screw in the two setscrews securing the distributor clamp to the block, tighten the clamp pinch-bolt and then tighten the two setscrews, thus ensuring correct alignment.

TABLE 2:II

IGNITION TIMING

Timing—degrees before t d c

Model	Static	Stroboscopic at rev/min
850 (before 14824)	*3½	6 @ 600
850 auto	*3	6 @ 600
850 others	*0	3 @ 600
997 Cooper	*7	9 @ 600
998 Cooper	*5	7 @ 600
998 Wolseley, Riley and Clubman	*5	7 @ 600
970 Cooper S	12	14 @ 600
1071 Cooper S	3	5 @ 600
1275 Cooper S	2	4 @ 600
1275 GT	8	10 @ 600

*When extended nose plugs are used the timing may need retarding by as much as 5° from these figures.

Finally, to set the timing, slacken the clamp pinch-bolt again and rotate the distributor body anti-clockwise until the points are closed. Disconnect the l t lead from the distributor and connect a small 12V lamp, in series, between the lead and the terminal.

Switch on the ignition and rotate the distributor clockwise until the lamp just goes out, indicating that the points are open. Tighten the pinch-bolt on the distributor clamp and finally recheck the timing by turning the engine back before t d c and slowly bringing it forward until the lamp just goes out, then check that the correct setting is indicated by the timing marks on the flywheel. Remove the timing light and reconnect the l t lead and suction advance pipe.

A further fine adjustment of timing is provided on distributors fitted with vacuum advance mechanism, this is a knurled nut situated next to the vacuum advance diaphragm. Turning this nut clockwise retards the ignition timing and turning it anti-clockwise advances it. Graduations are provided on the spindle barrel, each one representing approximately 5 degrees of timing movement and being equal to 55 clicks of the knurled nut. Experimenting with this fine adjustment should allow for finding the best setting for the grade of fuel being used. An alternative, and more accurate method of timing the ignition is using a stroboscopic light with the engine running. The principle of this device is to have a small neon lamp connected in parallel with No. 1 plug; the light is electronically triggered to flash at the precise moment each spark occurs at this plug and, if this light is now directed at a mark on the flywheel which indicates the crank angle required for correct timing, by normal stroboscopic principles the mark on the flywheel will appear stationary. Adjustment of the ignition timing will now allow this mark to be apparently moved until it appears directly beneath the stationary pointer on the clutch cover. This method eliminates errors due to wear in the distributor drive and allows an engine to be accurately timed under working conditions.

Fan belt adjustment
The fan belt tension and condition should be checked during the 6,000 mile service and preferably at regular intervals between services.

As with most modern engines, this transverse unit relies upon the water pump to maintain sufficient circulation to prevent overheating so that, should the fan belt (which of course drives the water pump) break, the engine can only be run for a short time before overheating.

Before adjusting the fan belt, check that it is not badly worn or damaged. An old frayed belt should be discarded as soon as convenient and replaced by a new one.

The belt should be sufficiently tight to prevent slip. This may be checked by turning the fan by hand, it should be difficult, but possible to turn. Check the lateral movement of the belt between the generator and crankshaft pulleys, this should be between ¾in. and 1in. Excess tension should be avoided as this strains the generator and water pump bearings, reducing their life.

To adjust the fan belt, slacken the two generator pivot bolts and the nut on the slotted adjusting strut. Raise the generator bodily until the tension is correct (only gentle leverage should be required to achieve this) and, with the generator held in this position, tighten the bolts and the nut on the adjusting strut.

Removing the fan belt

When removing the fan belt, first slacken the generator pivot bolts as above, push the generator down to the limit of its travel and release the belt from the generator and crankshaft pulleys. There is sufficient clearance between the fan blades and the top forward corner of the radiator cowling to allow the belt to be manoeuvred out from behind each blade of the fan as it is slowly rotated. Remember, however, that a worn-out belt may be quickly removed by cutting it through with a knife or tin snips. The refitting operation is similar to the removal procedure, the belt must be slipped over the fan, one blade at a time, and then over the generator and crankshaft pulleys, the tension finally being set as described in the previous paragraph. Always carry a spare fan belt in the car, it can save a lot of trouble.

Clutch adjustment

As the friction material on the clutch plate wears, the clearance between the clutch thrust race and the thrust ring diminishes and, if this is neglected, clutch slip will result. An adjustment stop is provided on the

Fig. 2:11. Clutch lever return stop, showing position for feeler gauge measurement and adjusting screw.

transmission casing between the clutch lever and the clutch housing to correct this. To check the adjustment, remove the return spring and pull the lever away from the clutch housing until all the free movement is taken up and then check the gap between the stop and the lever with a feeler gauge (fig. 2:11).

On early Minis this gap was set at 0·060in., this was to prevent the clutch pressure-plate from being pushed out too far and fouling the flywheel housing; on later models, a shouldered stop is fitted to the clutch throw-out plunger and may be seen at the end of the clutch housing. The stop is set and locked in position with a large lock-nut during assembly and should not require any alteration during normal servicing. Any adjustment necessary on these models should be carried out at the lever stop screw. In this case the gap between the stop and the lever should be 0·020in., this should be checked with a feeler gauge as above. Adjustment is simply done by slackening the lock-nut on the setscrew and screwing the setscrew in the appropriate direction, finally locking again with the lock-nut.

Brake maintenance

The brakes fitted to all the 850 Minis prior to 1964 were Lockheed drum front and rear having one leading and one trailing shoe, hydraulically actuated. A pressure limiting valve is fitted into the pipe line to the rear brakes so that no more than a pre-set maximum pressure can be applied to them. This reduces the tendency for the rear wheels to lock under heavy braking when considerable weight transfer takes place from the rear wheels to the front.

The Mini Coopers, introduced in 1961, had disc brakes fitted to the front wheels, these have rotating disc units with rigidly mounted calipers. The brakes are applied to the disc by a pair of hydraulic pistons, mounted in the caliper, one each side of the disc and interconnected by internal hydraulic-fluid passages, so that equal pressure is applied to each side simultaneously. When the Mk II Riley and Wolseley models were produced, yet another type of braking system was fitted to the front wheels; on these models, the front brakes have drums but with two leading shoes instead of the original one-leading, one-trailing type; at the same time the lining width was increased slightly to produce, in all, an efficient and satisfactory braking system. This system has since been adopted for all 850 and 998cc models while the disc brakes were continued on the Cooper models with the addition of a brake servo on the 'S' types and the 1275 GT.

The level of the brake fluid in the master-cylinder reservoir should be checked periodically and if necessary topped up to about ¼in. below the filler neck. The need for frequent topping up indicates a leak in the system and a thorough inspection of the brake pipes, master cylinder and wheel cylinders should be carried out at once and replacements made where necessary.

Provided the hydraulic system is functioning correctly, lack of stopping power and the need to push the brake pedal almost to the floor, indicates worn brake linings which should be inspected to ensure that they have not worn dangerously thin.

Front drum brakes—inspection

Set the handbrake and if necessary chock the wheels. Jack up the front of the car and remove the wheels. Take out the Phillips-pattern setscrews holding each drum to the hub; remove the brake drum, it may be necessary to unscrew the brake adjuster two or three flats to prevent the shoes binding on the drum. Light hammering on the outside of the drum will help to free it from the wheel studs.

Remove dust from the mechanism with a brush or an air line and check the lining thickness. If there is not more than 0·015in. above the rivet heads at the thinnest point, the linings should be renewed. If more than this is present, they may be adjusted for further use, bearing in mind the need for replacement in the future, depending on usage.

It will be noticed, on cars with the one-leading/one-trailing-shoe set-up, that the brake shoes do not wear evenly; the leading shoe, which is the lower one on the front brakes, always wears faster. It is sometimes possible to swap the shoes over from top to bottom to even up this wear but this can occasionally lead to 'grabbing' and care should be taken on the first few applications. When possible, and to achieve the most satisfactory braking system, the brake shoes should all be renewed together. While the brake drum is off, remove any dust from the inside and check the contact surface for scores. Badly scored drums should either be renewed or skimmed to a fine finish by an experienced turner.

Check that the square-headed brake adjusters, on the rear of the backplates, move freely; a little penetrating oil may help to free a seized adjuster. The wedges, which are to be found on the inside of the backplates of models having one leading and one trailing-shoe, should be cleaned and lightly greased on their working faces. Note that when adjusting brakes of this type, the wedges should sit squarely on the flats of the adjuster when correctly set. If possible, a brake-adjusting spanner should always be used, this avoids damage to the corners of the adjuster head.

Before replacing the drums, slacken the brake adjustment, on one-leading/one-trailing-shoe brakes, by turning the adjuster anti-clockwise and on two-leading-shoe setups by turning both adjusters in the direction of reverse rotation of the wheel. Replace the brake drum with its two setscrews and replace the road wheel. Pump the brake pedal to centralize the brake shoes in the drum.

Adjustment

With the car still jacked up, turn the road wheel slowly round and take up the brake adjustment until the brake shoes lock the wheel. If the brakes are of the one-leading/one-trailing-shoe type, check, by the feel of the adjuster, that the expanding wedges (described in the previous section) are seating squarely on the 'flats' of the adjuster; there are four 'flats' per revolution and these can normally be felt to click into place. Back-off the adjustment slightly until the wheel just turns freely. A slight high spot on the shoes may be tolerated but no drag.

With two-leading-shoe brakes, the adjustment should be carried out in the same manner but each shoe must be adjusted individually. The adjustment of this type of brake is by means of a cam and no 'flats' can be felt. Only slight movement of the adjuster should be necessary to cover the full range of adjustment.

Front disc brakes—inspection

The amount of friction material remaining on the front brake pads may be quickly checked as follows: Jack up the front of the car and remove the wheels. The friction pads can now be seen through the caliper assembly. Measure the thickness of the friction material on the pads and if this is less than $\frac{3}{32}$ in. (excluding the steel backing plate) new pads should be fitted as soon as possible. The surface of the disc is very quickly damaged if the pads are allowed to wear down to the steel backing plate. A replacement disc will cost far more than a new set of brake pads. Details of brake pad replacement will be found in chapter 3.

Rear brakes

The rear brakes of all the Mini models have one leading and one trailing shoe. Inspection and adjustment of these is as for the one-leading/one-trailing-shoe front brakes (page 28). Complete details for the overhaul of the brakes will be found in chapter 3.

Handbrake adjustment

If the handbrake lever moves more than three notches up the ratchet before the brake comes into operation, or the handbrake will not hold the car on an incline, adjustment is necessary. First check that both rear brakes are adjusted correctly, as detailed on page 28, also check that the handbrake mechanism is functioning correctly. If excessive brake lever travel is still present with correctly adjusted brakes it is permissible to take up the excess travel at the handbrake lever trunnion. Apply the handbrake until the pawl engages with the first notch on the ratchet, adjust the two nuts at the handbrake lever until it is only just possible to rotate the rear wheels by hand; it is important that the wheels offer equal resistance under heavy pressure, to get full braking power. Finally check that both wheels are still free with the handbrake in the 'off' position.

Tyres

As tyre wear is a subject of considerable interest to most Mini owners, the selection of the best tyre for the job is most important. There is now such a large range of special wheels and tyres available for the Mini that the prospective purchaser may be somewhat bewildered.

Tyres manufactured especially for racing are discussed in chapter 9. The tyres available for normal road use can be roughly divided into two main types by their construction, this is either cross ply or radial ply sometimes known as braced tread.

The tyres fitted by the manufacturer are usually cross ply and are quite suitable for normal road use, providing about 12,000 miles of normal motoring and possibly double this figure with very careful use. Tyres of this type are Dunlop D75, Goodyear G8, Firestone F7 and Pirelli Sempione.

Radial ply tyres such as the Dunlop SP series, Goodyear G800 or Pirelli Cinturato, have a textile braced tread and are designed to give better gripping and wear properties; although their initial cost is higher than the cross ply, tread life is generally about 30% greater.

An alternative radial tyre construction has a steel wire braced tread; typical of this construction are Michelin ZX and XAS. These tyres offer exceptionally long tyre life, in the order of 50% greater than cross ply tyres, and have good handling properties. The XAS with its asymmetric tread pattern is produced especially for the fast driver.

Several other specialist tyres are produced for use under rally conditions and on mud, snow and ice. These usually have a large block tread which can give rise to a certain amount of noise when used at speed on the road and their life is likely to be inferior to that of a normal tyre. However it is acceptable to fit them only to the driving wheels and to swap them with the rear wheels during the dry weather and thus extend their tread life.

Tyre care

It is essential that the tyre pressures are checked regularly and adjusted, if necessary, to the pressures recommended if the best tyre mileage and performance is to be obtained. It is also advisable to exchange the front and rear wheels as front tyre wear becomes apparent; this will even-up wear and maintain the handling characteristics of the car. It is always safer to have the better treads on the front wheels of these cars. The treads and side walls should be inspected regularly for cuts and splits or nails and any necessary repairs carried out.

The tyre pressures recommended by the manufacturers are as follows:

Dunlop D75 or equivalent cross ply tyres	Front 24 lb/in^2
	Rear 22 lb/in^2
Dunlop SP or equivalent nylon braced tyre	Front 28 lb/in^2
	Rear 26 lb/in^2
Michelin ZX or XAS wire braced tyre	Front 28 lb/in^2
	Rear 26 lb/in^2

Tyre removal

Note carefully. Tyre removal and refitting must always be carried out over the narrow bead seating, that is the inner rim of standard Mini wheels, both the normal width and wide wheels of reversed rim pattern, and the outer rim of Cooper S wheels; tyres cannot be removed or refitted over the other rim without damaging either the wheel or the tyre.

With tubeless tyres, as normally fitted to these cars, it can be very difficult to break the seal between the tyre beads and the wheel rim and it is therefore advisable to have tyres changed at a garage where equipment is available to do this. If a tyre has to be removed and no special equipment is available, proceed as follows:

The valve core should first be removed to deflate the tyre completely, then, starting at a point diametrically opposite the valve, push the tyre beads on both sides completely into the wellbase of the rim. This is best done by using spoon-shaped levers, insert one between the tyre bead and the rim with the outside of the curved end against the tyre and press the lever towards the tyre; then insert a second lever between the bead and rim with the inside of the curved end next to the tyre and pull the lever away from the tyre. Repeat this at intervals round the tyre until both beads have been freed, this may necessitate several circuits of the tyre. If it is found impossible to move the beads, using tyre levers, lay the wheel flat on the ground and carefully drive the front wheel of the car over the tyre and thus use the car's weight to break the seal. When this has been done, a little soap solution or 'Swarfega' may be applied to the tyre beads and rim to assist in removal. The cover edge is now levered over the wheel rim a little at a time until the bead on one side is completely free. Stand the wheel upright pushing downwards to keep the remaining bead in the wellbase, lever the tyre bead at the top over the rim and push the wheel away from the cover with the other hand.

If tubed tyres are fitted, it is usually much easier to break the seal between the tyre bead and the wheel rim and it should be possible to accomplish it with tyre levers in the manner just described.

Care must be taken not to damage the inner tube while levering the bead over the rim; when one bead is completely free, the inner tube should be withdrawn and the tyre then removed as already described. Replacement of the tyre and tube is the reverse of the above procedure. A little French chalk may be dusted inside the case, before refitting the tube, for lubrication.

Replacing the tyre

The tyre should be refitted using a similar method to that used for removal. Lubricate the tyre beads and the wheel rim as before. A new tyre will probably be marked with a white or coloured spot near the bead, this indicates the lightest position of the tyre and should be fitted on the outside and in line with the valve to assist in maintaining wheel balance.

With the tyre standing upright, insert the narrow rim of the wheel so that the bead edge is in the well base and lever the tyre edge, on the opposite side, over the wheel rim. When the bead has been levered all round this side, and with this bead in the well base, repeat with the other bead. Care must be taken, when fitting tubeless tyres, not to damage the tyre beads as this will result in a poor seal and possible air leakage. The levers should therefore be in good condition.

When inflating a tubeless tyre it is preferable to use a high pressure air pump but it may also be necessary, and if a foot pump is being used it will be, to tighten a rope tourniquet around the periphery of the tyre and so force the beads against the rims to obtain an initial air seal between the tyre beads and the wheel rims before the tyre can be inflated. During initial inflation it is preferable not to fit the valve core but *remember to insert it before finally inflating.*

AUTOMATIC TRANSMISSIONS

While the automatic transmission is functioning correctly there is little routine maintenance required, except for the regular changes of oil and filter element previously described. However, faults do occasionally occur which, if correctly diagnosed, may be corrected fairly easily.

The best way to identify and locate the cause of trouble in the automatic transmission is first to carry out a comprehensive road test, checking the following points:

Engage each of the seven selector positions and make sure that the engine will start only in the neutral position.

Check the engine oil level and top up if necessary.

Select '1' and check for drive but *no* engine braking on the over-run.

Select positions 2, 3, and 4 and check that there is drive and that there *is* an engine braking effect.

Select reverse and again check for drive with engine braking.

Now select the automatic drive position and check that gear change speeds with a light throttle agree with those shown in Table 2:III.

Now repeat this test using full throttle and again check that the gear change speeds agree with those in the table.

TABLE 2:III

Throttle position	Gear change	Mile/h		Km/h	
Light throttle	From 1 to 2	11		18	
'D' selected	From 2 to 3	16	±2	26	±3
	From 3 to 4	21		34	
Full throttle	From 1 to 2	28		45	
'D' selected	From 2 to 3	42	±4	67	±6
	From 3 to 4	54		88	
Kickdown	From 4 to 3	Below 43		70	
'D' selected	From 3 to 2	35	±4	56	±6
	From 2 to 1	22		36	
Over run throttle	From 4 to 3	18		29	
closed	From 3 to 2	12	±2	19	±3
'D' selected	From 2 to 1	6		9	

Do *not* select 3rd gear at speeds greater than 50 mile/h.
Do *not* select 2nd gear at speeds greater than 40 mile/h.

Select '2' and accelerate to approximately 30 mile/h, then select 'N', switch off the ignition and allow the car to coast. At 20 mile/h, switch on the ignition and select '2'. The engine should restart.

With the car facing up a steepish hill, carry out the following slip tests.

Select '1', release the handbrake and open the throttle fully. Check for excessive slip. At 5 mile/h, select '2' and open the throttle fully; again check for slip. At 10 mile/h, select '3' and again check for slip with the throttle fully open. At 20 mile/h, select '4' and repeat the test.

Finally, with the car facing downhill, select 'R', release the handbrake and open the throttle fully. Check for excessive slip in reverse and refer to Table 2:V to identify the fault.

Stall speed tests

When faulty transmission gears and/or clutches are suspected, a stall speed test should be carried out in each gear to check which of the clutch units and/or brake bands is not functioning correctly. The test will only

TABLE 2:IV

Symptom	Fault
(1) Incorrect gear selection	Faulty selector adjustment
(2) Engine stalls when a gear is selected	Engine idle speed too low
(3) Excessive creep when a gear is selected	Engine idle speed too high
(4) Kickdown changes obtainable outside of the normal range	Kickdown spring weak, broken or incorrect spring fitted
(5) Slip or no drive in all forward gears	Forward clutch or oil feed pipes faulty
(6) Slip or no drive in 'R'	(a) Reverse clutch booster piston faulty (b) Reverse shut-off valve faulty (c) Regulator valve booster sticking
(7) Slip or no drive in '1'	(a) One way clutch faulty (b) One way clutch reaction peg sheared
(8) Slip or no drive in '2'	(a) 2nd gear brake band, Servo or feed pipes faulty (b) 2nd gear valve sticking
(9) Slip or no drive in '3'	3rd gear brake band or feed pipe faulty
(10) Slip or no drive in '4' and 'R'	Top and reverse clutch or feed pipes faulty
(11) Slip or no drive in all gears	(a) Low oil level (b) Converter seals leaking or stator slipping (c) Flow valve sticking
(12) No drive in '1' accompanied by judder, tie up or drag in '2', '3', '4' and 'D'—car drives only in 'R'	Incorrect assembly of the one way clutch
(13) Judder, tie up or drag in '3' and '4' with 'D' selected, accompanied by no drive in 'R'	2nd and top gear valve sticking in 2nd gear applied position
(14) Judder, tie up or drag in '2' and '4' with 'D' selected, accompanied by judder, tie up or drag in 'R'	3rd gear valve sticking in 3rd gear applied position
(15) Car pulls away in either '1', '2', '3', or '4' or with 'D' selected, accompanied by no automatic gear changes	Governor or governor-valve sticking in 1st, 2nd, 3rd or 4th gear applied position
(16) Oil pressure warning light glows with engine running	(a) Pressure switch faulty (b) Engine relief valve sticking open
(17) Engine labours in 'R' accompanied by creep in 'N'	Forward clutch seized or dragging
(18) Engine labours in '1', '2' and '3'	Top and reverse clutch seized or dragging

Symptom	*Fault*
(19) Automatic gear changes occur at high engine revs only, irrespective of throttle pedal position	(*a*) Kickdown linkage out of adjustment (*b*) Oil level too high (*c*) Stiff governor operation
(20) Automatic gear changes occur at low engine revs irrespective of throttle pedal position	(*a*) Kickdown spring weak or broken (*b*) Kickdown linkage disconnected
(21) Erratic automatic gear changes	Governor or governor-valve not smooth in operation
(22) No tow start	(*a*) Tow start valve sticking in engine pump supply position (*b*) Auxiliary pump worn (*c*) Oil feed pipes faulty

be meaningful if the engine is running correctly and developing full power, otherwise the results will be misleading. The test, which requires the use of an engine tachometer, is carried out as follows:

Run the engine until it reaches its normal running temperature, this ensures that the engine will pull smoothly during the test and also circulates the oil in the transmission. Switch off the engine and allow the oil to settle for about 1 minute, check the oil level and correct this if necessary. Now connect the tachometer to the ignition system and apply the hand and foot brakes; preferably also chock the wheels. Select one of the drive positions and fully depress the throttle for a maximum of 10 seconds, check the tachometer reading and compare this figure with those in Table 2:V.

TABLE 2:V

Rev/min	*Inference*	*Action*
1,300–1,400	Transmission satisfactory	—
less than 1,000	Stator probably slipping	Probably requires a new torque converter. Consult agent
Over 1,500	Clutch or brake band slipping	Check which gear position is faulty and consult agent
1,100–1,200	Engine is probably not running correctly	Check ignition and carburetter settings

If the transmission appears to slip in all gear positions, it is possible that a low oil pressure is the cause and this may be checked as follows:

Remove the test-point plug from the oil filter head and using suitable adaptors and pipe, connect an oil pressure gauge, reading to at least 150lb/in². Run the engine until it reaches its normal running temperature and allow all the oil to settle for 1 minute and check the oil level, correct this if necessary. With the hand and footbrakes applied and preferably also with chocks under the wheels, start the engine and select one of the forward drive positions; a pressure of 80lb/in² should be obtained on the gauge. Now repeat this test, selecting reverse (and remembering to put the chocks at the rear of the wheels) a pressure of 120lb/in² should be obtained. If the correct pressure is not obtained, consult the fault diagnosis Table 2:IV.

Adjustments

Inhibitor switch. If there is no apparent cause for the starter failing to energize, with the gear selector lever at 'N' or if it operates in other gear positions, the starter inhibitor switch must be checked for adjustment. The switch is located at the rear of the gear selector lever housing. Before adjusting the switch, remove the clevis pin from the fork end of the transverse selector rod thus ensuring that the gear selector cable, which may also require adjustment, is not influencing the setting of the switch. Do not start the engine with the selector rod disconnected.

Select position 'N' and remove the starter solenoid wires from terminals 2 and 4 of the switch. (Terminals 1 and 3 are used for reversing light connections.) Slacken the lock-nut and unscrew the switch almost out of the housing. Now connect a test lamp, across the switch terminals 2 and 4, and screw the switch into the housing until the circuit is made; mark the switch body and continue screwing in the switch, counting the number of turns until the circuit breaks. Then remove the test lamp and unscrew the switch, half the number of turns counted; finally tighten the lock-nut against the housing. Now replace the starter solenoid connections on positions 2 and 4; the wires are interchangeable.

Before testing the operation of the switch, it is preferable to check the adjustment of the selector rod.

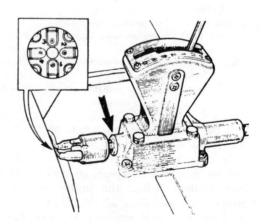

Fig. 2:12. The starter inhibitor switch on the gear selector lever housing. The arrow indicates the locking nut.

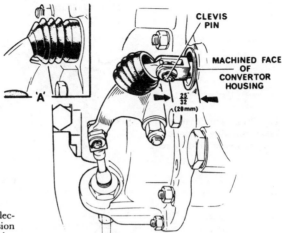

Fig. 2:13. The transverse selector rod showing the dimension to be checked and adjusted.

Adjusting the selector rod

Push the rod right into the transmission case, and measure the distance from the machined face of the converter housing to the centre-line of the clevis-pin hole in the forked end of the rod. This distance should be $\frac{25}{32}$in.; if this is not correct, slacken the lock-nut on the fork end and turn the fork in the appropriate direction to achieve the correct setting. Finally re-lock the nut and once again check the adjustment.

Adjusting the selector cable

With the selector rod still pushed right into the converter housing, and the clevis pin removed from the forked end, select 'D' with the gear lever and then slacken both lock-nuts on the selector cable where it passes through the boss on the converter housing. Now adjust the cable position, by means of these lock-nuts, so that the clevis pin may easily be replaced in the selector rod. Tighten the cable lock-nuts and then select each gear position in turn, checking that the clevis pin is free in each position; when this is satisfactory, refit the clevis pin and replace the rubber boots. Now apply the handbrake and footbrake before selecting 'N' and starting the engine; check the engagement of each gear in turn and, if satisfactory, carry out another road test.

Kickdown adjustment

The kickdown linkage consists of an adjustable rod from the carburetter to a bell-crank lever on the transmission case and thence to

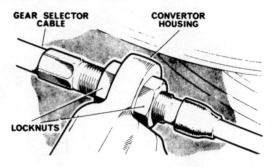

Fig. 2:14. The gear selector cable, showing lock-nuts on the converter housing boss.

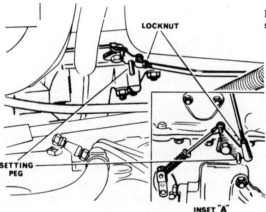

Fig. 2:15. Kick-down linkage showing the setting peg in position during adjustment.

the governor assembly. Adjustment is by altering the length of the rod whilst the throttle is closed and with the aid of a setting peg. Run the engine until it reaches its normal running temperature, then adjust the idling speed to about 650 rev/min, with a fast-idle speed of about 1,000/1,100 rev/min. (See carburetter slow running adjustment, page 13). Switch off the engine and disconnect the control rod from the carburetter by removing the clevis pin at its forked end; now insert a short metal rod, ¼in. diameter, through the hole in the intermediate bell-crank lever and into the hole in the transmission casing. Slacken the lock-nut at the lower end of the control rod and turn the rod in the appropriate direction to re-engage the clevis pin in the throttle lever, without opening the throttle. Tighten the lock-nut on the control rod, connect the rod to the throttle lever and remember to remove the setting peg from the bell-crank. Carry out a road test to check that the correct road speeds can be obtained.

CHAPTER 3

REPAIRING WEAR AND TEAR

The Mini, like all other makes of popular motor car, will not last for ever. After covering a certain number of miles and depending to a large extent upon the care taken by the owner, some wear will have taken place and faults will develop. The following chapter is written to help anyone with a Mini to deal with these problems as they occur and possibly to avoid some of them through timely warning.

Apparent low oil pressure

When the oil-pressure warning light fails to go out or takes more than a few seconds to do so after start up, or the oil pressure gauge fails to register very quickly, it is wise to investigate the cause as soon as possible. There are five possible reasons for this, assuming of course that the oil level in the sump is correct. These are:

1 A blocked oil filter
2 Sticking pressure-relief valve
3 Faulty pressure-indicating switch
4 Worn bearings
5 Worn oil pump

As the last two faults entail stripping the engine to put them right, it is best to eliminate the others first.

1 If the oil filter has not been changed within the last 5,000 miles, especially if the engine has done a high mileage, it should be renewed. If this fails to show any improvement, the pressure-relief valve must be inspected.

2 This valve is located behind a large hexagonal nut on the forward side of the cylinder block, just below the oil-pressure indicating switch. The nut is removed and the coil spring behind it lifted out. A steel plunger, behind this spring, forms the valve and this may be slightly difficult to remove from its bore. A piece of hardwood dowel will often serve as an extracting tool. Taper the end of a short piece of $\frac{3}{8}$in. dowel to about $\frac{1}{4}$in. so that it can be pushed into the block and jammed into the hollow end of the plunger, extract dowel and plunger. Check the sides of the plunger for signs of sticking or scores and the conical face for any sign of wear and mal-seating. If the plunger has been sticking in the bore, a new one should be fitted, after checking that the bore is perfectly clean. In some cases, when a plunger has not been seating correctly, it

can be lapped into place. A very slight smear of grinding paste should be placed on the conical face of the plunger and, using a tapered dowel as for removal, it may be pushed into the block and lapped in. When finished, the plunger should be removed and all traces of grinding paste wiped from it and the seat. Do not use small pieces of fluffy cloth to do this as these may become trapped in the bore and block the oilway but wipe it clean with lint-free cloth and/or with the clean plunger itself.

Before reassembly, check the spring for length; this should be 2¾in. long and if it is any shorter than this a new spring should be fitted.

3 and 4 The pressure indicating switch is screwed into the block just above the pressure relief valve. If the first two remedies for the lack of oil pressure have failed to effect a cure, the pressure switch should be renewed. On any model fitted with an oil pressure gauge, the reading will indicate whether attention to the filter or pressure relief valve has improved or cured the trouble but if the apparent lack of oil pressure still persists, then a genuinely low oil pressure is certain and the fault must be rectified immediately or severe damage to the engine may result. The most probable cause is worn big-end bearings and the engine must be removed from the car, stripped down and the big-ends inspected for wear. Details of these operations are given in chapter 4. Replacement of the bearing shells is usually a satisfactory cure so long as the crankpins are not oval or scored.

5 At the same time as the big-end bearings are inspected it is advisable to inspect the oil pump for excessive wear *i.e.* clearance in excess of 0·006in. between the inner and outer rotors.

If big-end failure is experienced, on a Mini which has not covered a high mileage, the oil pump should be suspected. If the car has done a large mileage, the oil pump is almost certain to be less efficient than it should be and replacement is advisable. Details of this are given in chapter 4, page 108.

Oil leaks

Minor oil leaks are a common occurrence on all Minis and are usually ignored but if they develop to the extent where the mess they make becomes objectionable a cure must be sought.

There are several likely places where oil leaks often occur and the ones listed below are likely to be encountered:

    1 Timing-case seal
    2 Cylinder-head gasket
    3 Clutch housing
    4 Tappet covers
    5 Differential output shafts

There are others of course but most of these are caused either by faulty gaskets or seals misplaced or damaged during maintenance. The cause and remedy is normally fairly obvious.

Points to note when curing the main sources of leakage are detailed below.

1 The timing-case seal is replaced as described in chapter 4, page 110 but be very careful not to bend the case when changing the seal. It is advisable to check the area of the case around the seal for squareness with the joint face of the case. This can be done by laying the case on a flat surface and measuring the distance from the seal housing to the flat surface at three or four points around its periphery. A bent case must be straightened or replaced with a good one. To aid centralization of the seal it is a good idea to enlarge the bolt holes in the case. The $\frac{1}{4}$in. ones can be opened up to $\frac{5}{16}$in. diameter and the $\frac{5}{16}$in. holes to $\frac{3}{8}$in.

2 The cylinder-head gasket sometimes leaks oil at the rear corner nearest to the by-pass hose where the oil feed to the rocker gear enters the head. The drilling is quite close to the edge of the gasket and the oil is under high pressure at this point. Oil escaping here attacks both the by-pass and bottom hoses. A leak at this point can easily be mistaken for a timing-case seal leak so take care to discover exactly which it is before starting the job. Cure of the cylinder head leak is by renewing the gasket and instructions for removing and refitting the cylinder head may be found in chapter 4.

3 If oil leaks from the small hole in the bottom of the flywheel housing, the cause is almost certainly a faulty flywheel-housing oil seal. Replacement is described in the section on the clutch on page 58.

4 The tappet-chest covers sometimes leak oil down the back of the engine. On occasions simply tightening the securing bolts will cure it. Do not overtighten these bolts however, they will not do up 'solid' and it is possible to distort the case. Two types of gasket are used on these covers, a cork one and a reddish rubber type. The cork one is meant for use on tappet covers which have a flat lip and the rubber type is used on covers which have a grooved lip.

5 If the nut securing the differential output-shaft flange to the shaft works loose, oil can creep up the splines and escape from around the nut. It is of course necessary to remove the inner rubber universal joint from the flange to get at the nut, this is described on page 62. Oil can obviously escape from the oil seals in the housing where the flanges pass into the gearbox casing but surprisingly a loose flange nut is a more common source of a significant leak. Very worn bushes in these housings, which bolt to the differential and support the drive flanges, can make a new seal wear very quickly and unless new housings are fitted seals alone may not be a lasting cure.

Generator overhaul

The only attention the generator should require, during normal use, is sparing lubrication of the brushgear-end bearing at the 12,000 mile service and inspection of the brushes at about 24,000 miles. A quick inspection of the brushes can be made by looking through the holes in the end bracket and observing the amount of brush that is sticking out of the top of the brush-holders. If the brush is worn level or below the top of the holder, or if one is in any doubt about which part is which in a dirty generator, it is best to remove and dismantle the generator for further inspection.

Removal is straightforward; remove the adjusting stay nut and washer from the cylinder block stud and the two upper pivot bolts. Unhook the fan belt from the generator pulley and the generator will be free. It is of course essential to first disconnect the two spade terminals from the end. It is not essential to remove the coil from its bracket on the generator if it is the type so mounted.

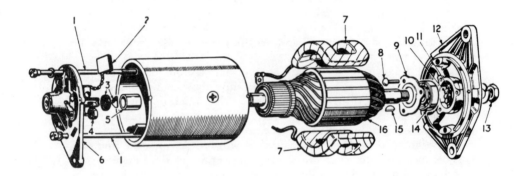

Fig. 3:1.
General assembly view of a Lucas C40-1 two brush, two-pole DC generator.

1. Bolts.	9. Bearing retainer plate
2. Brush	10. Corrugated washer
3. Felt ring and aluminium sealing disc	11. Felt washer
4. Brush spring	12. Driving end bracket
5. Bearing bush	13. Pulley retainer nut
6. Commutator end bracket	14. Bearing
7. Field coils	15. Woodruff key
8. Rivet	16. Armature

Brush replacement

Unscrew the two slot-headed bolts from the rear of the unit and remove the end plate together with bearing and brush gear. The armature, together with the driving-end plate may be withdrawn from the generator body. Check that the brushes are not worn down to less than $\frac{1}{4}$in. in length or badly worn at an angle. If this amount of wear has taken place, the brushes must be renewed. Also check that the brushes are not sticking in their housings and, if necessary, ease the sides of the brushes by rubbing them lightly on a file. While the generator is dismantled, check that the commutator is smooth and not badly burned. If it is worn, repair will usually require the services of a skilled turner and fitting a replacement unit is often a cheaper way. The commutator may be washed in clean petrol before reassembly.

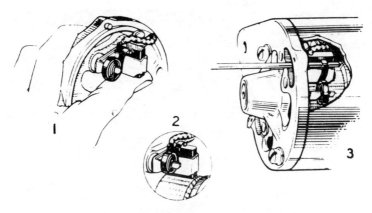

Fig. 3:2. Refitting the generator end plate

1. Trapping the brushes
2. Fitted position
3. Releasing the brushes

When reassembling the generator end-plate, the brushes should be pushed back through their housings until they are trapped in position by the side pressure of their springs (see fig. 3:2), this holds them away from the commutator until the end bracket is almost in position, when they may be released with a screwdriver. Before final assembly check that the brushes and springs have seated correctly.

Bearings

It is seldom that a generator will need new bearings during its useful life. The bronze bush at the brushgear end is not easy to renew without a suitable press and mandrel but the drive-end ball race is sometimes worth renewing if it becomes noisy.

To remove it, the nut must be taken off and the pulley extracted taking care not to damage its thin sides. The drive key can then be tapped out and the shaft driven out of the bearing. Use a soft drift here with great care to avoid damage to the threads. On older generators the bearing is retained by a plate held on by three rivets which must be drilled out. Later ones have a circlip to hold it. Obtain new rivets before starting the job. The new bearing should be lightly greased, but not packed solid, before fitting.

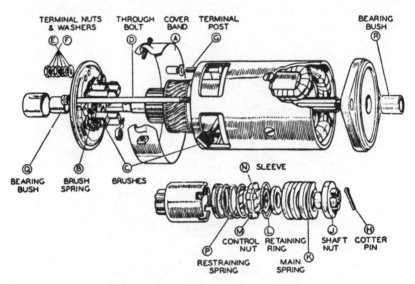

Fig. 3:3. An exploded diagram of the starter motor

Starter motor overhaul

Starter motors very rarely give any trouble but the brushes should be inspected after about 50,000 miles and if they are worn so that the flexible connection shows on the running face or so that they no longer bear on the commutator properly, they should be renewed.

Disconnect the starter cable from its terminal on the starter and remove the two bolts securing the starter to the flywheel housing. On normal saloon models it is easier to remove the grille and withdraw the starter through the aperture. On vans it is necessary to remove the distributor before removing the starter, but the Clubman starter is easily accessible.

Dismantling

Slacken the cover-band securing screw and remove the band from the starter. Hold back the brush springs and remove the brushes from their holders. Remove all the nuts and washers from the terminal post and take out the two big screws from the end of the unit. The end can now be withdrawn and the brushes examined.

Replacing brushes

Two of the brushes are connected to tappings from the field coils, the other two are connected to the terminal eyelets attached to the brush holders on the end plate. The flexible wires can be unsoldered from their connections and the new ones soldered into place. However, if aluminium field coils are fitted, it is better not to unsolder the flexible wire but to cut it off leaving a short length of copper wire to which the new wire can be more easily soldered. This avoids the difficulty of soldering to aluminium. The new leads should be shortened slightly so that the overall length is not increased.

Commutator

While the starter motor is dismantled, the commutator should be examined for excessive wear, burning or pitting. The segments may be cleaned with petrol and carefully polished with fine glasspaper while rotating the armature. As in the case of the generator, a badly damaged commutator is best replaced by an exchange unit.

Reassembly and replacement

This is a straightforward procedure, the new brushes require no bedding-in as they are pre-shaped on their working faces. Before re-assembling, ensure that the cable end and terminal nuts are clean and free from dirt and corrosion. Do not overtighten the terminal-post nuts when refitting the cable.

Drive mechanism

The Lucas inertia drive or 'Bendix' as it is often improperly named, sometimes becomes sluggish in action because it collects clutch dust. This is the usual cause of the starter 'spinning' when operated, without engaging with the flywheel. The cure is usually to wash the drive clean in paraffin which can be done without dismantling anything from the starter. When it has been washed clean and blown dry, the scroll, which is exposed when the drive gear is turned, should be given a few drops of thin oil. The plain shaft up which the gear slides must not be oiled or it will collect clutch dust.

The complete drive can be changed if the gear is damaged. It is secured by a circlip or nut on the end of the shaft. The circlip can be removed only after the large end washer has been pushed back against the spring.

Water pump

The water pump is sometimes troublesome on Mini engines and replacement is usually a matter of some urgency. Slackness in the bearings, which can be heard as a rattly grinding noise, soon leads to water leaks because the seal fails. A great deal of water can be lost in a short time through a defective water pump seal and it makes driving the car virtually impossible. Replacement is carried out as follows:

Drain the water and remove the bottom hose from the pump. Release the by-pass hose and clips. Remove the radiator top bracket and the screws securing the top half of the radiator cowling and remove it. It is possible to remove the water pump with the fan bolted to it if the pump securing bolts are undone a little at a time while the pump is pulled away from the cylinder block. It is located on two dowels and may require a tap to loosen it. This method, although fiddly, is probably less so than removing the fan bolts and fan with the pump in position.

When fitting a new pump, check that the locating dowels have not come out of the block and remained stuck in the old pump. They must be replaced in the block if this occurs. Always fit a new by-pass hose when fitting a new water pump as it is very easy at this stage.

There are now two different water pumps in use which complicates matters slightly. The early type pump will fit all the engines if there is any doubt. The later one, fitted to most Minis now produced, has a longer impellor and a larger bore outlet pipe. It cannot be fitted to early cylinder blocks without grinding a small amount of metal from the impellor to prevent it fouling on the inside of the block. Two types of bottom hose are used, as the larger pump requires a larger top end on the hose.

Water hose leaks: By-pass hose

If oil is allowed to leak from the engine onto the by-pass hose, the rubber will quickly deteriorate and the hose will split. Changing the by-pass hose can be a tedious job as it often means either removing the water pump (as detailed in the previous section) or alternatively lifting the cylinder head, and this will *almost* certainly mean fitting a new head gasket and resetting the valve clearances.

One alternative, which is sometimes possible, is to fit a new hose without disturbing either the head or the water pump. To do this, first slacken the clips on the old hose and remove it, this is probably best done by cutting the hose away. Next, position the new hose alongside the water connections and trim it to the minimum length necessary to make a complete seal on each pipe. Fold the hose in half and push it into place, taking care that the ends do not drop into the slots cut across the water pipe. Centralize the hose so that both slots are completely covered, refit and tighten both hose clips.

Broken exhaust pipe mountings

The main cause of failure of the rubber exhaust mountings used on all Minis is misalignment of the exhaust system. If the pipe is under any strain, the rubbers will quickly break so be sure that everything is nicely lined up when fitting a new system. Occasionally the pipe may have to be bent slightly to achieve this but it is worth the extra trouble. The bracket bolted to the differential side flange on Minis (but not Coopers) with remote gear changes is prone to breakage and should be examined carefully when any work is carried out beneath the car.

Worn engine tie-bar and exhaust leaks

If the engine tie-bar bushes become badly worn it will allow the engine to rock appreciably on its mountings and this puts a severe strain on the exhaust pipe. If a Mini is run for long in this condition, the exhaust-pipe

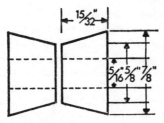

Fig. 3:4. Cones turned from steel, aluminium or brass to replace steel centre of engine tie-bar bush.

flange will crack, where it joins the manifold, and a leak will occur. It may also break the mounting lug from the pipe, where it is bolted to the transmission casing. The pipe can be repaired by welding but failing this a new exhaust system is required. The engine tie-bar steady-bush must be replaced when wear occurs. This is quite simply done by removing the two bolts that secure its mounting to the cylinder block and swinging the arm away from the block. The old bush is pushed out and a new one inserted. The steel centre from the old bush is pushed into the new one. To increase the life of the bush and the rigidity of the engine mounting on pre-1964 Minis, the steel centre of the bush may be replaced by a pair of cones obtainable from many conversion specialists. Alternatively they may be turned from steel, brass or aluminium and suitable dimensions are shown in fig. 3:4. They are inserted one from either side of the rubber bush and when the mounting bolt is tightened they are forced together, compressing the rubber.

The bolt securing the exhaust pipe to the gearbox extension, underneath the car, should be checked for tightness as this is important in avoiding fracture of the pipe. These troubles do not occur on Cooper models though occasionally the manifold cracks at the point where it bends underneath the car. If a crack is seen to start, it should be welded before it becomes serious.

Timing chain noise

The timing chain on all models (except the Cooper S and 1275 GT which are Duplex) is a single-row roller chain tensioned by two synthetic rubber rings set in machined grooves in the camshaft wheel. This chain wears and the rubber tensioners also wear and harden, allowing the chain to flap a small amount which causes a characteristic rattling noise. If the noise becomes excessive, the chain and tensioners should be renewed.

The job is straightforward and not expensive; it can be done with the engine in position and the procedure is as follows:

Drain the radiator.

Remove the top hose and disconnect the bottom hose from the heater pipe and from the water pump.

Remove the top radiator bracket.

Remove the small hexagon-head self-tapping screws, securing the top half of the radiator shroud and lift it clear. (If the Mini is a very early one with a one-piece radiator shroud, removal of the radiator is more difficult. All the shroud screws must be removed and the shroud moved away from the radiator in order to get at the fan bolts.)

Take out the two bolts which hold the bottom radiator bracket to the engine mounting. (These are reached through the small square hole in the wing valence, just underneath the radiator grille, which can be seen on removing the nearside front wheel.)

Remove the fan; the four setscrews at its centre are easy to remove, on a sixteen-blade fan, by holding a spanner on them and revolving the fan but with a four-blade fan more patience is needed—they must be unscrewed flat by flat.

The radiator may now be lifted out.

Pull the fan pulley off the water pump, after removing the fan belt.

The locking washer on the crankshaft pulley can be knocked back, using a long screwdriver passed through the radiator grille, after which the large hexagon-headed setscrew, securing the pulley, is removed. To do this, engage top gear and have someone apply the brake pedal. A hammer used on the end of a large spanner will help to free the screw.

The pulley may now be levered off the crankshaft. On the Minis fitted with a crankshaft vibration damper, the nearside engine mounting must be removed before this can be done. The bolts securing the mounting to the sub-frame and to the gearbox casing are removed after first supporting the end of the gearbox with a jack.

The timing case may now be removed to expose the chain and sprockets which are removed and examined as explained in chapter 4, page 109.

Reassembly is a straightforward reversal of dismantling but take the opportunity of examining the bottom radiator hose; it is so much easier to renew it while the radiator is removed.

Fuel pump overhauls

All models prior to October 1969 were fitted with SU electric fuel pumps. These are mounted beneath the car on the left-hand rear sub-frame and should be removed from the car for servicing. When removing the pump, plug the inlet pipe or squeeze it flat with a 'Mole' wrench as the pump is below the fuel level in the petrol tank.

Fuel pump failure was a common problem with early models but, although it can still occur, the later model pumps are very much more reliable and should run for 30,000 miles or more without trouble.

One symptom of fuel pump trouble, especially with PD type pumps, is a noisy buzzing from the rear of the car when the ignition is first switched on. This sound cannot be confused with the normal fuel pump noise which can be heard when the ignition is switched on; the buzzing is continuous and is much faster than the ordinary pump noise. Switching the ignition off and on again usually stops it for a while; if this does not succeed, check that the carburetter float chamber is not flooding because of a sticking float needle. In this case fuel will be seen running down the outside of the float chamber; remove the chamber lid and check the needle and seating. If the needle or seating are damaged new ones should be fitted.

The fuel pump should be heard ticking occasionally when the engine is running; if it is not ticking at all, it cannot be pumping. Reluctant fuel pumps can often be encouraged to work for a while if they are tapped with the fist or a piece of wood (leave the ignition switched on while doing this).

Before blaming the fuel starvation on the petrol pump, try removing the tank filler cap and running the engine for a short time. If this cures the trouble, the plastic vent-pipe should be removed from the tank (it is pushed on to a short tube at the top of the fuel tank) and checked for blockage. This is one cause of starvation which is often overlooked.

PD type fuel pumps

Up to August 1961 all Minis were fitted with PD type fuel pumps. These were distinguished by their dumbell shape and mounted vertically. However these pumps were fairly unreliable so the chances of a Mini still being driven with one is very remote.

If one is still in use and gives trouble the best plan is to throw it away and fit a new AUF type noting the comments about venting given below.

SP and AUF pumps

Cars fitted with electric fuel pumps after the Autumn of 1961 have either an SP or an AUF pump. These are removed from the car in the same way as the PD pump but their construction is slightly different; they should be dismantled as described below.

The contact breaker is under the end cover which is held on by the terminal nut and washer, a tape seal is also fitted around the cap when the pump is new. With the cover removed, the contacts may be inspected; if they are burned or pitted, they should be removed for cleaning. The contact blade is secured to the pedestal by a single screw which should be removed. If the contact points are only slightly burned or pitted they should be cleaned with a small oilstone and reassembled but when severe pitting has occured, a new contact assembly should be used. When the contacts are being fitted, adjust the contact blade so that the points on it are a little above the points on the rocker, when they are closed. At the same time adjust the blade so that, when the points make or break, each contact wipes over the centre-line of the contact opposite; a slot is provided at the fixing screw to allow this adjustment.

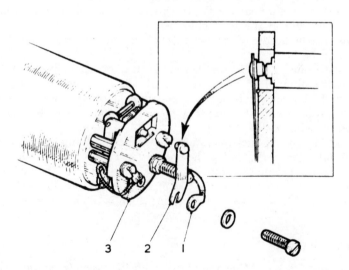

Fig. 3:5. SU fuel pump contact points showing the amount of offset necessary to give a self-cleaning action.

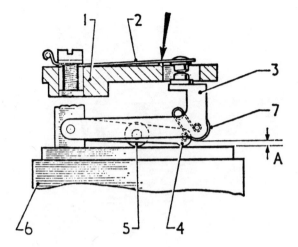

Fig. 3:6. SU fuel pump contacts (fibre roller type). The gap should be measured at point A.

Contact gap adjustment

First make sure that the outer rocker is pressed on to the coil housing and that the blade of the contacts rests lightly on the rib formed on the pedestal. If the blade is not touching this rib, the fixing screw should be slackened so that the blade is correctly positioned when the screw is retightened. Avoid bending the blade further than necessary as this may restrict rocker movement or damage the blade.

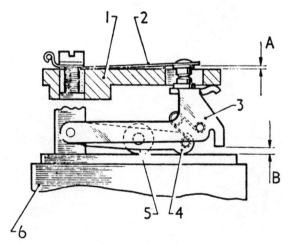

Fig. 3:7. SU fuel contacts (brass finger type). The gap should be measured at point B.

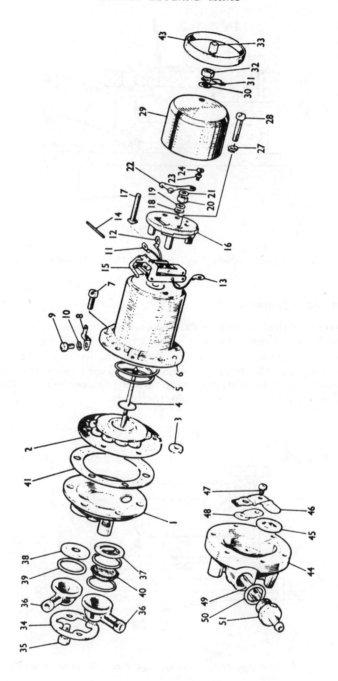

1. Pump body (AUF 200 only).
2. Diaphragm and spindle assembly.
3. Armature centralizing roller.
4. Impact washer.
5. Armature spring.
6. Coil housing.
7. Set screw.
8. Earth connector.
9. Set screw.
10. Spring washer.
11. Terminal tag.
12. Terminal tag.
13. Earth tag.
14. Rocker pivot pin.
15. Rocker mechanism.
16. Pedestal.

17. Terminal stud.
18. Spring washer.
19. Lead washer.
20. Terminal nut.
21. End-cover seal washer.
22. Contact blade.
23. Washer.
24. Contact blade screw.
27. Spring washer.
28. Screw.
29. End-cover.
30. Shakeproof washer.
31. Connector.
32. Nut.
33. Insulating sleeve.
34. Clamp plate (AUF 200 only).

35. Set screw.
36. Inlet and outlet nozzles. } AUF 200 only
37. Inlet valve.
38. Outlet valve.
39. Sealing washer.
40. Filter.
41. Gasket.
43. Sealing band.
44. Pump body.
45. Outlet valve.
46. Valve retainer. } SP type only
47. Screw.
48. Inlet valve.
49. Filter.
50. Washer.
51. Inlet nozzle.

Fig. 3:8. Exploded view of SU fuel pumps Types AUF 200 and SP.

Measure the gap between the fibre rollers and the coil housing while holding the contact blade against the rib of the pedestal; this should be 0·030in. (See fig. 3:6.) Adjustment, when necessary, should be made by gently bending the tip of the blade until the gap beneath the rollers is correct.

When adjusting a later model pump, with the modified rocker assembly now fitted, measure the lift of the contact blade tip above the top of the pedestal with feeler gauges, this should be 0·035in. and if necessary the stop beneath the pedestal should be bent slightly to achieve this figure. Also measure the gap between the rocker finger and the coil housing, this should be 0·070in. and may be adjusted, if necessary, by bending the stop finger.

Fuel-pump valve assemblies

If the pump ticks normally but does not pump fuel, the valves are probably faulty. To obtain access to the valves on an SP pump, remove the six screws which secure the coil housing to the valve body. The valve body can be prised off the housing but take care not to damage the diaphragm while doing this. A Philips screw secures the metal clamping plate that holds the valves in position and this should be removed. Take out the valves and inspect the plastic parts for deterioration and cracks. If they appear to be in good condition and the seatings in the valve body appear all right, all the parts should be reassembled. A quick check that the valves are working properly may be achieved by blowing and sucking on the inlet and outlet pipes. The valve retaining plate should be checked to see that it allows the inlet valve about $\frac{1}{16}$in. movement.

The valves of the AUF pump can be cleaned and examined without removing the valve body from the coil housing. The clamping plate which secures the inlet and outlet pipe stubs is first removed; then the stubs, together with the filter and valves, can be removed, cleaned and inspected. When reassembling, note that the inlet valve should be fitted tongue-side downwards in the recess marked INLET and the outlet valve fitted tongue-side upwards. The filter goes in the inlet side.

Most AUF pumps are fitted with a venting system; this is either a non return valve on the contact cover and a small pipe on the other end of the coil housing, or a small pipe at both ends. In either case the pipe or pipes should be connected with small bore plastic tubing to a region of dry air. The pipes are generally passed up into the boot of the car for this purpose.

Mechanical fuel pumps

The Mark III and Clubman Minis are fitted with a mechanical fuel pump instead of the electrical one used previously. This is an SU pump and it is driven by an eccentric on the camshaft, as is usual with mechanical pumps. It is positioned on the side of the cylinder block

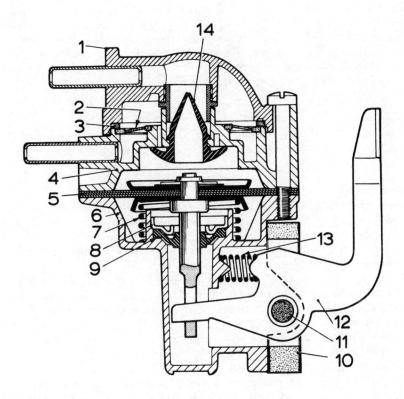

1. Cover
2. Filter
3. Sealing ring
4. Pump body, upper half
5. Diaphragm
6. Pump body, lower half
7. Spring

8. Cup
9. Seal
10. Insulation block
11. Spindle
12. Actuating arm
13. Spring
14. Valve assembly

Fig. 3:9. Section of SU mechanical fuel pump.

down behind the engine at the radiator end and is not very accessible. Apart from its low cost, it has the advantage that there is less to go wrong than with an electric pump and so should be more reliable. To check its operation, remove the fuel feed pipe from the carburetter, remove the l t wire from the distributor to prevent the engine starting and operate the starter. Good squirts of petrol should come out as the engine turns over. If petrol is not delivered, or if only a small amount appears, the pump is suspect. Before removing the pump, however, check that there is not a leak between the inlet side of the pump and the tank as this can cause the pump to suck in air.

Removal
The pump is held onto the block by two bolts and once these and the connecting pipes are removed it can be pulled from the block.

Dismantling
Three of the six screws in the pump retain the top cover for the filter which should be clean and undamaged. The other three screws hold the two halves of the pump together; when removed, the top half should be taken off leaving the diaphragm on the lower part. The top contains the synthetic-rubber valve which serves for both inlet and outlet control. It can be removed downwards from the body for renewal or inspection. The lower end of the valve's outer lip serves as an inlet valve and must be undamaged so that it forms a perfect seal against the pump body. The central pointed part must close properly to function as an outlet valve. Any dirt can prevent the valve from functioning so make sure everything is perfectly clean. The diaphragm need not be removed if it has no cracks or holes in it, but if damaged it will have to be renewed. To do this, hold the pump actuating arm against its spring pressure, push out its pivot and then the diaphragm and its rod may be pulled from the pump.

The larger sized lower part of the diaphragm push rod must be pulled through a rubber seal so, to avoid tearing this, see that the rod is oily before removing or refitting it.

Reassembly
Reassembly is straightforward but assemble the two pump halves in their original positions. Fit all the screws loosely and hold the pump actuating arm in so that the diaphragm is not stretched up or down but is in its mid-position while the screws are tightened. When re-fitting the pump to the block do not leave out the insulation washer or either gasket as their thickness determines the travel of the pump arm. The arm bears against the 'outer' side of the camshaft and does not pass beneath it so do not try to hook it underneath when refitting the pump.

Clutch slip or judder

If clutch slip or judder is experienced, the cause is almost invariably oil on the centre plate; though judder can be caused by broken engine mountings or a badly worn steady bush. Both of these should be checked and renewed if necessary. Oil can get onto the clutch plate if the rubber seal in the flywheel housing has deteriorated and is leaking or on cars manufactured before the beginning of 1963 through the seal in the flywheel. On cars after early 1963, the crankshaft primary gear was fitted with a self-lubricating bearing and this eliminated the need for a pressure oil feed to this point, thus the flywheel oil seal has since been dispensed with. If oil has found its way onto the clutch plate, a new plate and oil seal is the only cure.

If the engine has been removed from the car the job is quite simple. It is described in chapter 4 page 103. With the engine still in the car the job is carried out as follows: Remove the starter, and the coil if it is mounted on the clutch casing. Remove the bolts securing the engine tie-rod to the cylinder block and swing it away from the block; then remove the two bolts which secure the engine mounting to the sub-frame beneath the clutch housing. The nuts are on the sub-frame, under the wheel arch. The radiator top-mounting is removed from the thermostat housing on the cylinder head and from the radiator shroud. The clutch slave-cylinder must be unbolted from the clutch housing, after the return-spring has been removed, when it may be pulled off the pushrod on the clutch actuating arm. The clutch end of the engine may then be jacked up enough to enable the cover on the end of the clutch housing to be removed. When jacking up the engine, care must be taken to see that the fan does not foul the radiator. When all the bolts securing the clutch cover have been taken out, it may be lifted away, exposing the clutch and flywheel. To gain access to the clutch plate and centre oil-seal, the flywheel must be removed and the clutch dismantled as detailed in chapter 4, page 104.

When the clutch has been dismantled, examine the linings for signs of oil. In serious cases it will be found that the plate is wet with oil but do not confuse this with oil that may have been accidentally spilled from the flywheel centre when lifting the clutch from the car. If the lining has a uniform, dry, flecked greyish appearance and the rivets are well below the surface, it is in serviceable condition but if it is dark in colour because of impregnated oil, it must be renewed. It is impossible to wash oil off fouled clutch linings because only the surface may be cleaned in this way and, as the clutch is used, more oil will come to the surface. Sometimes only one side is affected but it is a mistake not to change the plate as the cost is trivial compared with the labour of getting at it.

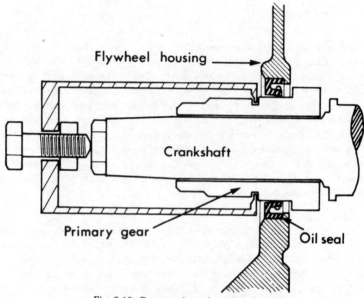

Flywheel housing

Crankshaft

Primary gear

Oil seal

Fig. 3:10. Cross section of crankshaft and
flywheel housing showing the operating
principle of a primary gear puller.

Flywheel oil seals—early models

Lever the old seal out of the flywheel from the back with a screwdriver.
It is well worth while renewing this seal whenever the clutch and
flywheel are removed from the crankshaft. Take care that the new seal
is seated squarely in its housing; the seals are quite easily damaged but
use of a cylindrical wooden drift, of just under seal diameter, will make
the job simpler. Before assembly, clean and de-glaze the pressure faces of
the flywheel and pressure plate. This is especially important in cases of
clutch judder. The working surfaces should be rubbed with a fine
oilstone and some thin oil or with medium grade emery cloth. The object
is to remove the very shiny glazed surface which forms after some time.
It is also advisable to lubricate lightly the contact lip of the new oil seal
to prevent the seal burning before oil reaches it. The modified type of
self-lubricating primary-gear bearing (already mentioned as being fitted
from early 1963 onward) may be substituted in the earlier models if
desired, but it does involve the expense of at least a new type primary
gear. This is described in chapter 4, page 105.

Flywheel-housing oil-seal

The flywheel-housing oil-seal can be replaced, once the flywheel has been
removed, without removing the engine from the car, if a primary-gear

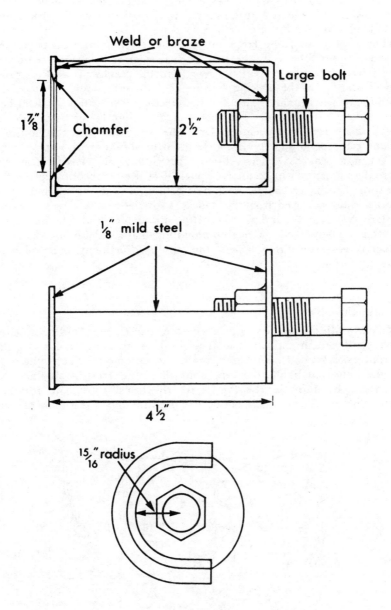

Fig. 3:11. Design for a simple primary gear puller.

extractor is used. This device has a thin horseshoe-shaped plate which fits between the splines and the shoulder of the primary gear. The plate is welded to one end of a piece of halved steel tube which has a plate on the other end carrying a large nut and bolt. A diagram of its operation is shown in fig. 3:10. With the primary-gear locating 'C' washer removed, the extractor is used to pull the gear from the crankshaft and it brings the oil-seal out of the housing with it. The new seal should be placed in position on the primary gear using a protector sleeve or tape as described in chapter 4 (page 108). The seal should be lightly lubricated on its working lip before reassembly. Drift the seal back into the housing, taking care not to damage it and to get it in absolutely square.

When a seal has been refitted, the clutch and flywheel are replaced as described in chapter 4 (page 106). Remember to replace the locating 'C' washer on the crankshaft before refitting the flywheel. The washer must be fitted from the top *i.e.* with the legs downwards when pistons No. 1 and 4 are at t d c. After fitting the flywheel, the clutch cover is replaced and the engine mounting bolts, radiator bracket and other pieces are refitted. Check the clutch adjustment as detailed in chapter 2 (page 26).

Gearbox troubles

The early Mini gearbox was plagued with defects, the main ones being poor synchromesh and rapid wear which leads to jumping out of gear. A conversion kit was available to cure the synchromesh by changing over to the improved baulk-ring type, and all new gearboxes obtained on exchange from British Leyland have the latest type synchromesh. Jumping out of gear which can occur on all the boxes is a more serious

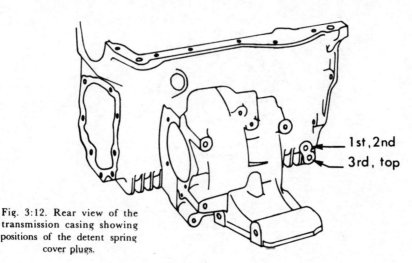

1st, 2nd
3rd, top

Fig. 3:12. Rear view of the transmission casing showing positions of the detent spring cover plugs.

fault however. There are several variations on the jumping out theme, some of which are listed in Table 3:I.

The list by no means covers all the possible causes of trouble but they are the most common and can be seen to be wrong when the box is removed and examined.

All that can be done from outside the box is to ensure that the bolts which secure the ball joint linkage at the back of the engine are tight and that the gear lever does not foul anything so as to reduce its travel. It is possible to change the detent springs from outside the box. They are fitted in the lower right hand side of the transmission casing as shown in fig. 3:12. New springs can be fitted without draining the oil if the job is done quickly and it is certainly worth trying new springs before removing the engine and stripping the box. If this fails to cure the trouble, the box must be stripped as described in chapter 4.

As a general guide, selector forks should be renewed if sideways play between the fork and sliding hub exceeds 0·025in. A certain amount of chipping of 1st gear, up to 30% of the tooth length, may not give

TABLE 3:I.

GEARBOX FAULTS

Symptom	Possible cause or remedy
Jumps out of 1st and/or reverse	Wear of 1st gear teeth – Replace 1st gear and possibly laygear
Jumps out of or fails to engage 1st and 2nd	1st/2nd selector fork loose on rod – Tighten securing bolt
Jumps out of 2nd gear	Worn selector fork – renew
Jumps out of or fails to engage 2nd and 3rd	Broken centre bronze thrust washer (early boxes 'A' type gears only) – Renew washer
Jumps out of 3rd	Worn selector fork – Renew
Jumps out of top	Worn selector fork – Renew
Jumps out of 3rd and top or fails to engage	Loose selector fork bolt – Tighten
All gears engage and speedo works but no drive	3rd motion shaft nut unscrewed – Fit new lockwasher and tighten

problems. If many parts of the box are found to be in poor condition however, an exchange box may well be the best proposition because the cost of replacement parts is quite high.

Deterioration of inner universal joints

The bonded-rubber spiders of the inner universal joints, on Minis with manual gearboxes, are in a position where they can be subjected to quite severe working conditions; oil saturation, high temperature and high loads occur, especially on tuned cars which are usually driven hard. The rubber gradually comes unstuck from the metal centre of the coupling and if it is allowed to reach a really bad condition, the coupling may disintegrate completely. In these circumstances the resulting loose drive-shaft has been known to knock a hole in the back of the gearbox.

Deterioration is gradual and so long as the rubber is inspected at regular intervals, every 6,000 miles or so, no trouble need be experienced. The first sign of age is a swelling of the rubber which eventually protrudes from the end of the coupling to the extent where it rubs on the back of the gearbox. If a coupling reaches this state it must be replaced. Another sign of failure is a small circle or hole appearing in the end of the rubber. This indicates that the metal interior is detaching itself from the rubber.

Replacement is carried out as follows:—Before jacking up the car, place a wooden wedge between the rebound stop on the front subframe and the top suspension arm; this will help removal of the top joint but it is not essential. Jack up the front of the car and remove the appropriate front wheel or wheels. Remove the nut and spring washer from the top suspension ball joint. The ball joint has to be extracted from its taper and this task can be greatly simplified if a ball-joint extractor can be obtained. If one is not available, however, the tapered joint can usually be freed from its socket in the suspension arm either by striking the end of the arm with a fairly heavy hammer and a solid steel drift whilst levering the bottom wishbone downwards with a long bar, or alternatively by striking the side of the joint with the hammer whilst holding a steel block of at least the same weight as the hammer on the opposite side of the joint to that being struck; this increases the effect of the blow and frees the taper more easily. Never hit the threaded end of the ball-joint spindle to try to knock it out of the arm, this will only ruin the thread without removing the joint. When the joint is free, the taper can be removed from the top wishbone, but it may be necessary to lift the wishbone with a long bar to achieve this.

Support the front hub assembly with some wire or rope so that it cannot flop over and strain the flexible brake hose. Remove all the nuts ($\frac{1}{2}$in. AF) and U-bolts which hold the inner universal together and push the driveshaft outwards and upwards to allow the rubber coupling to fall free. Place the new coupling in position and replace the U-bolts. It may be necessary to pinch the ends of the U-bolts together slightly in a vice to enable them to be replaced easily. Never overtighten the U-bolt nuts as this can damage the coupling, and always fit new self-locking nuts if the original ones are damaged. Tighten the nuts just enough to close the ends of the metal shells of the coupling together.

Alternative couplings can be obtained which are of the needle roller type. These are fitted with steel or nylon end pieces which are clamped to the standard flanges with 'U' bolts. They should outlast the rubber joints but a certain amount of extra engine noise may have to be tolerated as the cushioning effect of the rubber is removed. The last of the Cooper S types produced had Hardy Spicer solid couplings as used on the automatics in place of the rubber ones. These, although transmitting some noise to the interior, are much longer lasting. It is of course possible to convert a rubber coupling car to take the automatic drive shaft joints but it is an expensive conversion compared to the replacement steel or nylon cupped type. Make sure that the taper on the swivel ball-joint is clean before reassembling it to the top wishbone. Tighten the securing nut to 35/40 lb ft.

Drive shaft overhaul

At their outer ends, the shafts of both types are fitted with the Rzeppa constant-velocity joints manufactured by Hardy Spicer (fig. 3:13). In these joints, the drive is transmitted through six hardened steel balls running in curved grooves. These grooves are machined in the interior of one half of the joint, in line with the shaft axis, and on the exterior of the driving half. The steel balls engage the grooves of both halves, keying them together, while at the same time allowing them to hinge freely. In normal circumstances, the drive shafts require no attention but the rubber boots which cover the constant-velocity joints should be inspected periodically for signs of leakage or damage. Damaged boots should be replaced without delay as road grit entering the joint will soon ruin it. To replace a damaged boot it is first necessary to remove the complete drive shaft from the car.

Wear in the joints will cause them to make a clonking noise when the car is driven on full steering lock. This noise is slight at first, gradually becoming worse until a loud knocking noise can be heard even with moderate degrees of steering lock.

Some noise on extremes of lock is acceptable but if it becomes loud, the drive shaft must be removed and dismantled.

Removing the drive shafts

Jack up the appropriate side of the car and remove the road wheel. Remove the split pin from the hub nut and, either with the assistance of someone to hold the brakes on or by securing the hub with a long lever, undo and remove the hub nut. Slacken the nuts on the top and bottom

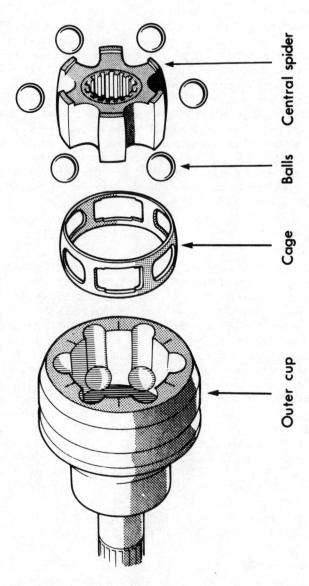

Central spider

Balls

Cage

Outer cup

Fig. 3:13. Exploded view of the constant-velocity joint, now described in B L parts lists as a 'ball-and-joint' assembly.

steering swivels and on the steering-arm ball-joint about two turns and loosen the joints from their taper sockets. This should be done with a ball-joint extractor if one can be obtained; if not, the tapers may be loosened by one of the methods described on page 62. When the suspension swivels are being freed in this manner, the bottom wishbone should be levered downwards.

After loosening the joints, remove the nuts and separate the steering ball joint. Push the bottom wishbone down, off the lower joint, this will allow the hub assembly to be removed and pulled from the splines on the drive shaft. Do this carefully and, to avoid straining the brake pipe once the hub is free, hang the hub from a piece of wire while working on the drive shaft.

The drive shaft is freed at its inner end by removing the four U-bolt nuts which secure it to the rubber universal or the four stud nuts if a Hardy Spicer flange is fitted. Before separating the joint, mark the relative positions of the two halves so that they may be reassembled the same way round. The shaft may now be removed from the car unless, as on some cars, the bottom wishbone fulcrum pin prevents it from coming through the hole in the sub-frame. In this case take the nut off the end of the fulcrum pin and knock it backwards about $\frac{1}{8}$in. to allow the other end to drop and clear the shaft.

Dismantling the shaft

Clamp the shaft in a vice and remove the band holding the large end of the universal-joint boot; fold back the boot to avoid damaging it. Remove the universal joint from the splines on the drive shaft by hitting the outer bell of the joint with a heavy soft-faced hammer while holding the splined part of the bell with the other hand. Take care not to strike the ball cage. This part of the joint is retained by an internal spring-wire circlip and a sharp blow is necessary to force this into its groove and allow the joint to be removed. Before dismantling the joint any further, remove the grease from the joint with paraffin and mark the relative positions of the individual components so that they may be replaced in their original positions. Tilt the centre and the cage of the joint so that the balls may be removed, one by one, from the ends of their tracks. Turn the cage and centre, vertically, and rotate the cage until the two opposite elongated windows coincide with two lands of the outer cup, one land will then fit into a window and allow the cage and centre to be removed. The cage and centre should then be separated by a similar process and the whole joint washed completely clean. The individual components should now be inspected for signs of wear or damage; wear should be evenly distributed over all components. British Leyland consider that the joint will remain serviceable until the end-float exceeds 0·025in. The balls should be inspected for chipping or wear in the form of 'flats'. The ball tracks on the centre portion and inside the outer cup should be inspected for wear, which occurs just on either side of the central circumference and causes the tracks to widen slightly at this point. This wear gives rise to the 'clonking', already described, when the vehicle is driven 'on lock'. The cage should be inspected on its inner and outer faces for any signs of 'picking up' and should also be checked for cracks especially across the thinner sections between the ball-retaining holes and the outer rims. The edges of the ball 'windows' may show signs of wear which can in some cases be a source of noise. Examine the end of the shaft for cracks in the splines and make sure that the square-section circlip is seated correctly in its groove.

If excessive wear or any damage has occured in the joint, it is usually necessary to fit a complete new ball and joint assembly. In some cases, where the ball cage only is damaged, it may be possible to fit a new cage

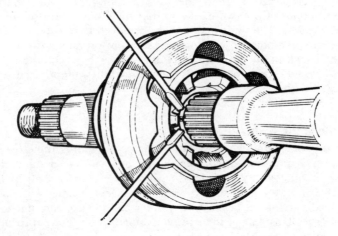

Fig. 3:14. Centralize the spring ring before tapping the shaft onto the splines.

but the original parts must be carefully measured as there are three sizes of cage which have been used and these are not interchangeable.

If inspection reveals no sign of cracking or damage and the joint was not clonking badly, the joints may be reassembled. The joint must be packed with Duckham's Q5795 grease (B L pack AKF 1457), obtainable from British Leyland agents in sachets sufficient for one joint. The whole contents of one sachet should be squeezed into each joint before the re-assembly. Difficulty may be experienced, when refitting the joint to the splined shaft, in getting the spring circlip to enter the splined central hole. Two screwdrivers and an extra pair of hands can be of great assistance. The circlip can then be held down in its groove with the screwdrivers while the joint is tapped back onto the shaft. (See fig. 3:14).

While the drive shaft is removed from the car, it is obviously a sensible

precaution to fit a new rubber boot over the joint unless the old one is
in very good condition. After fitting, it should be held in position with
either new steel bands or two turns of 18 swg soft iron wire in place of
the original band. The ends of the wire should be twisted together and
bent back, away from the direction of forward rotation of the shaft.
They should also be as close to the boot as possible but make sure that
in this position they cannot cut or chafe the boot. The drive shaft may
now be reassembled to the car. Remember, if the inner universals have

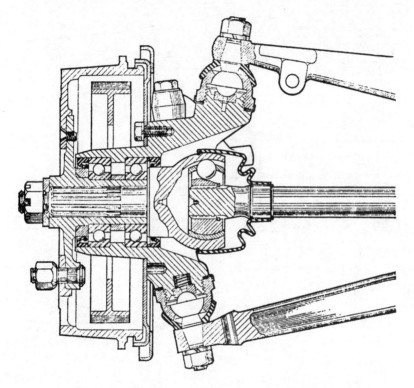

Fig. 3:15. A section through the front hub assembly, 850 Mini.

rubber bushed spiders, not to overtighten the nuts on the U-bolts. The
threads of these U-bolts should not protrude through nuts of the nylon
insert type by more than $\frac{1}{16}$ in., that is about two threads. If all-steel
self-locking nuts of the thinner type are fitted, three or four threads may
protrude.

Hub bearings

If play becomes noticeable in the hubs, as distinct from the steering
swivels, the bearings must be renewed as they are not adjustable.

Similarly if the bearings become noisy they must be dismantled and examined with view to replacement. Before stripping of the hub assembly is carried out it is worth checking to see that the large central hub nut is not slack which can cause looseness of the bearings. Some drum-braked Minis have been produced with front hub parts slightly out of tolerance, the most common fault results in the drive shaft (ball and joint) splined shaft protruding through the drive flange by a short

1. Drive shaft nut
2. Outer tapered collar
3. Inner tapered collar
4. Hub and disc assembly
5. Bearing distance piece
6. Taper-roller bearings
7. Outer oil seal
8. Inner oil seal
9. Drive shaft

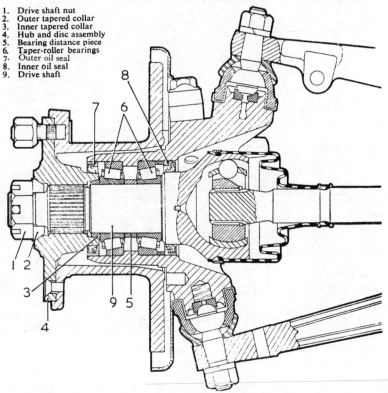

Fig. 3:16. A section through the front hub assembly, Cooper S.

distance and the nut and washer, instead of clamping the hub and bearings together, butts up on the protruding shaft. This fault is not easy to spot unless it is specifically looked for. The simplest remedy is to counterbore the thick washer in a lathe enough to allow the end of the shaft to be pulled into it. Alternatively, a large washer, big enough to go over the splined shaft could be fitted before the normal one is replaced. The amount of protrusion seldom exceeds 0·025 to 0·030in. so a thick washer is unnecessary.

When the hub has been dismantled and cleaned as described below, the bearings should be examined and discarded if there is any sign of chipping or crazing of the ball tracks or discolouration of the balls. If the hub has been run for any period with the central hub loose it is possible for the spacer between the bearings to wear. This results in excessive pre-load on the bearings causing stiffness of the hub and rapid bearing wear. Always replace the spacer as well as the bearings if there is any doubt. If the bearings are found to be slack in the hub it is best to replace the hub. If for any reason this is not possible, Loctite Bearing Fit may help to retain them but remember that wear of the register in the centre of hub will result in slackness unless the spacer is thinned down by exactly the same amount.

RENEWING THE BEARINGS

All drum-braked Minis, front hubs

First remove the brake drums, then remove the complete front hub assemblies from the suspension and drive shafts, as described in the previous section (page 63). Support the assembly, shoes downwards, on two stout wooden blocks (approx. 6in. × 4in. × 9in. high). Drift the drive flange downwards out of the bearings. The inner race of the outer bearing (and the outer grease seal) will probably come out with the drive flange from which it will require a puller to remove it. Remove the inner grease seal from the hub bore and the spring-steel spacer ring. Drift out the remaining races and remove the bearing spacer. Drift the outer races outwards from the bore, which is machined to leave a register between the bearings. Wash out the hub bore, taking care that no oil is washed on to the brake shoes.

Reassembly of the front hub. Carefully pack the new bearings with grease. Drift the outer bearing into position in the hub bore, insert the bearing spacer and drift in the inner bearing, making sure that the bearings are inserted thrust-face to thrust-face. Fit the outer grease seal, preferably not quite hard up against the bearing. Fit the spring steel spacer ring and the inner grease seal. Drift the drive flange through the outer bearing, turn the assembly over and drift the inner bearing on to the drive flange.

Reassemble on to the drive shaft, replace the drive-shaft nut.

Reassemble to the car, replace the brake drum and, with an assistant on the brake pedal, tighten the drive-shaft nut to 60lb ft torque and lock with a split pin.

997/998 Cooper front hubs

The procedure for Coopers is as for drum braked cars except that the caliper is removed from the hub and then the hub can be dismantled away from the car, thus simplifying the job.

Cooper S and 1275 GT front hubs

Remove the central drive-shaft nut and the split taper collar beneath it. Remove the brake caliper from the hub and pull the drive flange and disc from the end of the drive shaft.

Split the top and bottom steering swivels and the steering-arm ball joint. It should now be possible to pull the hub from the drive shaft whilst tapping the end of the shaft with a hide-faced mallet. The bearings, which are of the taper roller type, are removed from the hub as described for the other Minis. The bearings should only be fitted in pairs together with a matched spacer.

Rear hub bearings (all models)

All the rear hub bearings are the same angular-contact ball type except for the Cooper S which should have taper rollers.

Removal. Jack up the car and remove the appropriate rear wheel. Remove the brake drum and prise off the hub cap. Extract the split pin and remove the slotted nut from the stub axle, remembering that the left-hand wheel has a left-hand thread. Withdraw the hub assembly either using a puller or with the aid of two tyre levers or stout screwdrivers. Remove the grease seal and drift the outer races outward from the central shoulder, keeping them parallel to the bore during extraction.

If, as sometimes happens, the inner ball race disintegrates during removal of the hub, an inner race extractor or a tool of the type shown in fig 3:17 may be used to remove it.

Reassembly. Pack both bearings with grease and drift them into position (thrust to thrust) in the hub bore so that they are fitted hard against the central shoulder, not forgetting the spacer between them. Fit a new grease seal in the hub bore and refit the assembly to the stub axle. Make sure when doing this, that the bearing spacer is lifted over the shoulder on the stub axle before trying to push the hub assembly on. Fit the thrust washer with the chamfered bore towards the bearing, replace the nut and tighten to 60lb ft torque, lock with a split pin. Replace the hub dust cap, brake drum and road wheel.

Adjustment of steering swivels

If the top and bottom steering swivels become worn, usually through lack of lubrication, they should be removed and examined to see if adjustment or renewal is required. If the balls and cups are found to be pitted or worn oval they should be renewed but, if they are serviceable, they may be cleaned and readjusted. Removal and inspection is carried out as follows:

Separate the top and bottom swivels from their tapers as detailed for

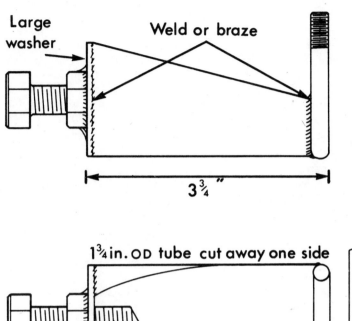

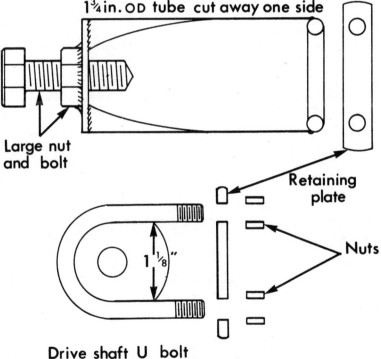

Fig. 3:17. Suggested design for rear-hub inner-race extractor.

the rubber universal joints (page 62). Take off the housing dust seal, remove the grease nipple and knock down the flats on the locking washer. The top of the housing may now be unscrewed with a large box spanner and the ball and seating removed. When the lower ball joint is removed, note that there is a spring beneath the seating which must not be omitted. To check the ball joint for correct adjustment, wash off all the components in paraffin or other solvent and assemble the joint without the packing shims, locking washers or, in the case of the lower joint, the seat spring. Tighten down the housing until there is no free movement between the ball and the seating and then measure the gap

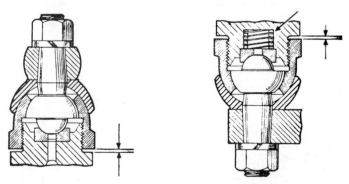

Fig. 3:18 Swivel hub ball joints, showing positions for feeler gauge measurements.

between the housing and the top of the hub with feeler gauges (see fig. 3:18). Remove the housing and ball, pack the joint with grease, remember to replace the spring beneath the lower seat and assemble the joint with lock washer, grease nipple and shims to the value of the feeler gauge measurement less the thickness of the lock washer (0·036in.) plus 0·002/0·003in. to allow free movement. When the joint is complete, tighten down the housing to the recommended torque figure and check that the ball pin can swivel freely and that there is now no significant end float. Knock up the locking washer and refit the dust cover. Refit to the top and bottom suspension arms. Tighten all the nuts to the recommended torque figure (see Appendix III).

Steering-arm ball joints

The steering-arm ball joints should be inspected occasionally for wear. This takes the form of shake or looseness in the joint and it must not be allowed to become excessive. A worn joint receives a considerable hammering when in use and it can break off with dire results. Worn joints should be replaced with new ones as follows: slacken off the ball joint lock-nut on the steering tie rod and remove the nut securing the joint to the steering arm. Loosen the joint from its tapered socket in the steering arm, either by striking the end of the arm with a hammer or by using a ball-joint extractor, and unscrew the joint from the steering tie rod. Fit a new joint and check the wheel alignment after assembly. (See page 77).

Steering rack and pinion

It is a quite common fault for older Minis to develop slackness in the steering rack as the components wear. Probably the most usual cause is the deterioration of the felt bush which, until fairly recently, was used as a support for the end of the steering rack which is further from the steering box; on later models or when renewing a felt type, a 'Vulkollan' plastic bush should be fitted and these should last longer. Wear also takes place on the rack and pinion teeth and although some adjustment is possible by swapping packing shims, accurate adjustment requires the use of a bearing preload gauge (B L part 18G207).

Removal. To remove the steering rack from the car, it is necessary to lower the front sub-frame about 3in. from the body of the car and this is done as follows:

Remove the nut and the clamping bolt which supports the steering column on the parcel shelf; remove the nut, bolt and washer which clamp the bottom of the column to the pinion shaft and pull the column off the shaft splines taking care not to strain the indicator wires. Jack up the front of the car, supporting it under the sub-frame and remove the front wheels and both front shockabsorbers. Release both steering arm ball joints from their tapered sockets (as described on page 72) and remove them. Take off the air cleaner and disconnect the exhaust pipe, both from the manifold and from the transmission casing. Remove the bolts fixing the engine steady bar to the cylinder block. Remove the four screws and nuts which attach the rear of the sub-frame to the floor and slacken the nuts on the sub-frame front-mounting bolts. Release the locking tabs on the nuts or bolts which hold the top of the sub-frame towers to the bulkhead. Inside the car, remove the four nuts (two are to be found beneath the carpet in each foot well) which hold the steering rack U-bolts to the floor.

Place some suitable supports under the vehicle body but not under the sub-frame and then carefully lower the sub-frame down from the body. It may be necessary to employ a couple of strong tyre levers, positioned between the sub-frame towers and the body, to lower the sub-frame far enough to remove the U-bolts from around the steering rack and get sufficient clearance to extract the rack assembly from the driver's side of the vehicle.

With the rack removed from the vehicle it can now be stripped down and examined for excessive wear.

Inspection of the steering rack and pinion

Slacken the lock-nuts on the end ball joints and unscrew these joints from the shaft. Remove the retaining clips from the rubber gaiters, remembering that they should have oil inside; drain off the oil and remove the gaiters. Take out the two bolts which secure the steering damper housing, these are the ones at right angles to the pinion shaft, and withdraw the housing and damper, watch out for the shims between the housing and the main casing, noting the number and thickness for replacement. Now remove the two bolts holding on the bottom plate; this also has packing shims and supports the lower bearing. Take out the thrust washer and bearing and withdraw the pinion shaft.

It is now necessary to remove the ball joint housing from, at least, the end of the rack opposite to the steering box and, for a complete inspection, from both ends. To do this, as recommended by the manufacturers, one should use a rack ball-joint spanner (18G707) but very careful use of a vice with soft jaws and some pipe grips will achieve the same result. Unlock the lock washer or locking ring (either may be fitted), slacken back the locking ring and then unscrew and remove the ball housing and take out the seat spring. The rack can now be withdrawn from the pinion end of the rack housing. Next remove the bush-securing screw from the rack housing and withdraw the bush and bush sleeve.

Wash off the oil from the component parts and examine them for wear or damage; check that the teeth of the rack are not pitted or badly worn on their mating faces, also check the ball joints for slackness. If wear is present, new pieces should be fitted. Before reassembling, examine the rubber gaiters; if these are deteriorating it is sensible to fit new ones as a hole in one of these would soon allow the lubricating oil to drain out of the rack housing.

When reassembling the steering rack, a plastic bush with a steel sleeve and spacer should be fitted instead of an original felt bush. The spacer is inserted plain-end first into the rack housing, the plastic bush then fits into the steel sleeve which is also inserted plain-end first. The flats on the plastic should be away from the retaining-screw hole. When the bush is correctly positioned, drill through the screw hole and bush with a $\frac{7}{64}$ in. drill. Remove the swarf and insert the screw, preferably with some oil resistant jointing compound on the threads and under the head; be sure to check that this screw does not project through the bush into the bore. Replace the top pinion bearing, if it has been removed, and insert the rack into the housing; refit the pinion shaft, lower bearing, bearing cover plate and cover screws but do not overtighten these screws. With a set of feeler gauges, measure the gap between the housing and the cover plate, remove the cover plate and fit shims to this value less 0·002in., this will

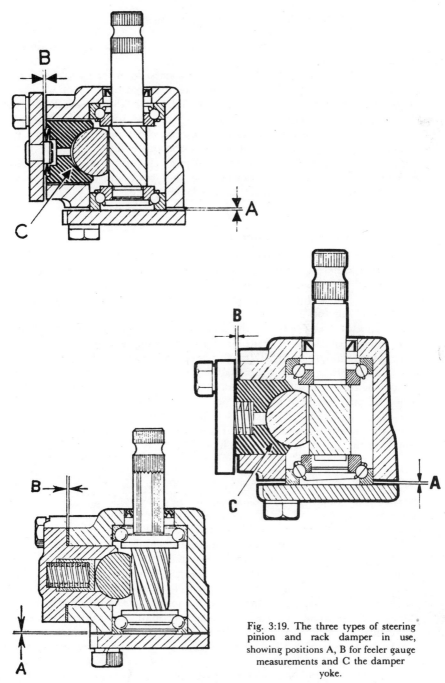

Fig. 3:19. The three types of steering pinion and rack damper in use, showing positions A, B for feeler gauge measurements and C the damper yoke.

give the recommended pre-load. It is also suggested that the jointing faces be coated with a thin layer of 'Hermatite' or a similar jointing to prevent leakage. Now refit the cover plate and shims and tighten down the retaining bolts.

On models fitted with ball-end lock washers, screw the ball-housing locking ring onto the rack as far as possible, followed by the lock washer; otherwise fit a new locking ring screwed right on to the thread. Replace the seat spring, seating, tie-rod and housing, tighten up until the ball-end is slightly pinched, screw up the locking ring, checking that the joint is still pinched, and then back-off the housing one-eighth of a turn, this should allow free movement of the ball joint. Tighten the locking ring, making sure that the ball housing does not turn, and finally re-lock either the lock washer (if fitted) or the locking ring.

Steering-rack damper adjustment

Three types of damper have been fitted since the Mini range started production, differing slightly in design but almost identical in operation. Adjustment of these dampers is as follows:

Assemble the damper housing to the steering box without damper spring or shims (do not overtighten the housing screws) and take feeler gauge measurements between the damper housing and the steering box. Now remove the housing, refit the damper spring and fit shims to the feeler gauge value plus 0·001/0·003in.; replace housing bolts and tighten down. If possible, the torque load needed to start movement of the pinion should be measured; the correct value of this will depend on the type of damper fitted but should be between 15lb in. for the earlier type and 35lb in. for the latest and in any case if it is too tight it will soon be noticed when the rack is refitted to the car and adjustment is possible without removing the complete rack assembly again.

Assembly of the steering rack

Replace the rubber gaiters, clipping them to the rack housing at both ends and to the tie-rod at the end away from the steering box. Stand the rack upright with the steering box at the top and pour ⅓ pint of 90 SAE grade oil into the top gaiter and then clip the gaiter to the tie-rod. Screw the lock-nuts onto each tie-rod followed by the ball ends. Turn the pinion so that the rack is centralized and, if there is no mark on the pinion shaft already, mark it so that the central position can be checked when the rack is refitted to the car; late models have a line stamped on the end of the pinion shaft which, when the shaft is centralized, should be vertical, below centre for right hand drive cars and above centre on left hand drive models. Refitting the rack to the car is straightforward if the removal instructions are reversed. Mk II racks have a centralizing peg hole. This is found beneath the floor at the opposite end of the rack to the pinion. If the rubber stopper in the floor is removed a plastic plug will be seen. Pulling this out exposes the hole into which a suitably sized metal peg is inserted to lock the rack while adjustments are made to the wheel alignment which must of course be checked when the rack has been refitted.

Wheel alignment

It is very important that the front wheel alignment is kept correctly adjusted. A very high rate of tyre wear occurs if the car is run far with the wheels out of track. If the front tyres wear unevenly or 'feather', the track should be checked. It is also wise to check the track if a kerb or other solid object has been struck hard with a front wheel.

Adjustment of wheel alignment is best done by a garage which has accurate equipment for the job, since the small size of the wheels make a correct setting very difficult to achieve using less precise methods. If such equipment is not available, the alignment should be checked by careful measurement.

With the steering in the straight-ahead position, each wheel should make an angle of 7 minutes 30 seconds with the longitudinal axis of the car; in this position the front of the wheels will be $\frac{1}{16}$ in. farther apart than the rear. To check this accurately, measurement should be taken on a 14·5in. diameter (this is on the side wall of the tyre) and at wheel centre level. Remember that as tyre manufacturing tolerances vary, these measurements should be taken with the tyres in several positions, that is by rolling the car half a wheel revolution back or forward between pairs of measurements, finally taking the average of a set of readings. If it is necessary to alter the alignment, slacken the lock-nut for each tie-rod ball joint and also the clips securing the rubber gaiters, turn each tie-rod about the same amount in the required direction, that is out of the ball joint to decrease the distance between the front of the tyres and into the ball joint to increase this distance. Tighten up the lock-nuts before taking the next measurements and remember to lock up finally when the correct alignment is achieved. When braced-tread tyres are fitted, it is advisable to have the wheels adjusted to run parallel.

Maintenance of the braking system

The brakes should remain in good working order if they are serviced regularly but they will deteriorate slowly and the faults which so develop do not always manifest themselves until an emergency arises. The main faults which cause braking inefficiency are outlined below.

1 Lack of lining material, usually at the front, which if not attended to allows the rivets to score the drums or the brake pad backing material to scrape on the disc with a loud 'graunching' noise.

2 A fluid leak either from the wheel cylinders, the master cylinder or

a brake pipe rusted or damaged. This allows air to enter the system and the pedal feels spongy when pressed.

3 Seized wheel cylinders or calipers causing pulling to one side.

4 Seized or worn handbrake mechanism giving inefficient handbrake.

5 Warped drums or discs causing vibration which can be felt through the car body and through the pedal under heavy braking.

Diagnosis of braking faults

A straightforward heavy-braking test from about 15 or 20 mile/h can show up several faults. It should be carried out on a smooth, dry, even surface, with the car lightly loaded. With the brakes in good condition, it should just be possible to lock all four wheels. The skid marks should be the same length for each pair of wheels although the rear ones may be longer than the front. There should be no noticeable tendency to pull to one side. Further checks must be carried out if any unevenness or inefficiency is apparent. Jack the car up so that all the wheels are free and get an assistant to apply the footbrake gently but not so as to prevent the wheels being turned by hand. Try all the wheels and check that the effort required to turn both front wheels is the same. Repeat the procedure at the rear. If a wheel requires less effort than its opposite number, a stiff or seized caliper or wheel cylinder must be suspected.

Having done this first check, apply the footbrake hard and then release it. Spin all the wheels round by hand to see if any of the brakes stay on or drag, which again would indicate seizure. Repeat both these checks with the handbrake. Unevenness here may be caused by maladjustment (see page 29) or seizure of the quadrants on the rear radius arm or the links inside the drum.

A very spongy feel to the pedal is usually caused by air in the system. If bleeding fails to cure it, the master cylinder may be faulty. To check this, borrow four brake pipe clamps and clamp all four flexible hoses. The pedal should then have very little travel and a very solid feel. If this is not the case, the master cylinder must be suspect.

Removal of the clamps, one at a time, can also be used as a method of finding which part of a system has air trapped in it. Pedal vibration when braking fairly hard from high speed is usually caused by distorted discs, drums or drive flanges. The drums can be changed round front to rear to see if the bad one can be isolated. Discs should be checked for run-out at the periphery. It should not exceed 0·004–0·005in.

The correction of these faults is described below.

Replacement of worn shoes

This should be carried out as follows:

Note where the pull-off springs are attached to the brake shoes and

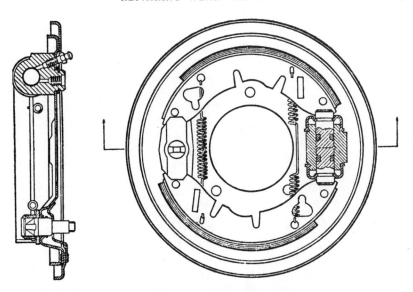

Fig. 3:20. The pre-1965 850 Mini right-hand front brake assembly showing the correct fitted position of the brake shoes and pull-off springs.

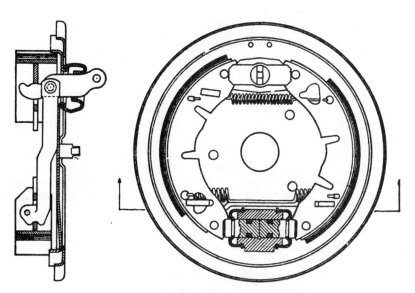

Fig. 3:21. The right-hand rear brake assembly (all models), showing the correct fitted position of the brake shoes and pull-off springs.

also that the springs are positioned so that the coils stand away from the wheel hubs. (See fig. 3:20, 3:21 and 3:22.)

Remove the shoes by levering the end of one shoe out from the slots in the adjuster and lifting it forward. The springs and shoes are now easily removed, care being taken not to displace the hydraulic pistons as this would necessitate bleeding the system. Never operate the brake pedal with the brake drums removed.

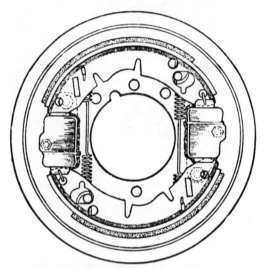

Fig. 3:22. Elf/Hornet Mk II, III and post-1965 Mini left-hand front-brake assembly showing correct fitted position of shoes and pull-off springs.

Before fitting the new shoes, it may be helpful and for competition linings almost essential to chamfer about $\frac{1}{8}$in. of the leading edge at about 45 degrees, to prevent grabbing while the shoes are bedding in.

To refit the shoes, hook the springs on to both shoes at the hydraulic cylinder end and on one shoe at the adjuster end. Holding the shoes apart to keep the springs in place, insert the hydraulic cylinder ends in their respective slots, position the other spring behind the hub and attach it to both shoes. Insert the end of one shoe in the adjuster slot and lever the other shoe outward and push into position in the slot.

Refit drum and adjust as previously indicated.

Pad replacement

Remove the pad-retaining split pins and the spring retainer. Pull one of the pads, together with its shim, from the caliper with a pair of pliers. Clean, by scraping, and blowing out any rust or dust from the pad recess in the caliper and also from the exposed portion of the piston. Check that the cutaway portion of the piston is uppermost and turn the piston in the caliper to correct this if necessary. Then, by levering steadily and squarely with a pair of large screwdrivers or similar implements, push the piston back into its recess in the caliper. During this procedure the fluid level in the master cylinder reservoir will rise and it may be necessary to siphon off a small quantity to prevent overflowing. In any

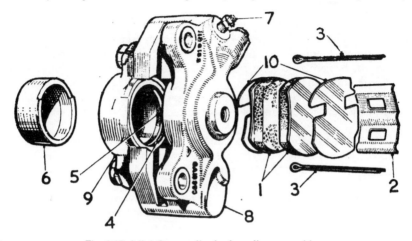

Fig. 3:23. Mini Cooper disc brake caliper assembly.

1. Friction pads.	6. Piston showing cut-away.
2. Pad retaining springs.	7. Bleeder screw.
3. Retaining split pins.	8. Mounting half-caliper.
4. Piston dust seal.	9. Rim half-caliper.
5. Piston fluid seal.	10. Anti-squeak shim.

case, remove the reservoir cap or excess fluid may squirt from the vent hole and could damage adjacent paintwork.

Before fitting a new pad into the caliper, clean any rust from the anti-squeak shim and smear the metal back of the pad and the shim with brake grease or fluid. Do this very sparingly and do not allow the fluid to contact the pad or disc. When the pad and shim have been replaced, repeat the procedure with the other side of the caliper. Fit new retaining clips and split pins (these come with new pads) and then pump the brake pedal a few times to adjust the calipers. Finally top up the master cylinder reservoir and replace the cap.

Fluid leaks

A brake-fluid leak is seldom difficult to find and the most likely places are the wheel cylinders which leak around the internal seals causing fluid to accumulate inside the rubber dust covers, eventually oozing out on to the brake linings. On disc-braked cars, the caliper seals may leak in a similar manner. Fluid leaking from the brake master cylinder will appear inside the car around the brake pedal linkage. The pressure-limiting valve is a possible source of leakage on old cars if the washer has not been changed but the hydraulic pipes themselves are seldom a cause of trouble unless damaged or severely corroded. Damage to the hydraulic lines usually means a complete failure of the brakes.

Wheel cylinders

Brake cylinders should be examined when the drums and shoes are removed. The pistons in the wheel cylinder should be free to move with hand pressure only. Never push the brake pedal right down with a drum removed. Seized or leaking cylinders should be removed by unscrewing the pipe and either prising off the spring retainer or circlip or removing the two retaining bolts according to type. Buy new spring clips before this job is started because old rusty clips are easily broken while being removed.

The pistons in the cylinders can be pulled out when the rubber dust seals have been removed. The bore of the cylinder should be bright and smooth and if rusting or pitting has occurred it should be replaced with a new cylinder assembly.

New rubber seals may be fitted if the cylinders are in good condition. All traces of cleaning fluid must be removed from the cylinders before assembly. Lubricate all the parts with brake fluid and fit new seals (using only the fingers, to avoid damage to the seals), with their largest diameter towards the inside of the cylinder. Reassemble the cylinder to the backplate, clean out the holes in the bleed valve and refit the brake shoes. Take care not to push the pistons out of double ended cylinders while refitting the shoes.

Dismantling the brake calipers

Unlock the locking tab and release the nut securing the tie-rod ball end to the steering arm. Remove the two screws and nuts holding the locking plate onto the disc dust cover. Remove the two bolts securing the caliper on to the front hub. Remove the upper and lower halves of the dust cover and remove the caliper assembly.

Do not remove the rubber hose but support the caliper assembly so as not to strain it. Remove the friction pads and clean the caliper assembly, removing all dust and any cleaning fluid.

With the help of an assistant, gently apply the foot brake; this will force the pistons out of the caliper and if care is taken, both pistons can be removed at the same time.

With a blunt-nosed tool, remove the fluid seal from its groove in the piston bore, taking care not to damage the bore or the retaining groove. The dust seal retainer can be removed by carefully levering it from the mouth of the caliper bore, the rubber seal may then be removed.

Only brake fluid or methylated spirit should be used for cleaning the caliper bore as other cleaning fluids may damage the internal rubber seals.

Reassembly

Lubricate the new fluid seal with Lockheed disc-brake lubricant and ease the seal into its groove. Make sure that the seal is the correct way round. Slacken the bleeder screw, in the caliper, one complete turn. Lubricate the piston with disc-brake lubricant and place in the bore with the cutaway facing upwards. Press the piston into the bore until only $\frac{7}{16}$in. of the piston protrudes, taking care that the piston is inserted squarely.

Refit a new dust seal in its retainer, having first lubricated it with disc-brake lubricant. Fit the seal assembly on to the protruding portion of the piston, with the seal on the inside, and press home the piston and seal assembly. Re-tighten the bleeder screw.

Both halves of the caliper assembly are dealt with in the same manner. Refit the caliper and the two halves of the dust cover to the hub. Refit and tighten the two screws retaining the dust cover to the tie-rod end-nut locking plate. Tighten the tie-rod ball-end nut and lock with the locking plate. A new locking plate should be used whenever possible. Tighten the caliper mounting bolts. Refit the friction pad assemblies as previously described and bleed the brake system.

Master cylinders

The master cylinder is removed from the car as follows: First remove the split pin from the clevis pin that secures the brake pedal to the master cylinder rod. It is found above the pedals inside the car and is rather inaccessible. If the pedal is lifted up hard it will prevent the clevis pin from turning and makes unbending of the split pin somewhat easier. Having removed the clevis, take off the nuts holding the cylinder down to the bulkhead in the engine compartment. If a spanner cannot be found that will remove the nut between the cylinders, the clutch cylinder will have to be removed first. Unscrew the hydraulic pipe from the union on the bulkhead and from the top of the cylinder and then lift the cylinder from the car.

Be careful not to drop brake fluid onto the wing or any other paint during the procedure.

Dismantling the cylinder

Empty out the fluid from the reservoir and take the rubber boot off the bottom. Press the piston rod down and remove the retaining circlip. Release the piston rod and the spring inside will push out most of the internal parts. A sectioned view of a master cylinder is shown in fig. 3:24. The cylinder should be washed out with methylated spirit or brake fluid. If the internal bore of the cylinder is free from scratches and roughness

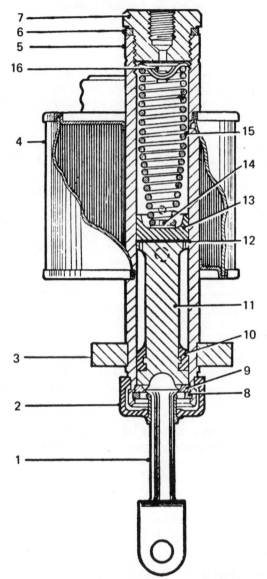

1. Push rod.
2. Rubber boot.
3. Mounting flange.
4. Supply tank.
5. Cylinder body.
6. Washer.

7. End plug.
8. Circlip.
9. Stop washer
10. Secondary cup.
11. Piston.

12. Piston washer.
13. Main cup.
14. Spring retainer.
15. Return spring.
16. Valve assembly.

Fig. 3:24. A sectional view of the brake master cylinder.

or pitting, generally caused by corrosion, it is serviceable and may be reassembled with new seals. Be careful to avoid scratching the piston when fitting the seals and before reassembly. The new seals, which come in a kit complete with a top valve, must of course face in the correct direction.

When the cylinder has been refitted to the car it often helps in bleeding the system if the cylinder alone is bled before the hydraulic pipe is screwed into it. To do this, fill the reservoir with fluid and very slowly depress the pedal. When the pedal is right down, get an assistant to pour fluid into the outlet hole in the top. Then release the pedal slowly and continue to pour fluid down into the top, keeping it full of fluid. Very slowly depress the pedal again when bubbles will come up through the fluid. Continue this procedure until no bubbles appear when the pedal is pressed. This process ensures that when the pipe is connected, and the normal bleeding procedure commenced, the cylinder will pump fluid straight away.

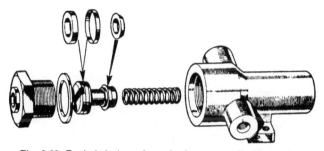

Fig. 3:25. Exploded view of rear-brake pressure-limiting valve.

Pressure-limiting valve

Pressure limiting valves are much less prone to faults than the rest of the system as they are better sealed against dirt and water. If they do deteriorate, the fault is less obvious than with other parts. They cannot normally leak and allow air into the system but dirt or failing seals can cause excessive rear wheel locking under heavy braking. They are straightforward to strip and reassemble (see fig. 3:25).

The rear-brake pressure-limiting valve is mounted on the inside of the right hand rear sub-frame. Some trouble has been experienced with this valve when an aluminium sealing washer was used on the end cap. Corrosion, especially from salt used to clear ice from roads, can cause the washer to deteriorate and eventually leak; this could occur suddenly when braking hard so that it is a sensible precaution to change to the later copper washer if an aluminium one is still in position.

The valve is quite easily removed from the sub-frame after the three hydraulic pipes have been unscrewed. It should then be dismantled and cleaned. The metal cylinder may be washed in petrol but all traces must be removed before reassembly. Rubber parts should be washed in brake fluid. Examine the seatings and rubber washers for bad seating and deterioration; if everything appears in good condition it should be lubricated with brake fluid and reassembled as shown in fig. 3:25. Fit a new copper washer under the end cap and refit the unit to the brake pipes and replace the bolts securing it to the sub-frame. It will then be necessary to bleed at least the rear brakes and, if the brake pedal is still spongy after bleeding, the front brakes should also be bled. (See page 87.)

Brake intensifiers and vacuum servos

On early Mini Coopers, a brake intensifier is fitted to the hydraulic brake system to increase the available pressure for the front brakes.

This cylinder is mounted on the right-hand wing valance of the engine compartment and is connected to the master-cylinder at its lower end and to the front brakes at the top connection. On later cars the fitting of an intensifier was discontinued and a modified master-cylinder was fitted instead.

When an intensifier is fitted and the brakes are to be bled, the intensifier system must be bled first before proceeding as normally with the brakes (page 87).

On 'S' type Cooper and 1275 GT models, a vacuum servo unit is a standard fitting to the braking system. This unit provides assistance when the brakes are applied, power is provided by vacuum from the inlet manifold and by atmospheric pressure. Little maintenance should be necessary for this unit, all that is normally required is to clean the air filter at least every 12,000 miles as follows: Release the outer end of the heater air-intake hose. Remove the five setscrews from the air-valve cover and remove the cover. Push the air valve off its seating and blow out the filter chamber. Do not lubricate the filter or remove it from the air valve cover. Replace the air valve in its seating and refit the cover.

A fault which can occur on a brake servo is an internal leak which lets fluid pass into the vacuum chamber and eventually into the inlet manifold and cylinders where it is burned. This is not an easy leak to find but once the servo unit has been dismantled it is obvious as the vacuum chamber will contain fluid. If a fault with the servo is suspected it should be removed and dismantled. If it is found to be in good condition, uncorroded and not scored on its working surfaces it may be rebuilt with new seals.

Two types of servos have been used, the earlier type has its vacuum chamber held together with a vee shaped band and a clamp bolt. The only difficulty with rebuilding this unit is that a special sleeve is needed to assist reassembly of the main piston to the cylinder bore. The

PLATE I

(a) Badly burned or eroded electrodes indicating overheating. Fuel/air mixture too weak or incorrect plugs fitted.

(b) Brown or grey light deposit indicates correct fuel/air mixture and correct grade of spark plugs.

(c) Dry black deposit indicates fuel/air mixture too rich. 'Choke' may be stuck or carburetter incorrectly adjusted.

PLATE II

(a)

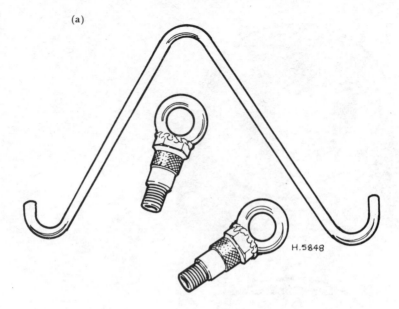

H.5848

(a) Alternative lifting hook and eyes made from old spark plug bodies with steel rings welded on. These are fitted into the plug holes of cylinders no. 1 and 4.

(b)

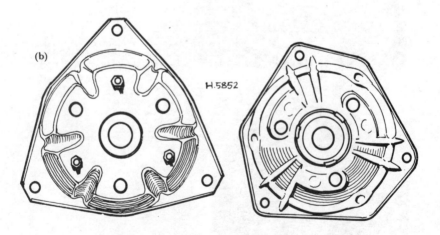

H.5852

(b) The two types of clutch spring covers; *left*, the coil-spring clutch type with its triangular thrust plate and *right*, the diaphragm-spring type with its circular thrust plate.

dimensions of this sleeve are length 1·61in. to 1·62in., diameter 0·746 to 0·748in. and bore 0·625 to 0·627in. Its function is to prevent damage to the edge of the new cup seal as it is refitted to the bore and it is placed in the large diameter outer end of the bore while this is done. The essential thing with a servo is not to dismantle all of it into tiny pieces and then try to obtain new parts but to fit new seals one by one so that the direction they face and their position is not forgotten. Obviously absolute cleanliness is essential, use only methylated spirits or clean brake fluid for cleaning and lubricate the working parts with fluid during reassembly. Always fit new seals and gaskets throughout.

The same principles apply to the later servo, as used on the 1275 GT, except that the method of dismantling is not as obvious. The vacuum chamber is removed by holding the slave cylinder gently in a vice and turning the end of the vacuum chamber anti-clockwise with a bar held down on to the end by the mounting studs. Considerable force may be necessary to release this end cover. When the end cover is removed, the diaphragm has to be unpeeled from its boss on the centre of the support piston. A clip, which slips into a slot beneath where the diaphragm fits, holds the support piston to the piston rod. Once this clip has been shaken out, dismantling is straightforward. No other special tools are required to reassemble this servo.

Check the size of new rubber seals against the old ones. Some of these servos have been made with different bore sizes and if one of a non-standard (for a Mini) bore has been fitted it could lead to confusion.

Bleeding the brake system

Should it be necessary to bleed the hydraulic system, obtain about 2ft of small bore tubing and a glass jar. Top up the fluid reservoir and ensure that it is kept above half-full throughout the operation, otherwise air may enter the system, necessitating a fresh start.

Clean the bleeding nipple, to be found on the backplate at the rear of the hydraulic cylinder and attach the rubber tube. With the brake drum in place, unscrew the nipple about one turn with a spanner and with the aid of an assistant in the car, work the brake pedal slowly up and down until the brake fluid being expelled into the jar is free from air bubbles; in some cases it may be necessary to stop and refill the reservoir once or twice before sufficient fluid has been passed through to expel all the air. When the fluid is clear, the brake pedal should be held down to the floor while the nipple is tightened. In order to ensure complete expulsion of air from the system, bleeding should start at the wheel cylinder farthest from the master cylinder, i.e. rear near-side, and proceed towards the master cylinder. Fresh air-free fluid must be used to top up the reservoir.

Handbrake overhaul

The handbrake mechanism usually works quite satisfactorily, provided that it is properly maintained. There are however, one or two points in the system which may give trouble and these should be checked during overhauls.

The worst offender, especially on early models, is the bell-crank swivel on the rear suspension arm, round which the handbrake cable passes. This seizes up and either prevents the handbrake being applied or causes it to stick on; it is located on the underside of the rear suspension arm just to the rear of the arm pivot point. To free this bell-crank, the nut underneath it should be unscrewed about ½in. On early models, the bell-crank swivels on a stud but on later models a bolt passes right through the mounting and it may be necessary to hold a spanner on the head when slackening the nut.

Recently a third type of bell-crank mounting has been fitted, this has the pivot pin welded on and is secured to the suspension arm by nylon and steel washers and a spring clip. Once the nut or clip is loose the bell-crank should be levered down and the bolt (or stud) oiled above it (thin lubricating oil or penetrating oil may be best at this stage), then twist the crank until it swivels freely. Lubricate with thick oil or grease and tighten up the nut, which is self locking, sufficiently to hold the crank in place but not so much that it clamps it tightly to the suspension arm and prevents any movement.

The other troublesome point in the handbrake system is the actuating mechanism inside the brake drum. Seizure of the swivel here prevents the handbrake working, even though everything else is in good order. To free this swivel, it is first necessary to remove the rear wheel and brake drum. Tapping lightly with a hammer on the outside of the drum may assist in removing it if tight but slacken the adjusters first and remember to take out the Phillips screws. The brake shoes are then removed, use of a screwdriver, as a lever will help here. The brake cable is attached to the handbrake mechanism behind the backplate by a clevis pin secured by a split pin. This pin must be removed to free the cable and allow the seized mechanism to be removed from the car. The offending part is best held in a vice and the swivel worked to and fro while penetrating oil is applied until it is quite free. When reassembling, ensure that the brake shoes and springs are replaced correctly as shown on pages 79 and 80.

Seizure of the brake adjusting screws is best cured by soaking with penetrating oil. It is essential to use the correct tool if adjusters are tight, as a normal spanner will merely round off the squared corners of the adjusters. The special spanner is available from British Leyland dealers.

Replacing the windscreen

Although this job would not normally be considered as 'wear and tear', and is not often undertaken by the amateur mechanic, a broken windscreen is quite a common occurrence and since a new screen will only cost about £5 and the job is not too difficult, it is described in this chapter.

Removing the windscreen whole

If the windscreen is to be removed but is not broken, the procedure is as follows:

Remove the windscreen wipers from their splined bosses. Prise one end of the outside finisher strip from its channel in the rubber surround and remove the strip completely. Push the glass at one corner from inside the car and ease the rubber surround from the edge of the windscreen, working along the screen until it is sufficiently free to be removed.

Removing a broken windscreen

If the glass is broken, great care should be taken when removing the pieces as, even with toughened glass, the splinters are very sharp. If the glass is shattered but there is no hole in it, it is most advisable before attempting to remove the screen, to cover the demister ducts with sticky tape to prevent small particles of glass from falling into the demister tube. If the screen is broken there will almost certainly be small pieces of glass in these ducts and they must therefore be disconnected and carefully blown out before a new screen is fitted. All traces of broken glass must be removed from the rubber surround. If this is damaged, a new one should be fitted to avoid water leaks. When the broken glass has been removed, it will be found that small particles have collected in almost every crevice and these should be carefully cleaned out. Places to check while cleaning are the rear of the seat cushions, the front of the parcel shelf and door pockets, and inside the starter-button shield on early models.

Fitting the new glass

Fit the rubber surround to the windscreen aperture and lubricate the channel into which the glass fits, with soap solution, rubber grease or 'Swarfega'. Fit the new screen into the bottom channel of the surround, pushing it as far into the channel as possible and, starting at the bottom corner, lift the rubber lip over the glass. Use the B L tool (part no. 18G468) to do this or else a tool made from an old screwdriver with the blade edges rounded off will also serve. Work right round the screen, pushing the glass into the channel.

When the screen is in place, lubricate the finisher-strip channel as before and starting at the middle of the screen *i.e.* one end of the finisher strip, ease the strip back into position. The tool used for replacing the glass will also help to spread the channel before the strip is pushed home.

If the old strip is being replaced, care should be taken to get the corners back in their original positions as this will simplify the job.

Screenwiper failure

The cable rack, which operates the windscreen wipers on Minis, wears and allows the toothed wheels which engage with it, to slip out of mesh. When this occurs the offending wiper fouls the other one and prevents it operating. It should be removed as soon as possible because, if used in this condition, it may damage the motor or the operating mechanism of the other wiper. Slackness in the meshing of the wheels and cable rack allows excessive travel and the blades flop over the edge of the screen.

To remedy either of these troubles, the wheel boxes and rack must be removed from the car. First remove the wiper blades by levering the underside of the cap at the bottom of the blade upward with a screwdriver and off its splined boss. The nuts round the spindles can then be removed. The union nut securing the cable to the wiper motor is undone next, the plate on top of the wiper motor taken off and the end of the cable removed from its crankpin, after removal of its retaining spring clip. The complete rack assembly can then be removed from the car. If the teeth on the wheels have stripped, at the point where they engage with the rack, they may sometimes be salvaged by dismantling the wheel box, rotating the wheel through 180 degrees to allow the unworn teeth to engage with the rack, and reassembling. Failing this, new wheel boxes will have to be fitted. Sometimes the spring wire helix, which acts as a rack, works loose on the cable. In this case a new cable must be fitted. It is sometimes possible to improve the meshing of wheel and rack by bending the tops of the wheel boxes down slightly but discretion must be used here or the assembly will become stiff.

Always grease the cable and wheel boxes before reassembly. It is advisable to fit lock-nuts or lock washers to the wheelbox screws as they tend to work loose with use. Careful use of the wipers will prolong their life. They cannot be expected to work on a dry screen and overheating of the motor and slowing up will occur if they are used for any length of time under these conditions.

If the motor stops working, it is worth dismantling it to see if it can be repaired. The trouble may only be worn brushes and these are easy to replace. They can be obtained quite cheaply but exchange motors are much more expensive. To obtain access to the brush gear, remove the wires from the end cap of the motor and undo the screws holding the cap. Removal of the cap exposes the brush gear.

The later type of permanent magnet motor which has a cylindrical motor body differs in that the brush gear is fitted to a plate on the gearbox end of the armature. The magnet body and armature must be removed to get at them. The body of the motor should be refitted to the gearbox in its original position and the armature end-float, which is controlled by the thickness of shims beneath a screw in the side of the gearbox, should be checked. It should be between 0·002 and 0·008in. and if it is greater than 0·008in. shims should be removed from under the screw head to correct it.

Window channels

One part of the body which is very susceptible to rusting, is the window channel; on old Minis these may have deteriorated almost to non-existence and their appearance can spoil an otherwise presentable car. Removal is a fairly simple matter provided the fixing screws have not also deteriorated too far. The fixings are self tapping screws located in the bottom of the channel and once they have been removed the channel and window glasses can be lifted out. When new channels are fitted they should be sealed to the body, with sealing compound, to prevent leaks.

Minis not fitted with sliding windows do not suffer in this way.

Dropped and ill-fitting doors

Many older Minis, with the external type of hinge, suffer to a certain extent from slight dropping of the doors on their hinges. This is easily put right by adjustment of the hinges and locating dovetails. It is easier to adjust the position of the hinges on the doors, rather than adjust their position on the body and, to do this, the hinge securing screws must be loosened. Each hinge has a Phillips-head screw securing it to the front of the door. This can be seen right at the edge of the door, behind the hinge, when the door is open. A stud and nut also secure each hinge to the door, these are located behind the door trim. The vertical corner pieces of the trim should be sprung out of position by lifting the edge of each away from the main door trim when they can be removed. The main door trim can then be slid backwards as far as it will go and the hinge stud nuts can be loosened with a $\frac{7}{16}$ in. AF spanner, slid in behind the trim. The door may now be lifted slightly and shut in its correct position, unless the nylon dovetail is set incorrectly. Loosening its securing screws will enable it to be tapped up or down to reposition it. When the door is shut correctly, retighten the nuts on the hinge studs. It may be necessary to move the lock striker plate on the rear door-pillar if the door does not shut properly. If it shuts correctly, i.e. flush with the body, but does not close properly against the draught excluder, the metal strip, over which the draught excluder is fitted, will have to be bent slightly towards the door.

Rust

Minis, in common with most other cars, rust away. The extent to which this occurs depends mainly on the amount it is used on salty roads in winter. There is no 100% cure but regular hosing down of the under parts obviously helps. The worst areas are the front wings, the sills and the rear sub-frame. The most important of these are the sub-frame and sills as rust here will fail an MOT test.

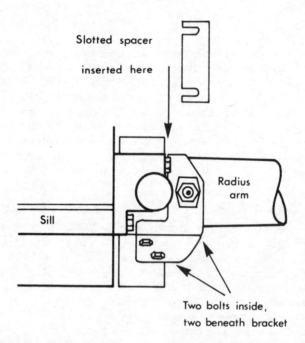

Slotted spacer

inserted here

Radius arm

Sill

Two bolts inside, two beneath bracket

Fig. 3:26. Rear radius-arm outer bracket showing shim adjustment of toe-in.

Rear sub-frame

Renewal of the rear sub-frame is a relatively straightforward job on a Mini with dry suspension but on a hydrolastic model the suspension must be depressurized as described in chapter 6. The sub-frame is held in by four nuts and bolts passing through the boot floor at the rear (or into captive nuts in the body on vans and estate cars), and by four bolts fixed into captive nuts at the front. If these bolts come out, the job is easy but the snags arise when the heads round off because they have rusted down undersize and/or they break off in the bracket. Worst of all is the captive nut escaping inside the end of the sill so that the bolt just turns round and round. The way out of these predicaments depends on the tools available but use of metric or single hexagon sockets can help undo bolts with undersize heads. Broken or more stubborn ones will have to be drilled away, an awkward and tedious process. Remember that the fuel pump should be removed from its bracket before the sub-frame is lowered and the top mountings of the shockabsorbers or auxiliary springs must also be removed.

Penetrating oil and patience is required to release the hydrolastic pipe unions. These sometimes rust onto the pipe to the extent where undoing them twists the steel hydrolastic pipe off. New front to back pipes can be obtained but they are almost impossible to fit on at the front without removing the front sub-frame! *You have been warned.*

The rear wheel alignment should be checked after a new sub-frame has been fitted. If, as is most probable, the rear wheels are found to be toeing in by up to $\frac{3}{8}$in., adjustment should be made by inserting packing pieces 0·030 to 0·040in. thick between the sub-frame and the radius arm outer end bracket. This moves the end bracket rearwards and reduces the toe in of the wheels. It is possible to insert the packing pieces without removing the bracket completely but the two forward facing bolts should be removed and the two lower ones slackened off. See fig. 3:26. The rear wheels should toe-in approximately $\frac{1}{16}$in.

Sills

The outer sill panels form a structural part of the car and therefore they should be welded into position when new ones are fitted. Pop-rivets and self tapping screws are not good enough. The old sill is removed by chiselling the remains away and sanding or grinding off protruding spot welds. Before clamping the new sill into position for welding, the car should be evenly supported on front and rear sub-frames and beneath the centre crossmember. This helps to avoid distorting the door aperture. Ideally the sill should be spot welded into position but normally gas welding is employed. Great care must be taken when tacking the flange below the rear body side because if this panel receives more than a very small quantity of heat it will distort quite badly. This wrinkling is very difficult to remove and somewhat unsightly although it does no structural harm.

If the inner sill is rusted, this also should be patched with steel sheet welded into position. If the inner sill is rusted through, across the end of the centre crossmember, it should be patched before the outer sill is replaced as any water which gets inside the sill will enter this crossmember and run out onto the floor. Opportunity should be taken to reinforce the seat belt anchorage while the job is being done.

Some very early Minis with foam filled sills only rust very slowly but when the time comes for repair the foam must be removed as it burns and emits a thick smoke. Always ensure that there is adequate ventilation while welding these cars.

Any rubbish that has fallen through the bottom of the rear glove pockets will catch fire when a sill is welded on, so remove the trim and check. Replace the trim when all welding is finished.

CHAPTER 4

MAJOR OVERHAULS OF THE POWER UNIT

Any major overhaul of the engine, gearbox or final drive unit necessitates the removal of the power unit from the car.

There are two ways in which this can be achieved: either the power unit is lifted out through the bonnet aperture, or the engine/sub-frame unit is released from the body which is then lifted away.

The first method is probably the easiest and quickest for most purposes and this requires lifting tackle capable of raising 330lb about 3ft; alternatively, if the engine and front sub-frame is released from the body it may then be lifted clear, leaving the power unit exposed for attention. This method will also require the use of lifting tackle or the assistance of several strong men as the body weighs approximately 900lb and the engine/sub-frame unit 430lb. Only the front of the body need be lifted, however, and this should be supported on blocks while work is carried out on the engine.

The second method has the disadvantage, on hydrolastic suspension models, that it is necessary to depressurize and disconnect the front suspension fluid pipes, which will need repressurizing when they are refitted (a job requiring the use of a Hydrolastic Suspension service unit), thus making the job difficult for the average amateur mechanic. However, in some circumstances, one or other method may be more useful and both will be described in some detail in this chapter.

Removal of the 850 Mini and Wolseley/Riley Mk I and II engine/gearbox unit

Drain the cooling system both from the radiator drain tap and from the drain tap on the rear of the cylinder block. Disconnect the battery and remove the bonnet from its hinges. Now raise the front of the car, far enough to allow work beneath the engine, preferably by jacking the front sub-frame onto blocks but the use of ramps or a pit will be satisfactory.

If a fresh-air heater is fitted, with the blower unit under the bonnet, disconnect the power-wire snap connector, release the air intake control cable and remove the earthing wire and the four securing nuts from beneath the wing. Disconnect the air pipe from the front grille and from the rear of the blower unit and remove the unit; secure the remaining air pipe to the bulkhead, clear of the engine. If the fresh-air heater has the motor mounted inside the car it is only necessary to remove the air hose

94

from the grille fixing and secure it to the bulkhead, clear of the engine. Disconnect first the heater inlet and outlet hoses and then remove the windscreen-washer bottle if it is fitted to the wing valance. Unscrew the sleeve nut to release the speedometer cable from the back of the instrument and release the cable from the clip on the bulkhead cross-member. If an oil pressure gauge is fitted, it will be necessary to remove the rubber connecting pipe. Disconnect the breather hose from the air cleaner and remove the air cleaner from the carburetter: also disconnect

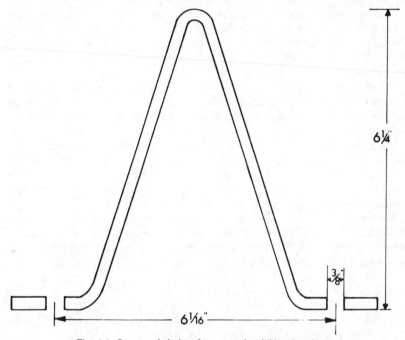

Fig. 4:1. Suggested design for an engine lifting bracket.

the mixture and throttle control cables from the carburetter, withdraw the throttle control cable from the grommet on the rocker cover. Remove the suction advance pipe and fuel pipe from the carburetter. Release the exhaust-pipe-to-manifold clamp and also the exhaust pipe mounting on the gear-change casing and lower the pipe to the ground.

Remove the nuts securing the inlet/exhaust manifold to the cylinder head and remove the manifold.

Unscrew the nuts and remove the two U-bolts which secure the flexible coupling to each drive shaft, marking the parts for reassembly in their original positions. Push these couplings and sliding joints outwards on to the drive shafts to enable the engine to clear these when it is lifted. Unscrew the hexagon plug from the gear-change casing and remove the anti-rattle spring and plunger. Inside the vehicle, remove the rubber gaiter at the bottom of the gear lever; through this aperture, remove the two setscrews securing the gear lever retaining plate and pull the lever out of the casing into the car.

Remove the tension spring from the clutch lever; take out the two setscrews securing the clutch slave cylinder to the flywheel housing and pull the push-rod from the slave cylinder which should then be secured clear of the engine. Disconnect the engine tie-rod from the cylinder block and swing the rod away from the engine, against the bulkhead.

Pull the caps from the spark plugs and remove the distributor cap, also disconnect the leads from the oil pressure warning-light switch on the front of the cylinder block, the coil, generator, distributor, temperature gauge (if fitted) and the starter motor cable, also do not forget to remove the earthing braid from the clutch cover.

When a remote solenoid starter-switch is fitted, unscrew the switch bracket retaining screws from the flywheel housing and lower the switch to the ground, clear of the engine. Remove the horn from the front crossmember.

It is now necessary to fit a lifting bracket or two lifting eyes and several alternatives are available. If the cylinder head is to be removed at a later stage remove the nuts from the second and fourth cylinder-head studs on the front of the engine and fit either two lifting eyes or a lifting bracket, manufactured approximately as shown in fig. 4:1.

However, if the cylinder head is not going to be removed it is unwise to slacken any head-nuts and in this case the rocker cover should be removed and the lifting eyes or bracket should be attached to the two long rocker shaft studs. Alternatively, two lifting eyes manufactured as in plate II (a) may be screwed into the outer plug holes. Now take the weight of the engine with suitable lifting tackle and remove the two bolts on each side securing the engine mountings to the sub-frame. Carefully raise the engine from the vehicle, making certain that the drive-shaft flexible couplings are held clear and that the clutch slave cylinder is also clear. A hardboard shield may be inserted between the radiator and the wing to prevent damage to the matrix while lifting. To clear the body with the gear-lever housing, it will be necessary to tilt the front of the engine up and backward slightly as it is raised. This is, of course, easier when the lifting eyes are on the front of the cylinder head.

If difficulties are encountered in lifting the motor, it is sometimes worthwhile draining the oil and removing the generator and ancillary equipment to lighten the load and simplify manoeuvering.

Removal of the engine/gearbox unit from other models

When removing the engine from models other than the 850, the following modifications to the procedure are necessary:

850 Automatic transmission. Remove the nuts from the drive-shaft flanges; pull back the rubber sleeve and disconnect the gear selector cable by removing the clevis pin. Slacken the yoke clamp-nut and remove the yoke, nut, and rubber ferrules and sleeve. Remove the cable front adjusting nut from the outer cable and pull the cable clear of the transmission. Remove the exhaust bracket from the final drive cover. (It should be noted that the larger nut is secured by a locking tab).

Models with 'remote' gear changes. Remove the exhaust pipe and silencer. Remove the four long bolts which attach the gear change extension to the transmission casing and lower the extension.

On models where servo-assisted brakes are fitted, when the engine is removed without the sub-frame, it is necessary to disconnect the vacuum and hydraulic pipes and remove the unit.

Replacement of the engine unit

As for removal, care should be taken, when lowering the engine into the engine compartment, not to damage the radiator matrix or cowling on the body. Keep the sliding joints pushed well onto the drive shafts while lowering the engine and refitting the rubber universal-joints. If a brake servo unit has been removed and refitted, the braking system must be bled throughout. (page 87.)

When refitting an engine with automatic transmission remember to check the adjustment of the gear rod and cable. Apart from these details the refitting operation is essentially the reverse of the removal procedure.

Removal of the engine and front sub-frame. 850 Mini and Wolseley/Riley Mk I and II

Remove the bonnet from its hinges. Disconnect the battery. Disconnect the heater water hoses and air hoses, as applicable. Unscrew the sleeve nut and release the speedometer cable from its clip on the bulkhead crossmember and secure it to the engine. Disconnect the breather hose from the air cleaner and remove the air cleaner. Remove the exhaust system by slackening the manifold clamp and releasing the pipe from the mountings on the gear-change extension and the two points on the rear sub-frame. Remove the manifold securing nuts and washers and lift off the manifold. Disconnect the spark plug leads and remove the distributor cap; also disconnect the leads from the oil-pressure warning-light switch, oil filter-light switch if fitted, the coil, generator, distributor and stop-light switch.

Remove the starter-motor cable from the motor and from the retaining clip on the sub-frame. Remove the earthing braid from the clutch cover. Disconnect the hydraulic-brake supply pipe from the union on the engine bulkhead and plug the union with a clean $\frac{3}{8}$in. UNF bolt to prevent the system from draining. Take the spring off the clutch slave cylinder and remove the cylinder from the flywheel housing. Secure the cylinder to the bulkhead, clear of the engine. Unscrew the hexagon plug from the gear-change casing and remove the anti-rattle spring and plunger.

Inside the vehicle, remove the rubber gaiter at the bottom of the gear lever; through this aperture, remove the two setscrews securing the gear-lever retaining plate and pull the lever out of the casing into the car. Disconnect the ball joints, at the steering-rack ends, from the steering arms. Remove the hydraulic shock absorbers fitted to cars with rubber suspension. Depressurize and evacuate the suspension system of hydrolastic suspension models. This will require the use of a Hydrolastic Suspension service unit, details of which will be found on page 128. Remove the engine tie-rod from the rear of the block and swing the rod away from the engine, against the bulkhead.

Support the engine, beneath the gearbox casing, on suitable blocks. Knock back the locking-washer tabs and remove the four bolts (or nuts on later cars) securing the sub-frame to the body; two are located each side on top of the bulkhead crossmember. Remove the four setscrews securing the rear of the sub-frame to the floor and also the two securing the front of the sub-frame to the bottom of the grille panel. The body should now be free from the sub-frame and may be lifted clear, taking care that while lifting, the body does not damage the radiator or cowling and that all cables are removed from the engine and safely secured.

On Cooper S models, when a brake servo is fitted, it is only necessary to disconnect the vacuum pipe from the inlet manifold.

Having raised the body it may either be supported on blocks, while the engine/sub-frame unit is removed, or be wheeled away leaving the engine clear for attention. It is usually necessary to remove the engine from the sub-frame to carry out further work.

Removing the engine from the sub-frame

Drain the water from the radiator and cylinder block and drain the oil from the transmission casing. Disconnect the drive shafts at the universal joints. Support the sub-frame under both side members with suitable blocks. Fit lifting eyes or a lifting bracket to the cylinder head, as described on page 96, and then take the weight of the engine with lifting tackle or with the help of two strong men, some rope and a long pole, then remove the two setscrews which secure each engine mounting to the sub-frame. The engine may now be lifted clear of the sub-frame. Replacement of the engine in the sub-frame is quite straightforward. When removing the engine/sub-frame assembly from models other than the 850 manual transmission, the notes on page 96, should be consulted, as these extra instuctions still apply.

Replacing the engine and front sub-frame

Reverse the removal procedure, taking care when lowering the body on to the engine/sub-frame assembly not to damage the radiator matrix or cowling and also not to trap the power cable from the battery, between the body and sub-frame. The braking system should be bled throughout when reassembly is complete. When reconnecting the drive shafts to the engine, the universal joints should be refitted in their original positions. Care should be taken when tightening the self-locking nuts to the U-bolts securing the rubber spiders; when correctly fitted, only $\frac{1}{16}$ in. of thread should protrude from the nuts. Overtightening will damage the joints and reduce their life. The steering arm ball-joint nut should be tightened to 25lb ft torque. On Hydrolastic models, when the suspension fluid hoses have been reconnected, the suspension system will need to be repressurized and, as previously mentioned, this requires the use of service equipment; if none is available at the workshop where the job has been carried out, the car may be driven very slowly, with the suspension resting on the 'bump stops' to the nearest agent, possessing this equipment, who will then complete the pressurization.

STRIPPING THE ENGINE

Ancillary equipment

Remove the radiator as follows:

Remove the upper support bracket from the thermostat housing and from the top half of the radiator cowling.

Release the top hose from the thermostat housing and the bottom hose from the water pump.

Remove the two bolts securing the bottom support bracket to the engine mounting and remove the radiator, taking care not to damage the core on the fan blades.

Remove the two generator-mounting bolts and the nut from the adjusting stay.

Remove the generator, and coil if both are mounted together.

Remove the two starter-motor securing bolts and the starter motor.

Mark the distributor body (see page 21).

Undo the clamp-plate pinch-bolt and withdraw the distributor body.

If the coil is fitted to the flywheel housing, remove the two mounting screws and the coil.

The cylinder head

Unscrew the two sleeve nuts securing the rocker cover and lift it off, taking care not to damage the cork gasket if a new replacement is not available. Slacken the four nuts securing the rocker-shaft posts and the nine cylinder-head nuts evenly, as shown in fig. 4:2, to avoid distortion of the head.

On 'S' type Coopers, the cylinder head is retained by 10 nuts and one bolt, the bolt is situated at the front of the cylinder head and identified by the figures 300 stamped on the head of the bolt. This bolt should be removed first and the remaining nuts removed evenly in the general sequence given in fig. 4:2.

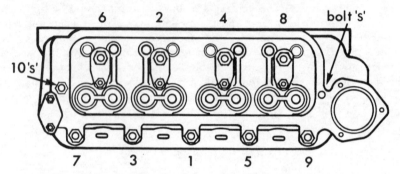

Fig. 4:2. Correct tightening sequence for cylinder head stud nuts.

Remove all the nuts and the complete rocker assembly and brackets. Withdraw the push-rods carefully, twisting them slightly as they are lifted, to avoid lifting the tappets out of their guides. Release the clip securing the by-pass hose to the cylinder head. The cylinder head may now be removed; in order to break the joint at the gasket it may be necessary to tap each side of the head with a hide-faced mallet or a hammer and wooden drift.

The head should then be lifted squarely from the studs.

Decarbonization and valve grinding

When the cylinder head has been removed, the combustion chambers should be cleaned to remove deposits and the valves and valve seats inspected for pitting or burning.

Valve removal

Before removing the valves, it is advisable to mark the head of each to facilitate replacement in the original seating. A number punch or centre-pop may be lightly stamped on the heads of the valves which are usually numbered from the 'front' (timing-case end) of the engine.

Remove the spring clips from the valve cotters and compress the valve springs using a valve-spring compressor. If a pillar drill is available, a useful and rapid valve spring compressor can be manufactured either from a piece of ¾in. pipe or from a piece of round bar or a long bolt and a large steel washer as shown in fig. 4:3.

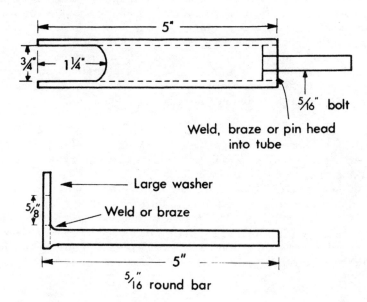

Fig. 4:3. Two designs for valve spring compressors for use with a pillar drill.

With one of the tools in the drill chuck and the cylinder head on the drill table, support the valve on a small piece of wood inserted in the combustion chamber. The springs may be compressed in turn by lowering the tool on to the valve-spring by means of the drill feed lever (but of course without setting the drill in motion).

Remove the two cotters from each valve stem and decompress the spring. Remove the valves and check the seating faces and the valve seats in the cylinder head, for serious pitting.

Scrape all the carbon from the cylinder head and combustion chambers with a blunt scraper, taking care not to scratch the valve seats, and wash off the head with petrol or paraffin. Remove any carbon from the valve stems or heads without damaging the seating face.

Carefully remove any carbon from the cylinder block and piston crowns taking care to prevent any dirt getting into the two exposed cylinders by stuffing them with clean rag. Avoid scratching the soft alloy piston crowns by using a blunt scraper, preferably made of softer material than the pistons.

Valve grinding

Stand the cylinder head, upside down, on two wooden blocks high enough off the bench to allow the valves to be inserted and to seat correctly. Lightly lubricate the valve stems with thin oil to ease rotation during grinding. Smear the seating face with a little grinding paste. If the seats are not badly damaged, only a medium or fine grade of paste is necessary. For badly pitted valve seats, grinding should start with a coarse paste. A suction-type grinding tool is applied to the valve head and the valve rotated back and forth several times before being lifted just off the seating, rotated about half a turn, reseated and rotated again. This should be continued until an even, mat finish is obtained on the valve face and seating. If a coarse paste is being used, it should be wiped off when an even finish is obtained and the valve finally seated with a fine paste.

When all the seatings are satisfactory, all traces of grinding paste should be washed from the head and valves with petrol or paraffin and the head finally dried, preferably with a compressed air-blast. Check that the valve guides are thoroughly cleaned.

If the seating faces of the valves are badly pitted, but have not been ground-in before, it is possible to have them refaced at a garage having a valve refacing machine. This may save hours of grinding by hand. Similarly, if the valve seats in the head are damaged, they may be recut with a valve-seat cutting tool. It is still necessary, however, to finish grinding-in the valves by hand.

Refitting valves

When the valves are all seating correctly, and all traces of grinding paste have been removed, they should be replaced in their original positions. Replace the valve springs, shrouds and caps. Compress the valve spring as for removal and fit a new rubber valve-stem oil-seal on the stem at the bottom of the waisted section, below the cotters. Replace the cotters, ensuring that both seat properly, and carefully decompress the spring. Replace the cotter-retaining spring clip.

When all the valves have been replaced, the head is ready for refitting to the block.

Refitting the cylinder head

Always use a new cylinder-head gasket when replacing the head. Fit the gasket on to the cylinder block, checking that it is positioned correctly. The gasket is stamped 'front' and 'top'. Fit a new by-pass hose on to the water pump. Replace the cylinder head squarely over the studs; replace the push-rods, preferably in their original positions. Replace the rocker shaft and the four thick washers on top of the bearing posts. Replace the cylinder-head nuts and washers and the rocker-shaft securing nuts, finger tight. Now tighten all 13 nuts evenly, a turn at a time, in the same order as for removal (see fig. 4:2). If possible use a torque wrench for final tightening to 40lb ft for head nuts and 25lb ft for the four rocker post nuts.

When an 'S' type Cooper head is being replaced, where the head is secured by 10 nuts and one bolt, the head nuts should be tightened in the general order given in fig. 4:2 to 42lb ft torque. The single bolt, which is replaced last, and the rocker-shaft mounting nuts should be tightened to 25 lb ft torque. On no account should this figure be exceeded on the head bolt, as damage to the cylinder head may result.

The 1275 GT has high-tensile head studs and the nuts should be tightened to 50lb ft.

THE CLUTCH AND FLYWHEEL

Remove the nine setscrews which secure the clutch cover to the flywheel housing. Remove the clutch cover. For identification of the spring type, see plate II (b).

Coil-spring type clutches

Knock back the tab washers on the three nuts securing the thrust plate to the centre of the clutch. Remove these nuts and the thrust plate. Knock back the tab washer locking the central flywheel-securing bolt and remove this bolt. Lever out the flat driving washer and insert a short $\frac{1}{2}$in. diameter bolt or similar piece of metal into the end of the crankshaft for the flywheel puller to tighten against. *The flywheel must now be turned so that the 1/4 mark is at the top;* at this point pistons Nos. 1 and 4 are at t d c, in which position the 'C' washer, that locates the crankshaft primary gear, will be prevented from dropping inside the clutch when the flywheel is removed. The flywheel has now to be released from its taper and, to do this, either a service tool or a puller manufactured as detailed on page 107, is required.

To remove the flywheel, pass the screws of the adaptor set through the plate and screw them into the three recessed holes in the clutch spring housing, taking care to keep the puller plate parallel with the flywheel. Tighten the centre screw in the puller and thus break free the flywheel from its taper. If the flywheel is very tight on the taper, a sharp blow on the head of the centre screw while tightened may help to free it. The extractor tools should now be removed together with the flywheel retaining bolt and the driving washer behind it. The flywheel and the clutch may now be pulled off the crankshaft. (Care should be taken to keep the flywheel upright while moving it, in order to prevent any oil, trapped in the centre, from running on to the clutch lining.) It may now be swiftly laid flat on a bench.

Dismantling the coil-spring type clutch

To dismantle the clutch, screw the three screws of the service tool set through the recessed holes in the pressed steel spring housing and into the flywheel. Tighten the nuts down finger tight against the housing and remove the three bolts from the corners of the housing. The nuts may now be evenly slackened off until the spring pressure is fully released, when the screws may be removed and the clutch assembly taken apart. The positions of all the component parts should be noted so that they may be reassembled in their original positions to maintain correct balance.

It should be noted that the letter 'A' has been stamped on a corner of the thrust plate, on the spring housing and on the pressure plate, indicating the correct assembly positions.

Diaphragm spring clutches

A modification, now incorporated on all models, is the replacement of the original six coil springs in the clutch assembly by a single diaphragm spring. This modification has simplified the dismantling procedure, for the clutch spring may now be decompressed before the flywheel is removed.

With the clutch cover removed, the type of clutch fitted can be identified by the appearance of the pressure spring housing. Coil spring clutches have a triangular, cast-steel thrust plate which covers the central flywheel setscrew and is retained by three nuts. Diaphragm spring housings have a circular thrust plate which is retained by a wire circlip. When dismantling these clutches, first remove the wire circlip and then remove the thrust plate. Evenly slacken the three bolts which secure the spring housing to the clutch pressure plate, this will release the pressure on the diaphragm spring and allow the bolts and spring housing, complete with spring, to be removed.

Knock back the tab washer locking the central flywheel-securing bolt and undo this bolt two or three turns. Turn the flywheel, so that the 1/4 mark is at the top, and release it from its taper as previously described on page 103. When the flywheel has been removed from the crankshaft, the clutch plate and pressure plate have only to be lifted off. It is possible to remove the diaphragm clutch and flywheel without first dismantling it, as just described, but in this case a very large socket spanner (1½in. AF) is required to undo the flywheel-securing bolt and few owners will possess one of these. To remove the assembly complete, the wire circlip and clutch thrust plate are first removed, when the flywheel bolt can be undone and the puller used as described previously for a coil-spring type clutch.

Removal of the flywheel housing

It is assumed that the oil has already been drained from the transmission case but if not it must be done now.

Flatten the tabs on the internal locking washers and remove the nine setscrews which secure the flywheel housing to the cylinder block and transmission casing. Note the positions of the screws for replacement. Carefully remove the flywheel housing. A new oil seal should always be fitted into this housing before it is replaced.

Removing the flywheel-housing oil seal

The old seal should be tapped out of the housing from the engine side. The new seal is inserted (taking care to get it in squarely) from the flywheel side of the housing.

Replacing the flywheel housing

When refitting the housing it is necessary to use either a special sleeve (or see page 108), to enable the oil-seal to pass over the splines and shoulder of the crankshaft primary gear without damage. This sleeve is placed in position over the gear splines, before the housing is replaced. Check that the joint faces of the cylinder block, transmission casing and flywheel are clean and that all traces of the old gasket have been removed. Fit a new flywheel-housing gasket. It is advisable to pack the rollers of the gearbox first-motion shaft bearing, which fits into an outer race in the flywheel housing, with stiff grease to prevent them tilting as the housing is refitted. Also remember to lubricate the lips of the housing oil-seal before reassembly.

The flywheel housing may now be manoeuvred into place and the sleeve removed from the primary gear splines. The flywheel-housing setscrews and nuts should be evenly tightened to 18lb ft to give the correct compression thickness of 0·030in. (0·762mm) to the gasket. A small cutaway will be found in the gasket which enables a feeler gauge measurement to be taken between the two machined faces to check this.

Fitting a modified primary gear bearing

On the very early vehicles, the crankshaft primary gear is pressure lubricated through drillings in the crankshaft. Later models have been fitted with a type of bearing requiring no external lubrication, thus reducing the possibility of oil leaking on to the clutch lining. When one

of these bearings has been fitted, there is no need for an oil-seal in the
flywheel. These parts were available from B L agents or stores.

After removal of the crankshaft primary gear, the oil-feed hole in the
crankshaft is plugged with the tapered brass plug supplied. This is
knocked down about 0·005in. below the surface of the crankshaft with a
punch. It may be necessary to shorten the plug slightly to ensure that it
can be driven into the required depth. The new primary gear is then
fitted, together with the new spacers provided, but check that the end
float is between 0·0035in. and 0·0065in., this must be measured with a
feeler gauge. A range of thrust washers is available to correct deficiencies
here. The oil-seal in the flywheel should be removed and discarded and
the clutch reassembled in the normal manner. In some cases it is possible
that fitting a new crankshaft primary gear, without fitting new idler and
first-motion-shaft gears, will lead to an undesirable amount of transfer-
gear noise and if this proves to be the case, fitting new gears is the only
immediate cure. However, the noise may lessen with running-in and in any
case does no mechanical harm.

Reassembling the coil-spring type clutch

The dismantling procedure detailed on page 104 is now reversed, taking
care that the corner stamped 'A' on each part is assembled next to the
timing marks on the flywheel. Place the pressure plate, back downwards,
on a bench but raised about 1in. off the bench on wooden blocks and
placed in such a manner that the central hole is not obstructed. The
driven plate is laid on this with its boss downwards. Great care must be
taken to get the driven plate centralized or it will be impossible to fit the
assembly to the crankshaft. The use of the service tool, which was used
for removal, will facilitate this but is not absolutely essential. The normal
working position of the plate can usually be seen by the markings on the
pressure-plate face. Place the flywheel on top of these parts in the correct
balance position, and fit the springs in their locating registers. Next put
the three thrust-plate securing studs on top of the three springs nearest
to the pressure-plate boss holes in the flywheel and place the spring
housing in position, compress the springs, using the tool in the same way
as for dismantling, until the three driving bolts, which pass through the
corners of the spring housing can be inserted. Fit new shakeproof washers
under the heads of these bolts and ensure that the shouldered shanks of
the bolts pass right through the driving straps. The compressing tool can
now be removed.

Refitting the flywheel (coil spring clutch)

Make sure that the mating tapers on the crankshaft and in the flywheel
are completely free from oil and dirt and that the engine is at t d c on

cylinders 1 and 4. The flywheel must be placed on the crankshaft with the timing marks at the top. The keyed driving washer can now be tapped lightly into position in the end of the crankshaft, a new locking washer fitted and the flywheel-securing bolt screwed home. This bolt must be done up really tight, 110lb ft is the correct torque-wrench setting. One side of the locking washer should then be knocked up against the bolt head and the other side down against the flat on the driving washer. Place the clutch thrust plate in position and tighten its securing nuts, using new tab washers to lock them. The clutch-housing end cover may now be replaced and the engine and accessories reassembled. When this has been done the clutch adjustment must be checked as detailed on page 26.

Refitting the flywheel and reassembling the diaphragm spring clutch

This is more easily carried out by reversing the dismantling procedure, as this method avoids the necessity of centralizing the driven plate before assembly. Before refitting the flywheel to the crankshaft, place the pressure plate in position over the end of the crankshaft, with the corner marked 'A' at the top. Slide the driven plate on to the primary gear splines. Refit the flywheel on to the crankshaft as described for coil spring clutches. When the flywheel is locked in position, refit the pressure spring housing to the flywheel, lift the clutch pressure plate into position at the back of the flywheel (this can be done through the starter motor mounting), and screw in the three housing mounting bolts. New shakeprooof washers should be fitted to these. Tighten these bolts and refit the thrust washer and circlip.

Flywheel pullers

A serviceable flywheel puller is shown in the diagram (fig. 4:4). It should be at least $\frac{1}{2}$in. thick and the centre bolt should be at least $\frac{1}{2}$in. diameter. If no $\frac{3}{8}$in. UNF studding is available, three bolts or setscrews four inches long will do the job almost as well, but, for use when dismantling the coil-spring type clutch, either studding or long setscrews and nuts are essential. A modification to the design, which the Authors have found useful, is to use a piece of plate of sufficient thickness to allow a $\frac{1}{2}$in. diameter hole to be drilled in the edge. A stout tommy-bar may then be used to steady the tool as the centre bolt is turned.

Clutch dismantling tool (coil-spring type)

The three long setscrews or pieces of studding used for the previous tool can be used for dismantling and reassembling the clutch. The setscrews are screwed into the flywheel and the nuts screwed on to the spring housing.

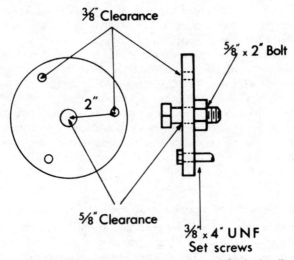

Fig. 4:4. Design for an easily manufactured flywheel puller.

Flywheel-housing oil-seal replacer sleeve

The function of this sleeve is to enable the flywheel-housing oil-seal to be fitted over the splines and sharp edge of the primary gear without damage. If it is not possible to borrow one, the following method will serve instead. A strip of Sellotape or pvc insulation tape, at least 1in. wide is wrapped round the primary gear, overlapping the sharp edge by about $\frac{1}{16}$in. and continuing down to cover the splines. This must be put on evenly and tightly. The tape surface is then covered in oil and the flywheel housing and seal fitted. When the housing is in position the tape can be peeled off easily.

Oil pump removal

The oil pump is situated on the flywheel end of the block and driven from the end of the camshaft. Several types of pump have been used but only the latest ones should be fitted to an engine during overhaul. All the cars except the 1275 GT now use 'Concentric' pumps which have three securing bolts and are driven by a peg in the camshaft which engages with a slot in the pump shaft. Two versions of this pump are supplied, the only difference between them being that the type needed for the Cooper S has a slightly longer driving shaft.

The 1275 GT uses either a four or two bolt pump which is driven by a three eared 'dog' or 'spider' which engages with the camshaft and the splined shaft of the pump. Both pumps appear to have four securing bolts but it will be found that on the later, improved, two-bolt type only two of the bolts pass right through into the block. These pumps are interchangeable and the two bolt type is preferred.

All the pumps are removed by knocking back the lock washers, if fitted, and taking out the bolts. Take care that the pump drive is refitted correctly and preferably, turn the engine over, or rotate the camshaft a few times to centralize the pump as the bolts are tightened. The automatic transmission cars use a much larger pump designed for use with the AP gearbox. It is a four-bolt spider-drive type and obviously no other pump is suitable.

Dismantling the oil pump

The pump bodies are manufactured in two pieces; the end cover, through which runs the drive shaft, is secured to the main casting by one screw and is located by either one or two dowels. The inner end of the driveshaft is lobed and runs in a rotor which is mounted in the pump body. When the end cover has been removed, examine the bearing surfaces of the lobes on the driveshaft and the inside of the rotor for scores and check the rotor end-float and lobe clearance as follows:

Place the rotors in the pump body and measure the clearance between the peaks of the inner and outer rotor lobes; if this is greater than 0·005–0·006in., the pump should be renewed. Lay a straight-edge across the joint face of the pump body, measure the clearance between the top face of the rotors and the underside of the straight-edge with suitable feeler gauges. This clearance should not exceed 0·005in. If it is found to be greater than this it is permissible to remove the locating dowel(s) and carefully lap the joint face of the body until the correct clearance is obtained.

When refitting the pump to the block, always use a new paper gasket. Care must be taken, when fitting this gasket, not to obstruct the intake and outlet ports. It is advisable to fill the pump with oil before refitting.

Removal of the timing chain and sprockets

Flatten the tab locking the crankshaft-pulley securing-screw and remove this screw. Carefully lever the pulley and damper off the crankshaft. Remove the ten setscrews which secure the timing chain cover to the block and remove the cover. Remove the oil thrower from the crankshaft. Bend back the tab washer from the camshaft-sprocket nut and remove the nut and lock washer. Remove the timing chain and sprockets by levering each forward a little at a time, until both are free of their keys. Care should be taken not to use excessive force on the camshaft sprocket, as the rims of the tensioner grooves are fragile. Note the presence of packing washers behind the crankshaft gear. Check the timing chain for wear and renew it if any slackness is present in the links. Also check the rubber chain-tensioners fitted in grooves on the periphery of either side of the camshaft sprocket; unless these are very new it is a sensible precaution to replace them with new ones, while the engine is stripped, as they are comparatively cheap and easily changed at this stage.

Refitting the timing chain and sprockets

Unless new camshaft or crankshaft parts have been fitted, which may have altered the alignment of the two sprockets, replace exactly the same number of packing washers as were removed. If the alignment of the sprockets has been altered, check the number of washers needed by placing a straight-edge across the sides of the camshaft-sprocket teeth and measure, with a feeler gauge, the gap between the straight-edge and the crankshaft-sprocket teeth.

To replace the timing chain and sprockets, first set the crankshaft with its keyway at t d c and set the camshaft keyway in approximately the 2 o'clock position.

Assemble the sprockets into the timing chain with the dots on the faces adjacent to one another. Engage the crankshaft-sprocket keyway with the key in the crankshaft and, still keeping the marks on the sprockets aligned, rotate the camshaft slightly until the camshaft sprocket keyway and key are aligned; push the sprockets on to the shafts and secure the camshaft sprocket with its lock washer and nut. Before refitting the timing cover, it is advisable to fit a new oil seal as these seals are a common source of oil leaks.

A new cover gasket should be fitted and the crankshaft pulley should be positioned in the oil-seal and lightly lubricated before the cover is fitted. The oil thrower should be fitted with the concave face outward. Push the pulley and cover on to the crankshaft and check that the keyway in the pulley is in line with the Woodruff key in the crankshaft before finally drifting the pulley into position.

Replace the cover setscrews and tighten evenly. Refit the pulley securing screw and lock washer. Tighten the pulley securing screw to 70lb ft and bend up the tab of the lock washer.

Removal of the camshaft

Remove the timing chain cover, timing chain and sprockets as described on page 109. Remove the distributor complete with clamping plate from the distributor housing. Extract the single setscrew, which secures the housing to the block. Remove the tappet covers and using one of the tappet-cover bolts as an extractor, screw it into the tapped end of the distributor drive and pull the spindle from the block. Remove the eight tappets from their guides, noting their positions so that they may be refitted in their original guides. Remove the three setscrews and shakeproof washers which secure the camshaft-locating plate to the block. The camshaft may now be removed from the block.

It should be noted that the 1275 GT engine does not have tappet covers and it is therefore necessary to invert the engine before removing the camshaft, to allow the tappets to fall clear of the cam lobes.

Refitting the camshaft is the reversal of the removal procedure, preferably replacing the tappets in their original guides.

Refitting the distributor drive spindle

Turn the crankshaft until No. 1 piston is at t d c on its compression stroke. At this point the two timing marks on the camshaft- and crankshaft-sprockets will be in line. If the cylinder head and valve gear is in place, the exhaust valve of No. 4 cylinder should be just closing and the inlet just opening. Screw the bolt ($\frac{7}{16}$in. by $3\frac{1}{2}$in. UNF) used for removal, back into the threaded distributor drive gear and, holding the gear with the large offset above the slot, *i.e.* with the slot horizontal and just below centre, replace the drive in the block. When the gear engages with the gear on the camshaft, the drive will turn slightly in an anti-clockwise direction until it is fully engaged. Remove the bolt and refit the distributor housing and secure with the correct setscrew and washer, ensuring that the head of the screw does not protrude above the face of the housing. Replace the distributor complete with the clamping plate and check the ignition timing, as described on page 23.

Removing the cylinder block

Remove the 12 setscrews from the flange of the transmission casing, noting their different lengths and positions for replacement. Lift the cylinder block from the transmission casing.

Inspection of the big-end bearings

If the big-end bearings are thought to be badly worn or the crankpins oval, they should be removed as follows: Release the securing tabs on the big-end-cap lock washers and remove the big-end bolts. Number the sides of each cap and rod so that they may be replaced together in their original positions. Remove the big-end cap. Push the connecting rod off the crankpin and inspect the bearing shells. These should be mat grey; slight scratches may be ignored but if the bearings show any trace of copper colour, the bearing material has worn away and in this case, or if any scores are present, new shells must be fitted. Before fitting new bearing shells, and while the big-ends are removed, the crankpins should also be inspected for score marks or for ovality. The diameter should be carefully measured with a micrometer at different positions round the crankpin. A difference of more than 0·001in. indicates a worn crankpin which will need regrinding or replacing by an exchange crankshaft. Also any score marks present on the crankpin must be removed by regrinding, as they would damage any new shells fitted.

If no undue wear or damage is present on the crankpins, it is unlikely that the main bearings are damaged. If however there is any damage or wear on the crankpins, the main bearing caps should also be removed and the shells inspected before refitting the big-end bearings.

To replace the big-end bearing shells, push the old shells from their seatings and fit the new shells into place so that their locating tabs fit in their respective grooves. When the big-end caps are refitted these tabs should both be on the same side of the connecting rod.

Tighten the big-end bolts to 35lb ft torque and re-lock with new tab washers. The torque setting for the Cooper S is 46lb ft.

Removal of pistons and connecting rods

If the pistons are to be removed with the crankshaft in position, it is only necessary to remove the big-end caps as described and push the piston and connecting rod out upwards through the block. It is advisable to refit the big-end cap on to each rod immediately and to number its position in the block, on the rod and piston, in order to avoid confusion when refitting.

Removal of piston rings

The piston rings should be removed over the top of the piston to avoid damage to the surface of the skirt. To remove each ring from its groove it may be helpful to use an old feeler gauge or piece of shim. This is inserted between the ring and piston at one end and moved round the piston, while lifting the ring on to the land above the ring groove from where it can easily be removed. Care must be taken not to expand the rings too much if they are to be refitted, as they are fragile. Before refitting or fitting new rings, the piston-ring grooves should be cleared of any carbon deposits, taking care not to damage the edges of the grooves in doing so. An old broken piston ring used carefully will make an efficient scraper.

When fitting new compression rings to a slightly worn bore, special 'quick-seat' rings should be fitted in the top grooves. These rings have a relieved top edge to clear any ridge worn at the top of the bore.

The gap of new rings must be checked before assembly. To do this, insert each ring in the bottom of the cylinder bore, to avoid taking the measurement where the bore is worn. If a piston is now inserted, and the ring pushed down on to the crown, it will ensure that the ring is square with the bore while the gap is measured, using suitable feeler gauges. The gap should be between 0·006 and 0·011in. If the gap is too small, the ring should be removed and the ends carefully filed away until the correct gap is obtained. The top compression ring is machined parallel but the second and third rings are tapered and stamped with the letter T on the upper face for identification when fitting.

Oil-control rings

If the engine is burning oil and the bores are not badly worn or damaged, it is possible to replace the standard scraper rings with special oil-control rings. These may be of two or three types and the manufacturers' instructions should be consulted before fitting.

It is essential that the piston-ring groove depth is measured and that the oil-control rings are matched to the pistons when purchasing, as the ring groove depth may vary from one engine to another. If the bore wear is excessive (*i.e.* greater than 0·010in.) it will be necessary to have the engine rebored.

If an internal micrometer is not available, place the piston, without rings, near the top of the bore and if a 0·012in. feeler gauge can be pushed down between the piston and the cylinder wall at the side of the block, wear is excessive.

Four sizes of piston are available for rebored engines, these are +0·010, +0·020, +0·030, +0·040in.

These oversize pistons have the actual oversize bore dimensions, for which they are suitable, stamped on the piston crown and enclosed in an ellipse. The size indicated is the actual bore over-size to which they must be fitted; running clearances have been allowed for during machining of the pistons.

Removing the pistons from the connecting rods

The 850 and 998 pistons are removed from the connecting rods by pushing out the gudgeon pins after removing the retaining circlips. New pistons may require heating in hot water to expand them while the pins are fitted or removed. It should not be necessary to use force to move the pins.

The Cooper S and 1275 GT engines are different in that the gudgeon pins are not retained by circlips. The pins are an interference fit in the small end of the connecting rod and a special extractor is necessary to remove and refit them. If the engine is being fitted with new pistons, the reboring specialist or an Austin/Morris distributor will be able to do this for you. When the pistons have been fitted, they should rock freely on the gudgeon pins and move sideways easily. Make sure, however, that the connecting rod eyes are in the centre of their gudgeon pins and that the pins cannot protrude from the pistons, in either direction, so as to score the cylinders.

Refitting rings and pistons

The piston rings are fitted in the opposite order to removal, *i.e.* the scraper or oil-control rings first, followed by the two tapered compression rings and finally the parallel top ring. Before replacing the pistons, lubricate the cylinder bores with a little oil. To refit the piston in the bore, it is advisable and, if oil-control rings have been fitted, almost essential, to use a piston-ring compressor to contain the rings in their grooves while the piston is pushed back into its bore. Ensure that the word 'FRONT' which is stamped on the piston crown is at the front, *i.e.* 'radiator' side of the bore.

Before refitting the big-end caps, check that the connecting rods are the correct way round, *i.e.* with the centre two rods offset toward each other and the outer two rods offset towards the ends of the engine. The gudgeon-pin clamp bolts and big-end bolts must face the camshaft side of the engine. Tighten the big-end bolts of all models other than the Cooper S to 35lb ft torque and lock with new tab washers. The torque setting for the Cooper S is 46lb ft.

Removal of the crankshaft

If the crankshaft is found to be oval or damaged it should be removed as follows.

Unlock the tab washers holding the main-bearing-cap securing bolts and remove the bolts. Remove the main-bearing caps complete with bearing shells, keeping the shells and caps in their respective positions. The bottom halves of two thrust washers will be removed with the centre bearing cap. The corresponding top halves will be removed with the crankshaft. Withdraw the three camshaft thrust-plate securing bolts and remove the thrust-plate, noting which side faces the camshaft. Remove the remaining bolts securing the steel plate to the front of the engine block, and remove it. The crankshaft may now be lifted out.

Inspect the main journals for wear, scores, scratches or ovality, as for the crankpins. Examine the main bearing shells for wear, pitting or picking-up and renew if necessary.

Refitting the crankshaft

Refitting is simply a reversal of the dismantling process described above, but the following points should be noted.

Lubricate the bearing surfaces with clean engine oil before refitting. Also ensure that the thrust washers on each side of the centre main bearing are fitted correctly, *i.e.* with the oil grooves facing outwards and with the locking tabs on the bottom halves in the slots in the bearing cap.

The main-bearing securing bolts should be tightened to 60lb ft torque.

THE GEARBOX AND FINAL DRIVE—
MANUAL TRANSMISSION

Removal of the differential assembly

With the engine removed from the car, as previously described, the differential assembly may be removed from the gearbox, with or without first separating the engine from the transmission.

Release the lever clamped to the top of the remote gear-change shaft. Take out the nylon seatings and tension springs from the remote control shaft and the lever, if these are fitted, and discard them, as these seatings and springs have been discontinued on later models, to allow more freedom of movement. Remove both the split pins and nuts securing the drive flanges which may then be removed from their splines. The five setscrews may now be removed from each of the end covers and the covers taken off. Mark the components for replacement in their original position. Note carefully the number of shims fitted between the differential bearing and the housing. Unlock the tab washers on the four differential-housing stud nuts, remove these and the other two nuts and withdraw the differential unit from the gearbox.

Dismantling the differential

Using a bearing extractor (or by very careful use of two tyre levers) withdraw the differential bearings. Unlock the locking tabs and remove the six setscrews which attach the driving gear to the differential cage. To make sure of refitting the components in their original positions, mark the driving gear and differential cage before dismantling. Remove the driving gear from the differential cage and withdraw the differential gear and thrust washer. Tap out the taper pin from the differential cage and pinion shaft and remove the shaft, pinions, pinion spacer and thrust washers.

Reassembly

This is essentially a reversal of the dismantling procedure. The differential-gear thrust washers are refitted with their slightly chamfered bore against the machined face of the differential gears.

Refitting the differential assembly

Replace the differential assembly in the gearbox casing, offset slightly towards the flywheel-end of the engine.

Replace the differential housing, preferably with new joint washers,

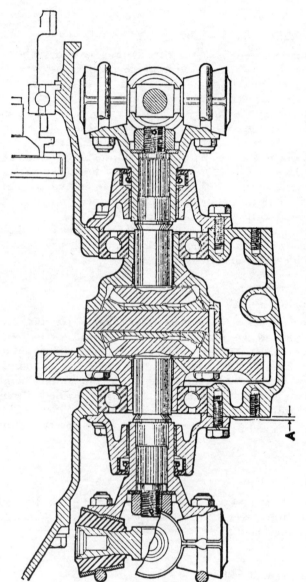

Fig. 4·5. A section through the differential assembly and final drive end covers. To obtain the correct preload on the differential bearings a feeler gauge measurement should be taken at 'A' as described in text.

and tighten the securing nuts sufficiently to hold the bearings firmly but so as to allow the assembly to move slightly when the right hand final-drive end cover is fitted. Replace this end cover and its jointing gasket, ensuring that the holes in the cover flange are correctly aligned with the tapped holes in the transmission casing and differential housing. Insert the setscrews and tighten evenly, maintaining maximum contact between the register and the inner face of the differential bearing. As the setscrews are tightened, the differential assembly will be displaced slightly away from the flywheel end of the engine. The left hand final drive cover should now be fitted *without its jointing gasket.* The cover flange will not seat correctly and the setscrews should only be tightened sufficiently to seat the bearing outer race and not so tight as to distort the flange. Feeler gauge measurements should now be taken between the cover flange and the differential housing and transmission casing in several positions (fig. 4:5). Variations in measurements indicate that the setscrews have not been tightened correctly, with the result that the differential assembly is out of alignment or the cover flange is distorted. Adjust the tension on the cover screws accordingly, avoiding excessive tension and measure again with the feeler gauge.

If it is not possible to insert any feeler gauge in the joint between the cover flange and the housing, shims to the value of 0·008in. must be fitted between the bearing outer race and the register on the end cover. The correct compressed thickness of the cover joint gasket is 0·007in. and the required gap for pre-load on the bearings is 0·001 to 0·002in. Therefore the correct gap is 0·008 to 0·009in. Any deviation from this figure must be corrected by shimming.

Remove the end cover, fit the necessary shims and the jointing gasket, replace the setscrews and tighten.

Tighten all the differential housing nuts, using new tab washers, and lock them. Refit the drive flanges to the differential gear shafts with the split-pin holes at right angles to the flange and secure with slotted nuts and split pins.

Refit the *ball-ended lever* to the splines of the gear change shaft, making sure that the recess in the shaft is correctly aligned with the drilling in the boss before attempting to insert the setscrews. Now fit the socket of the other lever over the ball end and engage the splines of the lever on those of the shaft. Carefully replace the clamping screw and tighten.

Dismantling the gearbox

With the transmission casing separated from the engine and the differential assembly removed from the transmission casing, as previously described, remove the clamp screw from the selector lever and withdraw the gear-change operating shaft, taking care when doing so not to damage the oil-seal in the casing.

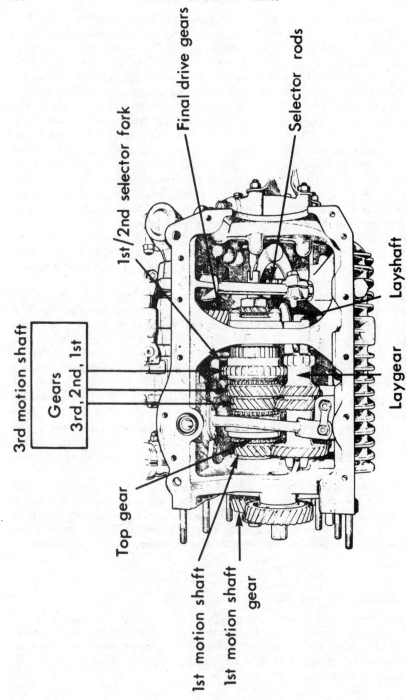

3rd motion shaft

Gears
3rd, 2nd, 1st

1st/2nd selector fork

Final drive gears

Selector rods

Top gear

1st motion shaft

1st motion shaft gear

Laygear   Layshaft

Fig. 4:6. Top view of the gearbox showing location of major components.

PLATE III

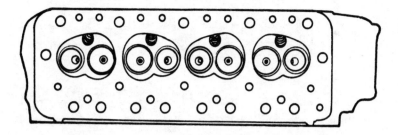

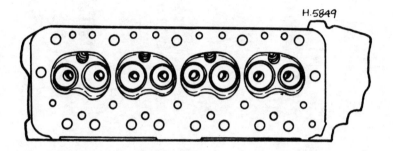

H.5849

(a) Unmodified and modified Cooper S cylinder heads. The reshaped combustion chamber and cutaway valve-guide bosses can be clearly seen.

(b)

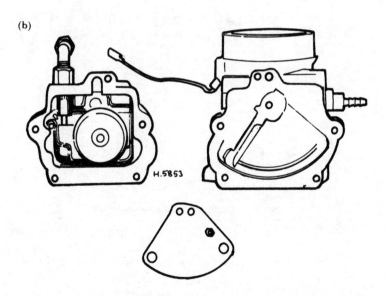

H.5853

(b) A dismantled Fish type carburetter showing the float chamber and fuel pick-up arm. The tapered fuel metering groove and dividing plate with its non-return flap valve are also shown.

PLATE IV

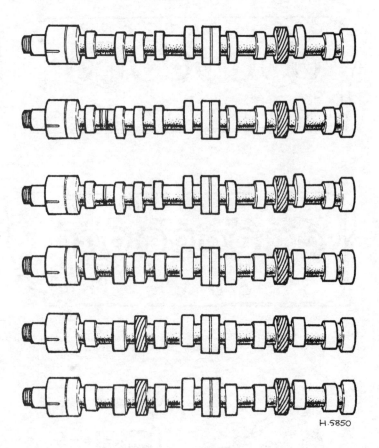

H·5850

A selection of Mini camshafts

1 850 Mini, no markings, narrow lobes and a fuel-pump cam.

2 AEA 630, 1100 type with two turned rings, narrow lobes and a fuel-pump cam.

3 88G 229, Mini Cooper 997 type, similar to AEA 630 but with only one turned ring.

4 1275 GT camshaft with wide lobes, a fuel-pump cam and no markings.

5 Racing C–AEA 648 with stamped markings and two driving gears.

6 Sprint type C–AEA 597 stamped 'AEA 598' with spider type oil-pump drive.

Unscrew the speedometer-pinion housing screw, remove the housing and withdraw the pinion.

Remove the speedometer gear. Remove the setscrews from the end cover of the transmission casing and remove the cover. Remove the setscrews securing the oil pipe to the lug on the transmission casing and the pipe flange to the rear wall. Remove the oil pipe from the gauze filter. Remove the third-motion-shaft drive pinion nut, locking washer and pinion. The shaft may be locked by selecting both first and reverse gears. Unscrew and remove the setscrews and locking plate, securing the third-motion-shaft bearing retainer to the central web of the casing, and extract the retainer together with the packing shims. Remove the circlip from the end of the first-motion shaft and slide off the caged roller bearing. Unlock the tab washer and remove the nut from the end of this shaft. Remove the driving gear from the first-motion-shaft. Remove the locking plate from the lay and reverse shafts, push the lay-shaft out of the casing and remove the lay-gear and thrust washers. Unscrew the external retaining plugs and extract the selector-rod interlocking plungers and springs. Remove the first-motion-shaft bearing circlip and withdraw the bearing from the casing. Service tool part No. 18G284 and adaptor 18G284B may be useful to facilitate this.

Release the lock-nut and locking setscrew securing the first- and second-gear selector fork to the selector rod; withdraw the selector rod and remove the selector fork from the casing. Drift the third-motion-shaft forward to displace the bearing from the central web of the transmission casing, far enough to enable the bearing to be levered from the web bore. Great care must be taken when carrying out this operation not to damage the selector fork. Once the bearing has been removed, the third-motion shaft may be removed from the casing.

Remove the remaining oil-strainer bracket screw and locking plate and withdraw the strainer assembly. Release the lock-nut and slacken the locating setscrew of the third and fourth-gear selector fork. Slide out the selector rod and remove the selector fork from the casing. Remove the reverse-gear shaft, gear and selector fork and also the detent spring and plunger. Remove the circlip from the gear-shift-lever pivot and remove this lever.

Dismantling instructions for the third-motion shaft are given at the end of this chapter.

When dismantling the Cooper S gearbox or one from any of the more recent models, note that the layshaft bearings and third-motion-shaft spigot bearing in the first-motion-shaft, are now caged needle roller.

Reassembling the gearbox

Although this is only a reversal of the dismantling procedure, detailed instructions have been included. If it has been removed from the casing, replace the reverse-gear shift-lever pivot pin in its drilling and fit the shift lever; secure it to the pivot with the retaining circlip.

Insert the reverse selector-rod detent spring and plunger; insert the reverse selector rod into the casing from the front, passing it through the reverse-gear fork on the way. Put the third- and fourth-gear selector fork in position in the casing and push the selector rod through from the front, engaging the selector fork as before. Replace the selector-fork locating setscrews, to engage in the indentations of the selector rods, tighten and carefully secure with the locking nuts; *should one of these screws work loose, it is usually necessary to dismantle the gearbox completely to retighten it.*

Position the oil pick-up strainer in the casing and insert the fixing screws through the mounting bracket and the lug on the casing, leaving them slack in the bracket. A little grease should be smeared on to the sealing ring, fitted between the bracket and the strainer, to help the oil pick-up pipe to pass through easily and not push out the seal when it is inserted. Place the third-motion shaft assembly in the casing, with the slotted end through the central web and with the first- and second-gear selector forks engaged in the sliding hubs. Refit the ball race to the first-motion-shaft assembly and insert into the casing. Insert the third-motion-shaft bearing into the central web of the casing and check that the first- and third-motion shafts are correctly aligned before drifting the bearings carefully into their registers.

Fit the first-motion-shaft bearing-retaining circlip. Replace the first- and second-gear selector fork and fork rod and secure the fork with its locating screw and locking nut. Refit both selector-rod detent plungers and springs, preferably with new sealing washers under the heads of the retaining plugs. Replace the drive pinion, locking washer and nut on the end of the third-motion shaft. Engage first and reverse gears, tighten the pinion nut to 150lb ft, and bend up the locking washer. (Looseness of this nut used to be a common fault and it should always be checked while the engine is split.) It is advisable always to fit new locking washers throughout the transmission assembly to reduce the possibility of failure.

Refit the first-motion-shaft driving gear, ensuring that the locating tongues on the locking washer are engaged in the two holes in the gear, tighten the nut to 110lb ft and bend up the locking washer. Refit the lay-gear with the slotted end of the shaft to the front and with a thrust washer at each end. When the lay-gear and the thrust washers have been fitted there must be an end clearance of between 0·002 and 0·006in. Thrust washers ranging in thickness from 0·121 to 0·132in. are available to enable this clearance to be obtained.

Rotate the lay-shaft and reverse shaft so that the slotted ends face each other, to enable the shaft-locating plate to be refitted. Replace the third-motion-shaft-bearing retainer, fitting shims as necessary to take up the gap between the bearing outer race and the retainer. These shims should be positioned underneath the reverse and lay-shaft locking plate. Secure in position with the four setscrews and the lock washers. Remove the front screw, of the two holding the pick-up filter bracket, and insert the oil suction pipe into the filter. Take care not to push out the sealing rubber between the strainer and strainer bracket. Replace the two paper gaskets between the pipe flange, the outer blanking plate and the casing. Refit the two setscrews and tighten. Replace the strainer bracket locking-plate and setscrews and tighten both bracket setscrews, bend up the locking plate. Refit the selector interlocking arm and the front end cover and gasket. Examine the seal in the speedometer pinion-shaft housing and renew if necessary. Renew the paper gasket, push the housing over the shaft carefully and secure with the setscrew. Replace the gear-change operating shaft in the casing with the Woodruff key fitted in the lower end of the shaft.

Place the selector lever inside the casing with the end engaged in the interlocking arm and push the shaft through the lever boss into the bearing in the bottom of the casing. Align the recess in the shaft with the drilling through the lever boss, insert and tighten the setscrew. Refit the reverse-gear detent plunger, spring and plug. Refit the differential assembly as described on page 115.

If the idler-gear bearing, in the flywheel housing, requires renewal, great care should be taken, during the pressing-in operation to support the area of the housing around the bearing boss. This bearing should not be pressed in to the full depth of the machining in the housing as this will mask off the oil supply hole. Replace the idler gear with a thrust washer on each side, fitted with the chamfered bore against the gear face. Refit the roller bearing and circlip to the first-motion shaft and fit the flywheel housing and gasket to the transmission casing. With the housing nuts tightened there should be between 0·003 and 0·008in. end-float in the idler gear. Thrust washers of varying thicknesses are available to achieve this.

Remove the housing and gasket and refit the engine unit to the transmission.

Dismantling the third-motion-shaft: 'three-speed-synchromesh' gearboxes

Should this be necessary, while the shaft is removed from the gearbox, it may be carried out as follows: Remove the first-gear hub and baulk rings from the rear of the shaft. Remove the top- and third-gear hub and baulk ring from the front of the shaft, noting the correct orientation on the shaft for refitting. Remove the thrust washer by depressing the spring-loaded locating plunger and rotating the washer so that the splines register with those on the shaft. Remove the plunger and spring. Remove the third-gear pinion from the shaft, and then the third-gear bush and interlocking ring. Remove the second-gear pinion and bush and the rear thrust washer.

If it is required to separate the synchromesh hub and cone assemblies, these should be wrapped in a clean cloth to catch the three spring-loaded steel balls which are located in each hub.

When dismantling the gearbox from a Cooper S or any Mini later than engine no. 815140, it will be noted that needle roller bearings are fitted in many places where bronze bearings were originally fitted *e.g.* the spigot bearing of the third-motion-shaft in the first-motion-shaft and the second- and third-gear bearings. This alteration necessitates a slightly different third-motion-shaft. The later shaft has a built-in spacer for the needle roller bearings of the two gears and a locking collar for each gear. The collar locating second gear is locked by two sprung plungers diametrically opposite each other, and the third-gear collar is locked by a single sprung plunger. These plungers must be depressed with a fine pointed instrument before the collar can be moved.

Reassembly of the 'three-speed-synchromesh' third-motion shaft

Replace the synchromesh springs and balls in the hub and secure in place with a Jubilee clip or piston ring clamp. Fit the gear assembly on to the hub and ease off the clamp.

On the later models, where the gearbox is fitted with baulk-ring synchromesh, special attention must be given to the correct positioning of the first- and second-gear assemblies if these have been dismantled, as incorrect assembly will result in the loss of first gear. When reassembling the gear to the hub, check that the plunger in the hub aligns with the cut-away tooth in the gear assembly (fig. 4:7).

The first- and second-gear synchromesh hub is fitted with the cone side at the same end of the assembly as the straight side of the first-gear teeth and away from the bearing.

Fit the rear thrust washer and the plain half of the split bush, the plain end of which is positioned against the thrust washer. Next fit the second-gear pinion, the interlocking ring and the splined half of the centre bush. The dogs on each half should engage with the central interlocking ring. Since the bushes are retained by an interference fit, when first assembled, it is necessary to fit new bushes when reassembling. The bushes should be heated to about 180°C in oil, expansion will then allow them to be fitted without force and on cooling ensure a tight fit.

The latest type of gearbox has needle roller bearings in place of the split bush which makes dismantling and reassembling simpler. Refit the third-gear pinion, the plain side first, and insert the spring and locking plunger. Depress the plunger and push the thrust washer into position. Turn this washer until the plunger engages a spline and so locks the washer. When the second- and third-gear pinions have been assembled on the third-motion shaft, their end float must be between 0·0035 and 0·0055in. If the end float is outside these limits, new parts should be fitted to correct tolerance. Replace the top- and third-gear

Fig. 4:7. The baulk-ring first and second gear assembly, showing the gear and hubs correctly assembled. The plunger is shown by the arrow.

synchromesh hub, with the plain side towards the thrust washer. Refit the first- and second-speed hub as previously described. Refit the assembly as described on page 120.

Dismantling the third-motion-shaft: 'four-speed-synchromesh' gearboxes

With the shaft removed from the gearbox as previously described, remove the top- and third-gear synchromesh hub and baulk rings from the shaft. Depress the front thrust washer plunger and turn the washer until its splines align with those on the shaft when it may be removed, complete with plunger and spring. Remove the third-gear pinion complete with caged needle-roller bearing. Now take off the first-gear pinion and bearing from the other end of the shaft. It is now necessary to remove the needle-roller bearing journal from the shaft; the best way to do this is to carefully lever the journal along the shaft until there is enough clearance to fit a puller and then carefully draw the journal from the shaft. Now remove the reverse-gear mainshaft pinion, the first/second gear synchronizer assembly and baulk ring. Depress the two plungers which secure the rear thrust washer, and turn it so that it aligns with the splines on the shaft; remove the thrust washer followed by the second-gear pinion, and the split caged needle-roller bearing.

Reassembly of the 'four-speed-synchromesh' third-motion-shaft

When reassembling the third-motion-shaft it is necessary only to reverse the dismantling procedure but the following points should be remembered. If the synchromesh assemblies have been separated, ensure that the long boss on both the sleeve and the hubs are on the same side.

When refitting the third-and top-gear synchromesh assembly, the long boss on the synchronizer sleeve must face the first-motion-shaft bearing. The first- and second-gear synchromesh assembly must be fitted with the long boss towards the first gear.

Automatic transmission

Any major overhaul of an automatic transmission unit will require some knowledge of the general principles of its operation, precise adjustment details and access to a large number of special tools. It is therefore recommended that where possible these units are serviced by experienced mechanics at B L agents. Routine maintenance of these units including minor faults, is dealt with in chapter 2. Anyone contemplating more than the routine checks and minor adjustments described in that chapter, is advised to consult *Foulis' Overhaul Manual: AP Automatic Transmission* by John Organ.

CHAPTER 5

THE SUSPENSION SYSTEMS

The suspension is independent on all four wheels, the front consisting of double wishbones located on the side members of the front sub-frame with their outer ends attached to the swivel hubs by ball joints. The rear suspension incorporates long trailing arms mounted on the rear sub-frame.

When the cars were first produced, the suspension was achieved with rubber-cone spring units, the front ones being mounted in the front sub-frame towers with tubular struts interposed between the springs and the suspension upper support arms.

The rubber-cone springs for the rear suspension were mounted horizontally in the rear sub-frame, behind the trailing arm, and once again tubular struts were used to connect the spring to the suspension arm.

Telescopic, hydraulic dampers were used on both the front and rear suspension.

Following the success of the hydrolastic suspension system introduced by B M C on the 1100 models in August 1962, the Mini suspension system was changed to the hydrolastic type in September 1964, with the exception of the van and countryman models which retained the rubber suspension. After several years production, the economics of fitting the more expensive suspension system to what are moderately priced cars dictated a return to the original rubber system on all models.

The hydrolastic suspension retains a rubber spring-unit but these springs are hydraulically interconnected front-to-rear and incorporate their own damping system, making shockabsorbers unnecessary. The springs are built into pressurized fluid-filled hydraulic spring-displacer units, illustrated in fig. 5:1. As shown, the units comprise a rubber spring bonded into a pressed-steel housing which has two chambers formed on to it below the spring. The lower chamber is closed at the bottom by a tapered pressed-steel piston and sealed by a reinforced rubber diaphragm whose movement is restricted by a tapered steel cylinder. The upper chamber is formed between the rubber spring at the top and a pressed-steel dividing member which forms the top of the lower chamber. This dividing member has a damper valve in it which restricts the movement of the fluid from one chamber to the other. On either side of the car, the front and rear units are interconnected by steel and rubber pipes.

When a front wheel hits a bump, the tapered piston is pushed up into the lower chamber and fluid is forced through the damper valve into the upper chamber where the resulting pressure-increase compresses the rubber spring. At the same time some of the fluid is forced out of the upper chamber and along the connecting pipe into the upper chamber of the rear unit. The fluid passes through the rear damper valve and into

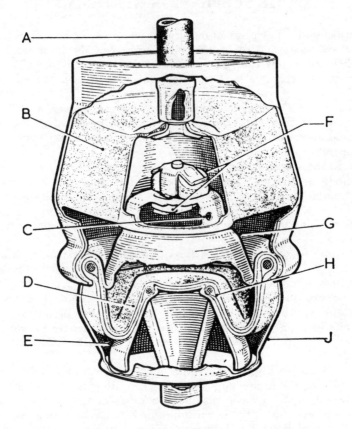

Fig. 5:1. Hydrolastic spring displacer unit.

(a) Flexible connecting tube.

(b) Rubber spring.

(c) Fluid bleed hole.

(d) and (h) Reinforced rubber diaphragm.

(e) Tapered piston.

(f) Damper valve.

(g) Dividing member.

(j) Tapered cylinder.

the lower chamber where it pushes out the piston and thus raises the rear of the car. The tapered pistons and cylinders and the conical rubber springs are arranged to give a progressive spring rate which stiffens with increased load to prevent excessive wheel travel. The effect of the interconnection is to raise the rear of the car by the same amount as the front is raised, and *vice versa,* as each wheel traverses the bump. Fore and aft pitching is thus almost eliminated and a vertical movement is experienced which is rather less uncomfortable than pitching. The system, although using fairly stiff springs, gives a comfortable ride and has good handling characteristics.

Dismantling the front suspension—Rubber type

To remove the front suspension struts from beneath the rubber springs, it is first necessary to compress the spring. This requires the use of a B L service tool and since this is not the sort of tool one would require often enough to be worthwhile buying, the best solution is to try and borrow one from a garage.

Jack up the car and remove one of the front wheels, remove the shock absorber from its top and bottom mountings, knock back the locking tabs of the two nuts (bolts on early cars) on top of the front bulkhead crossmember which secure the appropriate sub-frame tower. Remove the nuts and locking tabs which will expose a hole between the studs. If working on the right-hand side of a car, fitted with a fresh-air heater, it will be necessary to remove the air pipe from the heater motor or grille, according to the type, and lift it to expose the nuts on the crossmember.

Insert the central bolt of the spring compressor in the hole through the top of the sub-frame tower and engage its threads in the thread of the spring unit; screw the bolt nine complete turns into the spring unit. (If the thread on the spring compressor centre bolt is not in perfect condition it must be replaced with a new one. Always oil this thread before use.) Screw the wing nut of the compressor down on to the body of the tool, compressing the spring enough to allow the suspension strut to be withdrawn.

When decompressing the spring, ensure that the wing-nut of the compressor is screwed away from the body of the tool, before attempting to remove the centre bolt. Replacement of the suspension struts is quite straightforward, take care that the knuckle joint is correctly seated before completely decompressing the rubber spring.

Dismantling the rear suspension—Rubber type

When removing the suspension struts from the rear units, it is first necessary to remove the appropriate rear shockabsorber upper mounting. On the right-hand side, this is quite straightforward but, on the left-hand side, the upper mounting is behind the fuel tank and this must first be moved. It is possible to get to the nut by loosening the tank-securing strap, removing the filler cap and swinging the tank towards the centre of the boot, pivoting it about the flexible rubber pipe leading from the bottom front part of the tank to the fuel pump. On earlier models, a fuel drain tube is fitted to the tank and this must be removed from underneath before the tank can be moved. Care must be taken, while moving the tank, not to damage the flexible rubber fuel pipe. If difficulty is experienced, the tank will have to be disconnected from the fuel pump, drained and removed from the car. Disconnect the fuel-gauge wires from the tank.

When replacing the tank, ensure that the breather pipe is not kinked, or flattened; it should pass through the same hole in the floor as the wiring loom.

Having removed the nut from the shockabsorber upper mounting, jack up the car, supporting it beneath the rear sub-frame. Remove the wheel and allow the suspension arm to swing down to the lowest position. The strut may then be removed from the spring unit and pulled out of its socket in the suspension arm. When replacing the strut, be sure to see that the knuckle on the end is properly located in the socket on the suspension arm or damage to the strut may occur.

Before refitting shockabsorbers, especially if they have been laid down while off the car, hold them upright and extend and compress the unit two or three times to expel any air which may have become trapped in the hydraulic fluid.

Hydrolastic suspension

Before any of the suspension units can be dismantled, the hydrolastic system must be depressurized and eventually, before it can be repressurized, it must be evacuated. The complete job requires the use of a Hydrolastic-suspension service unit. This is a large and fairly expensive (£30/£40) piece of equipment and private owners are unlikely to have access to them at home.

One solution, for the amateur who wishes to work on the suspension, is to obtain a depressurizing connector, as used on the suspension service unit, depressurize the suspension and, after the work has been completed, drive the car to a garage which has a suspension-service unit and have it repressurized. It is permissible to drive the car without any fluid in it at all, provided that 30 mile/h is not exceeded and the road is not rough, as, without fluid, the car rests on rubber bump stops front and rear.

On some cars, especially if large section tyres are fitted, it may be difficult to drive the vehicle with no suspension at all as the tyres may touch the body, in this case it is possible to inflate the suspension with compressed air from an air line or foot pump; 50–75lb/in^2 should raise the car sufficiently but great care must be taken when driving it in this condition as the suspension will be extremely soft.

The connector should be fitted with a piece of rubber hose and used to depressurize the system as follows:

Attach the connector each side in turn, to the valve on the hydrolastic pipe which is situated under the car at the back of the rear sub-frame.

The cap is first removed from the valve and the connector is then fitted on with its knurled knob fully unscrewed. The end of the rubber tube should be placed in a clean can and the knurled knob on the connector may then be screwed in gently to release the fluid into the can. When no

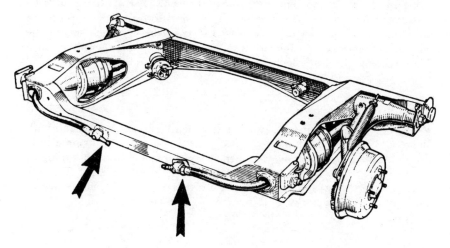

Fig. 5:2. Hydrolastic system pressure valves, showing position on the rear sub-frame.

more fluid comes out, the connector may be removed and the work on the suspension carried out. Arrangements should be made beforehand with a garage who, when the work is completed, will evacuate the system to remove any air which may have leaked in and repressurize.

REMOVAL OF THE SUSPENSION STRUTS AND DISPLACER UNITS

Jack up the car and support the body beneath the sub-frame front and rear.

Depressurize the suspension as described in the previous section, then remove the appropriate road wheel.

Front suspension units

It should now be possible to remove the dust seal from the nylon seating of the front suspension strut and lift the strut out of the displacer unit. If it is necessary to remove the complete displacer unit, disconnect the suspension fluid hose from the union on the engine bulkhead. It is now necessary to remove the upper support arm from the sub-frame; first remove the nut from the upper swivel-hub ball-pin and extract this pin from its tapered socket as described on page 62. Remove the nuts from the pivot pin and also the front thrust-washer retaining plate. Lever the pivot pin forward and remove the rear thrust washer, it should now be possible to manœuvre the arm out from the sub-frame. Now push the displacer unit upwards and remove the two screws which locate the displacer bracket inside the sub-frame tower. With these removed, turn the displacer unit anti-clockwise and withdraw it from the sub-frame.

Rear suspension units

With the car jacked up and supported beneath the sub-frame and with the road wheel removed, take off the coil helper-spring from its mounting on the trailing arm. Remove the suspension fluid pipe from the union at the rear of the sub-frame and then take out the displacer strut from the trailing arm socket and the displacer unit. It is now only necessary to turn the unit anti-clockwise a quarter of a turn and lift it out of its socket.

Refitting the suspension units front and rear

The refitting instructions for both front and rear units are essentially the reversal of those for removal, remember that the displacer units must be turned clockwise to lock them into their sockets. Lubricate the knuckle joint and nylon seating with grease (Manufacturer's recommendation for this point is Dextragrease GP) and replace the dust covers.

Do not exceed 30 mile/h, even on good roads, before the suspension has been evacuated and repressurized to the correct figure.

When the system is correctly pressurized and with the car loaded to kerb weight, that is with oil, water and 4 gallons of petrol, the wing heights should be checked and compared with the figures in Table 5:I.

TABLE 5:I

WING HEIGHTS

Early models (see Table III)		Later models (see Table III)	
Front	Rear	Front	Rear
13in. ± ¼in.	13½in. ± ¼in.	12⅝in. ± ¼in.	13⅛in. ± ¼in.
330mm ± 6mm	343mm ± 6mm	321mm ± 6mm	333mm ± 6mm

The wing height is the vertical distance from the wheel centre to the underside of the wheel arch.

TABLE 5:II

SUSPENSION PRESSURES

Early models (see Table III) ... ... $263lb/in^2$
$18{\cdot}5kg/cm^2$

Later models (see Table III) ... ... $282lb/in^2$
$19{\cdot}7kg/cm^2$

TABLE 5:III

The suspension changes referred to start at the following car numbers

Austin	Morris	RHD	LHD
Mini		830899	832055
	Mini	370004	370197
Cooper		830061	829417
	Cooper	830127	829490
Cooper S		820487	820514
	Cooper S	820705	820706

If the correct pressure does not give sufficient wing height, the system should be pressurized to about $60lb/in^2$ above the normal figure and left for half an hour. The pressure should then be reduced until the wing height is correct even if the pressure is then slightly above normal.

CHAPTER 6

IMPROVEMENT OF BRAKES AND SUSPENSION

It is often found that Mini brake drums are not truly round and this fault can occur to an extent where it markedly reduces braking efficiency. Scored brake drums also reduce efficiency and these faults must be rectified before any modifications, to improve engine performance, are carried out. If skilled machining facilities are available, at a reasonable price, the defects can be cured by lightly skimming the drum but only the minimum of metal must be removed. If much ovality or deep score marks are present the drum must be renewed but beware, not all *new* drums are perfectly round and if possible these should be checked and if necessary corrected before fitting.

Standard Mini brakes are good enough to cope with normal everyday motoring, if they are maintained in good condition, but if the car is driven fast, the brakes can sometimes prove inadequate. Stopping the car quickly from a high speed, several times in quick succession, will induce severe brake fade on the Mini. This is especially noticeable when a load is being carried. Pushing harder on the pedal in such cases only serves to bend the pedal itself and some modification of the braking system is required to achieve good stopping power. There are several possible approaches to this problem, these are: fitting different lining material, fitting a brake booster and changing the front brakes over to either two-leading-shoe operation or disc brakes. These different ways are covered in the following section.

Alternative lining material

Relining the brake shoes with a harder type of brake lining will improve the fade resistance. The harder the grade of lining material fitted, the higher will be the fade resistance of the brakes but also the higher will be the necessary pedal pressure. This is because the 'hard' linings have a lower coefficient of friction than normal ones and thus require more pressure than do the standard linings when working in an unfaded state. For example, if a car is being braked hard from 30 or 40 mile/h, a normal lining will not heat up sufficiently to reduce its coefficient of friction and so the braking will be effective with comparitively light pedal pressure. On the other hand, braking from high speeds with a hard lining which does not suffer from a decrease in coefficient of friction on heating up, will require less pedal pressure than a normal lining which

132

has overheated. With racing linings, it is desirable to fit a vacuum servo unit to increase the hydraulic pressure as these linings have a still lower coefficient of friction.

The standard lining material was changed in 1963 from Mintex M32 to DON 202. This lining is fitted to all brakes (*i.e.* front and rear) and is an improvement on the earlier type. Fade can still be induced however and if a harder grade is required, the use of Ferodo AM4 linings (or equivalent) on the front and standard linings (Ferodo AM3, DON 202, etc.) on the rear will improve matters further. The pedal pressure of a Mini with this grade of brake lining will be by no means excessive but the following points should be noted.

To realize their proper performance, the linings require fully bedding-in and this takes longer than with a standard lining. The leading and trailing edges of the lining should be chamfered slightly with a file before they are fitted in the car as this helps the bedding-in process. It is essential that the brake drums are thoroughly cleaned out when the new linings are fitted; the inside of the drums should be cleaned with emery cloth at the area along the edges of the working face which the old lining did not contact. The new lining may be slightly wider or may run in a slightly different position and if rust or dirt is present it may cause grabbing or pulling to the right or left.

In cases where an even harder grade of lining is needed, for instance, in competition work, it is advisable to ask the brake lining manufacturers for their recommendations. The following table suggests linings suitable for different purposes.

TABLE 6:I

ALTERNATIVE BRAKE LINING MATERIAL

All drum-braked models

	Front	*Rear*
Standard Lining (for normal use)	DON 202 Mintex M32 Ferodo AM3	DON 202 Mintex M32 Ferodo AM3
Fast road or competition use	Ferodo AM4	Ferodo AM3 DON 202
Racing (using booster)	Ferodo VG 95/1	Ferodo VG 95/1

With the hardest of the grades given above, a vacuum brake servo should be fitted, to make excessive pedal pressure unnecessary.

Vacuum brake servos

Fitting a vacuum brake servo increases the hydraulic pressure at the wheel cylinders whilst reducing the pressure required on the pedal. With a servo fitted, the standard brake linings will need much less pedal pressure and give a good stopping power, whilst a servo used in conjunction with hard linings will give excellent results. The disc brakes fitted to early Mini Coopers leave much to be desired and fitting a servo unit will help but it is preferable first to bring these brakes up to the late-type specification, as detailed in this chapter. Vacuum brake servo units are obtainable from Lockheed, Mot-a-Vac etc. and their manufacturers are very willing to supply details about them. They are normally supplied as conversion kits with all parts necessary for fitting included.

Installation is not a difficult job. A hole must be drilled and tapped in the manifold, to provide a vacuum take-off point for the servo unit and the brake-pipe, from the master cylinder to the union on the bulkhead, must be removed and replaced by the longer ones, provided in the kit, which run to and from the servo unit.

The unit itself is mounted on the side wall of the engine compartment, above the clutch housing. If the screen-washer reservoir is mounted on the side wall, it must be moved on to the bulkhead, to the left of the speedometer recess, i.e. on the opposite side to the hydraulic master cylinders. If an old-type fresh-air heater is fitted there is not enough room to fit a servo unit inside the engine compartment and in this case it is fitted to the outside of the engine compartment side wall, underneath the offside front wheel arch. A remote air filter must be fitted inside the engine compartment, in a clean dry position when the servo is fitted externally. This filter is connected to the servo by a breather pipe, passing through the engine compartment wall, together with the brake pipes. If much rallying is contemplated or other conditions are likely to be often encountered where a servo, mounted under the wing, might be damaged by large stones flung up from the road, it may be thought advisable to mount the servo inside the car. Some B M C works rally cars were equipped with brake servos mounted underneath the parcel shelf on the passenger's side of the car.

After fitting a brake servo, the unit itself and the new pipes have to be filled with brake fluid and this is done by bleeding the brakes in the normal way as outlined in chapter 2 (see page 87).

Changing the braking system

In some cases it may well be more practical to change the front brakes to a later type rather than fit special linings or a servo to the system as it stands. The least effective standard systems are those fitted to the 997cc Mini Cooper (very small discs) and all early 850s (single leading-shoe type). The best modification is to fit the backplates, cylinders and shoes used on all the latest type of drum-braked Minis. These parts will fit the hub of the old 850 Mini but if an old Cooper is to be modified, a pair of 850 hub castings must be obtained as well. These can of course be found very cheaply secondhand. It is a good idea to change the master cylinder and the pressure limiting valve for new ones at the same time.

The ultimate luxury is to fit Cooper S or 1275 GT type discs but unless these parts can be obtained secondhand in good condition it is a very expensive conversion. The discs, drive flanges, hubs, constant velocity joints and calipers are all different from any other Mini.

For serious racing, however, most people use the S-type system as it is the only really satisfactory one for this application.

The 'S' and GT type brakes need no major modification. A servo is fitted as standard to these cars and without one, although effective, the brakes need quite high pedal pressure. Some people prefer to race with no servo but the racing Mini is often very much lighter than its road-going counterpart so it is obviously easier to stop. Alternative lining materials for use with all disc braked Minis are listed below.

TABLE 6:II

ALTERNATIVE BRAKE LINING MATERIAL

All disc-braked models

	Front	Rear
Standard Lining (for normal use)	Ferodo DA3 (S types DA6)	DON 202
Competition use	Ferodo DA6	DON 202 Ferodo AM3
Racing (using servo)	Ferodo DS11	Ferodo VG 95/1

MODIFICATION OF THE SUSPENSION

The suspension of the Mini in standard form is quite suitable for fast motoring because its road-holding capabilities are such that very few people will ever exploit them to the full, on the road. There are, however, some modifications which can be carried out to improve the high speed handling and if the car is to be used in competition or driven very fast on the road, they are worthwhile.

DRY (NON-HYDROLASTIC) SUSPENSION

Shockabsorbers

Although the latest type of shockabsorbers are a vast improvement on the old, very short-lived type, one of the proprietary makes with stiffer settings will improve the handling. The quality of the ride is adversely affected by the use of very stiff shockabsorbers and this may not be acceptable if the car is to be used on the road, though an adjustable damper can help here. Several makes of adjustable shockabsorber are available and these can all be adjusted to give a stiff setting suitable for racing. Alternatively a non-adjustable damper made and set either for rallying or for racing can be used. For example the Armstrong.

Before buying new shockabsorbers, it must be remembered that cars with lowered suspension need special short rear shockabsorbers to avoid bottoming of the shockabsorber itself.

Cars used for production-car trials and autocross are best fitted with 'rally-setting' shockabsorbers, as circuit racing varieties are generally too stiff for rough going. The manufacturers can advise the owner about special applications if they are given all the details.

Lowering the suspension

If a road-going Mini is seldom used for carrying more than one or two people, the suspension may be lowered by about one inch all round and the handling will be improved but if the car is used for rallies or autocross, much lowering of the suspension is inadvisable; some owners raise the suspension for very rough work. For circuit racing, where passengers are never carried in the back, the suspension may be lowered by as much as $2\frac{1}{4}$in.

The easiest way to determine the suspension height, prior to lowering it, is to measure the distance from the centre of the wheel hub to the top of the wheel arch opening. This distance should be the same front and rear and is about 12in. according to the age of the car and how much it has settled. A reasonable minimum measurement for a road car is 11in. while a racer can go down to $10\frac{1}{4}$in.

The lowering is achieved by cutting a small amount of metal from the end of the suspension struts which act on the rubber springs. The struts must be removed from the car and the steel knuckles which plug into the end of the struts must be tapped out. The strut is then shortened at the knuckle end by $\frac{1}{8}$in. or more, according to how much lowering is required. Removal of $\frac{3}{16}$in. from the strut is the normally recommended maximum. $\frac{1}{8}$in. removed lowers the suspension by about $\frac{3}{8}$in. If the car is lightened much, as most club racers are, the car will rise, especially at the rear, and the suspension height calculations go somewhat awry. It is necessary in this case to cut more metal off the rear struts than off the front ones. Dismantling the suspension is described in chapter 5.

Unfortunately, the complications do not stop here, because the reduced weight of the car allows the rear rubber springs to decompress which reduces the spring rate and gives a very softly-sprung rear end. In this condition, with low-set suspension, the tyres will tend to rub on the wheel arches on corners and bumps. Probably the simplest way to increase the rear spring rate again is to fit large soft-rubber bungs inside the rubber springs before the suspension is reassembled. *A word of warning:* it is possible to shorten the rear struts so much that when the car is jacked up the springs are no longer compressed at all. This must be avoided at all costs as it is then possible, if the car becomes airborne, for the strut to fall out causing total loss of suspension.

Fouling the brake pipes

If the car is lowered by the absolute maximum amount, it is possible for the rear brake pipes to foul the sub-frame or the body on full bump deflection. The offending portion of the brake pipe is the joint between the Bundy tubing and the flexible hose at the bracket where the pipes are fixed to the top of the rear trailing arm. The remedy is to move the bracket down onto the inside of the arm. Make sure it is in such a position that the pipes do not suffer any strain in any suspension position or chafe on the sub-frame. On no account must the pipes be removed from the bracket and left unsupported, as the Bundy tubing may break because of the flexing and vibration.

HYDROLASTIC SUSPENSION

Displacer units

As well as the normal displacer units, fitted in standard form, alternatives are available with stiff settings for rallying and with hard settings

TABLE 6:III

ALTERNATIVE HYDROLASTIC DISPLACER UNITS

Use		Marking	
		Early cars	Late Cars
Normal setting,	front	no marking	1 orange band
	rear	no marking	1 orange band
Stiff setting,	front	1 yellow band	2 orange bands
(rallying)	rear	1 yellow band	2 orange bands
Hard setting,	front	1 red band	1 blue band
(racing)	rear	2 red bands	2 blue bands
Running pressure		263lb/in^2	282lb/in^2

for racing. The displacer units are colour coded and can be identified by the marking bands surrounding them. Early cars were fitted with displacers with no markings and also with early type helper springs and rear struts. The displacers suitable for early and late cars are listed in Table 6:III.

To prevent the front of the car rising during fierce acceleration, progressive rear bump rubbers are available in a kit. (Part no. C-AJJ 3313.)

Raising the suspension

For rallying, where extra ground clearance is needed, it is possible to lengthen the displacer struts by up to 0·15in. by fitting spacers between the strut and the knuckle which plugs into the end of it. Spacers of 0·050, 0·080, 0·100 and 0·150in. thickness are available from British Leyland Special Tuning Department. Increasing the pressure to above 300lb/in^2 is not recommended but if an early car is nose down because of the weight of the sumpguards etc. the stronger rear helper spring 21A1806, as used on late cars, may be fitted.

Lowering the suspension

For circuit racing, the suspension of hydrolastic cars can be lowered by shortening the displacer struts in the same way as is done for rubber-cone sprung cars. Up to 0·2in. may be machined from the front struts and up to 0·3in. from the rear ones. The standard rear bump rubbers should be replaced by the ones in kit C-AJJ 3313 unless these prove too stiff, when the parts 21A1728 and 21A1729 should be used.

The suspension pressure may be reduced to allow the car to ride just clear of the bump stops, but it should not be reduced to below 220lb/in^2. It does not matter if the pressures are not quite the same both sides as may be the case if there are slight differences in the displacers or struts from side to side.

Some owners have obtained a further improvement on cars used for circuit racing by blanking off the hydrolastic pipes completely and running with differential pressures, front to rear. This is done by putting small high-pressure-type taps in the hydrolastic pipes. These are sited either at the rear beneath the boot floor or alternatively, when the pipes are re-routed inside the car, just behind the front seats. In use, the suspension is pressurized to 250lb/in^2 with the taps open, the taps are then shut tight and the rear suspension then let down to 190lb/in^2. The best pressures vary from circuit to circuit however and must be found by experiment.

Anti-roll bars

Fitting an anti-roll bar to the rear of a Mini interconnects the trailing arms and reduces body roll on corners. As this keeps the front wheels more upright, it has the effect of reducing the understeer experienced when cornering a powerful Mini fast. The change of attitude of the car, normally experienced if the throttle is closed suddenly in a bend, is however accentuated, in fact, any modification of the suspension designed to decrease the understeer will tend to make the car less stable on the over-run. The method of fitting anti-roll bars varies with each make and the manufacturer's instructions should be followed.

Alteration of camber and castor angles

A popular modification, among racing Mini owners who are not tied to standard suspension angles by regulations, is to reduce the wheel camber. This modification causes the wheels to lean inwards at the top which means that the outside wheels, on corners, are held upright even though the body rolls.

At the front, the decrease in camber angle is achieved by lengthening the bottom suspension link by $\frac{1}{4}$in. This reduces the camber by $2\frac{1}{2}$ degrees which is about the optimum. The link may be heated and stretched or cut and welded back together again but in this case it should be reinforced by welding metal rods or strips along the channel section of the link. If the owner is in the slightest doubt about his ability to carry out either of these modifications it should be left to an expert because it is obviously a very vital component. Some tuning firms can supply adjustable lower links which enable the ideal camber setting to be found more easily.

It will be necessary to adjust the wheel alignment after the suspension has been lowered or the camber has been changed. The steering tie rods need adjusting for extra length but first check, by unscrewing the rods, that there will be enough thread left in the ball joint after making the adjustment. If the rods are too short they may pull the thread out of the ball joints which would be disastrous.

At the rear of the car, the camber angle is decreased by moving the position of the outer end of the trailing arm pivot pin in its bracket on the sub-frame. To do this, the bracket should be released by taking off the large nut at the end of the pivot pin and then removing the four bolts which hold the bracket to the sub-frame. Two of these will be found beneath the bracket and the other two are located, one above and one below the trailing arm. The pivot hole in the bracket is then welded up and redrilled $\frac{1}{4}$in. further up the bracket which decreases the camber by about $1\frac{1}{2}$ degrees.

Increasing the castor angle has the effect of decreasing the camber of the outside front wheel when the car is cornering and the steering is on lock. This modification is useful to a certain extent in this respect as well as for the increased self-centering action which it imparts to the steering. Some cars, when lowered and decambered, have very light steering which has insufficient feel; around 2 degrees of extra castor angle will correct this.

Extra angle is attained by shortening the tie rod which joins the outer end of the lower link to the front of the sub-frame. To do this, remove the tie rod from the car and, in a lathe, turn off the weld that holds the large flat washer to the rod. Weld the washer on again $\frac{1}{4}$in. further along the rod and extend the thread along the rod by the same amount. After this modification has been carried out, it is necessary to correct the wheel alignment, checking that there is adequate adjustment as mentioned above.

Wheels

The standard wheel rim width fitted to Minis was $3\frac{1}{2}$in. Later a $4\frac{1}{2}$in. optional extra was produced for the Cooper S types; the wider wheels were found to improve the road holding by maintaining a more upright posture of the tyre walls and thus keeping the tread on the road. A slight increase in ride harshness and steering weight could be noticed with some tyres but the improved handling far outweighs these faults.

Wider steel wheels (commonly known as reverse rim) are also available to fit standard Minis. Rostyle wide wheels are provided as basic fitments to the 1275 GT. When fitting different wheels to a Mini it must be remembered that Cooper S type wheels cannot be fitted to other models without modification, because the rims are offset inwards and the tyres would foul the suspension arms and shockabsorbers.

If these wheels are to be used, a spacer at least $\frac{7}{8}$in. thick must be fitted between the wheel and the brake drum. This should preferably be of the solid type with one piece studs; the R A C insist on spacers being of this type if used for racing and set a maximum thickness of one inch.

An alternative method is to use the Cooper S brake drums, which have a built-in spacer, together with Cooper S rear-wheel studs. The alternative to using Cooper S or wide steel Mini wheels it to fit specially made cast alloy ones.

Several firms are manufacturing high quality wide wheels both for general use in aluminium and for racing in aluminium/magnesium alloy.

The aluminium/magnesium alloy wheels manufactured by firms such as Dunlop, Mamba and Minilite for racing purposes, are very much lighter and stiffer than steel ones and some types are made in widths of up to $7\frac{1}{2}$in. to suit the very wide racing tyres now available. The aluminium wheels are better able to resist corrosion than those containing magnesium and are thus more suitable for general purpose use.

For road cars, a maximum width of about 5½in. is recommended as suitable tyres are not produced for the very wide rims.

The normal 145 section radial tyres fit comfortably on a 4½in. rim but the 165–70 low-profile types should be used on a 5 or 5½in. rim.

All 850 Minis produced up to 1961 had wheels with thin centres and because of the danger of failure under stress of racing B M C supplied special competition wheels for this purpose. When the Mini Cooper was introduced it was fitted with these stronger wheels as standard equipment and after 1961 all Minis were fitted with wheels with reinforced centres for extra safety. It is extremely unlikely that an 850 Mini fitted with early-type wheels would be allowed to compete in any form of racing competition so that any danger of wheel breakage would seem to be small. The Authors however have had personal experience of early Mini wheels collapsing on a car driven only on public roads and would recommend anyone, who perpetually corners hard in an early Mini, to consider replacing the wheels, especially if they have covered a high mileage. In any case they should be regularly inspected for signs of cracking which occurs in the area round the retaining-stud holes. The difference between the two types of wheel can be measured if there is any doubt, the centre portion of an early wheel is about 0·080in. thick and the later ones are 0·120in. thick. These measurements are approximate, to within three or four thou., as they include paint thickness. Some thick centred wheels also have the number 11 stamped on them which enables them to be quickly recognized.

There have been instances of thick centred Mini wheels and even Cooper S wheels breaking when used for racing. With careful use and regular examination this can be avoided. Overtightening of wheel nuts is a major contributing factor as this pulls the area round the nut down onto the hub. The wheel is designed to bear against the hub on four raised pads and not on the areas behind the nuts, as some people seem to think. The correct tightness for wheel nuts is 38 to 43lb ft.

The wheels on any car that is used for racing should be given a regular thorough inspection, especially round the stud holes. It is obviously an advantage to keep them clean and free from rust. If a car is raced most weekends, a new set of wheels at the beginning of the season is a wise investment, as are new studs and nuts.

Magnesium wheels can corrode and become liable to failure if they are not properly looked after. When new, they should have had an anti-corrosive coating put on by the manufacturers and this must be carefully preserved. Scratches can be the start of corrosion faults which penetrate deep into the metal yet are very difficult to see on the surface. Balance weights should be stuck on with double sided adhesive tape. The normal type of lead and steel clip-on weight should not be used because of the danger of the clip cutting through the coating on the wheel and starting rapid electrolytic corrosion of the magnesium.

Wheel arch extensions

It is both illegal and a contravention of the R A C vehicle regulations to run a car on which the tyre tread protrudes beyond the wheel arch. If Minis are fitted with very wide rims, or very thick spacers, the wheel arches must be extended to cover the tyre. Fibreglass extensions are available from British Leyland Special Tuning Department and from some accessory dealers. These screw onto the wheel arches after the removal of the plastic trim which may afterwards be replaced along their outer edges.

A skilled panel beater could, of course, modify the metal arches and, when filled and sprayed, a very neat and professional job would result but unless the owner can do it himself it would cost much more than the fibreglass parts.

CHAPTER 7

MODIFICATION OF THE ENGINE FOR ROAD USE

All Mini engines are of sturdy design with a large margin of safety built-in which ensures long life and reliability. As a result of this, a quite considerable increase in performance may be obtained without impairing reliability provided that the car is sensibly driven. It must, however, be fully understood that extensive tuning does narrow down the makers' safety margins and at the same time removes some of the 'safety valves' built into the standard engine. The limitations of standard valve springs and restricted breathing prevent the standard engine from being over-revved but when it is tuned the onus is upon the driver.

This chapter is concerned mainly with cars that are to be used for everyday transport whilst modifications to cars to be used for competition work are dealt with in chapter 8.

TABLE 7:I

850cc MINIS

Suggested stages of modification

Stage	Cylinder Head	Exhaust System	Induction System	Camshaft
A	Reshaped chambers Polished ports Increased c r Special valve springs			
B	As above	Straight-through silencer		
C	As above	As above	Larger single carburetter, twin 1¼in. carburetters or twin-choke carburetter	
D	As above but with larger valves	Special exhaust manifold and larger tailpipe	As above	AEA 630 or AEG 148

Before any modification is carried out, the owner should consider exactly what he wants in the way of improved performance and then think carefully how it is best achieved. Tables 7:I to 7:IV are intended as a general guide to engine modifications suitable for road cars. They indicate the order in which the modifications should be carried out for best results. The modifications given in the tables are described in detail later in this chapter.

TABLE 7:II

998cc MINIS

Suggested stages of modification

Stage	Cylinder Head	Exhaust System	Induction System	Camshaft
A	Reshaped chambers Polished ports Increased c r Special valve springs			
B	As above	Straight-through silencer		
C	As above but with larger inlet valves	As above	Large single carburetter, twin 1¼in. carburetters or twin-choke carburetter	
D	As above or modified 12G295 head	Special manifold and larger tailpipe	As above	
E	As above	As above	As above	AEA 630 or AEG 148
F	As above	As above	Twin 1½in. carburetters	AEG 510 or 2A948 (88G229)

Although it is difficult to give exact figures for the improvement in performance obtained with modifications, an idea can be gained from these approximate formulae. Stages A and B should improve the acceleration by up to 20% and increase the maximum speed by around 5%. Stage C should give up to 27% more acceleration and 8–10% higher speed, while stages D and E give 30–35% more acceleration and 12–15% higher top speed. There are definite advantages, for the owner who does not want to carry out the modification work himself, in going to a specialist (such as Downton or

British Leyland Special Tuning) who carries out a complete conversion instead of simply supplying bolt-on bits. Buying a cylinder head from one source, a carburetter set-up from another and an exhaust system from a third, may lead to disappointing results and is seldom cheaper in the long run.

TABLE 7:III

MINI COOPER AND COOPER S TYPES

Suggested stages of modification

Stage	Cylinder Head	Exhaust System	Induction System	Camshaft
A	Reshaped chambers Polished ports Increased c r			
B	As above		Twin 1½in. carburetters	
C	As above	Competition type exhaust manifold	As above	
D	As above but larger valves in Coopers	As above	As above	AEG 510 (exception post 1965 'S' types) or 2A948 (88G229)

TABLE 7:IV

1275 GT

Suggested stages of modification

Stage	Cylinder Head	Exhaust System	Induction System	Camshaft
A	Reshaped and polished, increased c r		Matched and polished manifold	
B	Modified with larger inlet valves	Competition type exhaust manifold	Twin 1½in. carburetters	
C	As above	As above	As above	C-AEG 542

Cylinder heads

Several different types of cylinder head are fitted to the Mini range in standard form and all of them can be improved by careful attention to the ports, passages and combustion chambers. Many specialist tuning firms supply cylinder heads on an exchange basis and these cost from £20 upwards according to the degree of modification. It does not necessarily follow that a highly modified and expensive head will give better results than one modified to a lesser extent. The head used should be carefully matched to the rest of the engine for best results; a head with large valves and ports for instance will show little improvement on an engine

TABLE 7:V

B L 'A' TYPE CYLINDER HEADS

The marking is found on top of the head and can be seen with the rocker cover removed

Marking	Normal use	Possible other use
2A629	850 Mini, A35, A40, & Morris Minor	Will fit 998 also 1100 and Cooper as a standby
12A1458	Late 850 & 998 Minis	Similar to 2A629 but with boss at front for temperature gauge
12G185	997cc Mini Cooper	Will serve as large-valve head for 850 & 998
12G202	Austin/Morris-1100	Similar to 12G185
12G206	Early MG 1100	Improved 12G202
12G295	998cc Cooper, MG 1100, Mk III Sprite	Suitable for 998 requiring larger valves
12G940 (with 9 studs)	1275 GT, Austin/Morris 1300, Mk IV Sprite, Marina 1·3	Can be modified to specification below
12G940 (with 11 studs)	Austin 1300 GT, MG 1300 Mk II, late Cooper S	Suitable for 1275 GT where larger valves are needed
AEG 165	Mini Cooper S	Can be used in place of 11—stud 12G940

which still retains its standard camshaft and carburetter. It is very difficult to choose between a number of professionally modified heads and comparison of performance figures can be misleading as they depend to such an extent on the conditions under which they are obtained. There is no risk though, in buying a head from an established company of good repute, for reputation and racing successes have to be earned, not just claimed, and these are a reliable guide.

For a moderate increase in performance, attention to the standard head without alteration of valve sizes is the best scheme. In some cases, as outlined in the tables on pages 143–5, enlarged valves are helpful, these are readily obtained for all the heads concerned and details are given as each head is described.

Modification of cylinder heads

The general methods of cylinder head modification will be dealt with first as this information applies to all the heads fitted to the Mini range. The precise details which apply directly to each type of head will be given later.

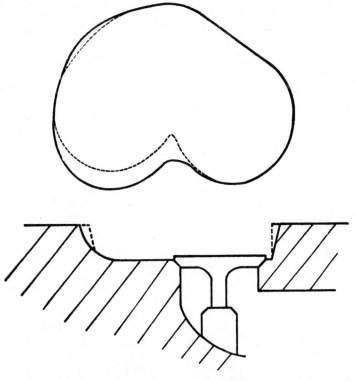

Fig. 7:1. Modified combustion chamber shape for 850 and 998 Minis in stage A tune. Dotted line shows outline of unmodified chamber.

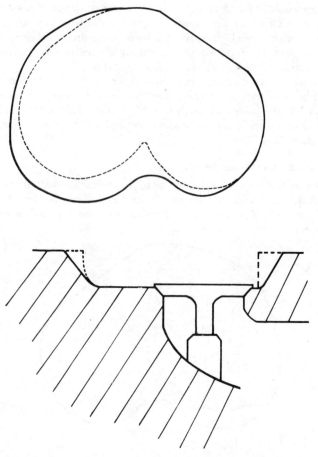

Fig. 7:2. Modified combustion chamber shape for 850 and 998 Minis in stage D
tune. Dotted line shows outline of unmodified chamber.

Modification of combustion chambers

All the cylinder heads can be modified to improve the gas flow past the
inlet valve by removing metal from the combustion chamber walls as
shown in figs. 7:1–4. This is best done by using a small grinding stone or
rotary file in a high–speed electric drill but the work must be most
carefully carried out. When modifying combustion chambers, do not
remove metal from the walls to the extent that the gasket will overlap
the edge of the chamber or bad sealing and gasket burning will occur.

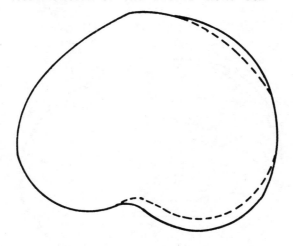

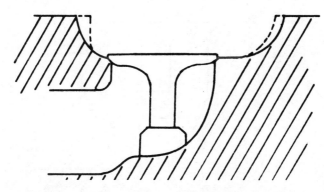

Fig. 7:3. Modified combustion chamber shape for 998 Cooper. Dotted line shows outline of unmodified chamber.

If the outline of the gasket is drawn on the head before work is commenced it will help in avoiding this. Care must be taken to avoid damaging the valve seats with a stone or cutter. It is very easy to ruin a valve seat in this way and recutting the seat 'pockets' the valve into the head which is very bad for gas flow. A pair of old valves, with their heads thinned down, should be left in position to protect the valve seats while the work is carried out. The roofs of the combustion chambers, of old heads, which have suffered from recession due to seat erosion, should be ground away to counteract this as shown in fig. 7:5. This is especially important in the case of the inlet valves.

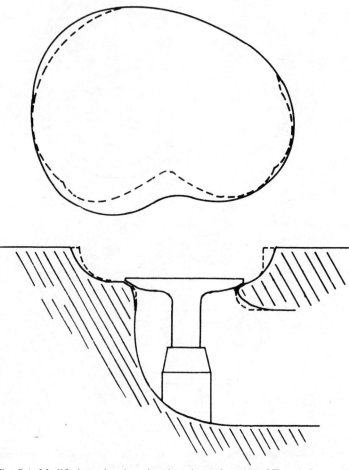

Fig. 7:4. Modified combustion chamber shape for 1275 GT and Cooper S.
Dotted line shows outline of unmodified chamber.

When the roughing-out of the combustion chambers has been done,
the roof and walls should be smoothed out all over to remove all lumps
and bumps. This is done with emery cloth strip, 1in. wide, wrapped and
tied with 20 swg soft iron wire, over a tool of the type shown in fig. 7:6.
The higher the speed of the tool used for this job the better; the
professionals use a flexible shaft running at 10–15,000 rev/min. However
the electric drill serves well enough, even if it takes longer. Quite coarse
emery may be used to start with, 50 or 60 grit, finishing with 150–200

PLATE V

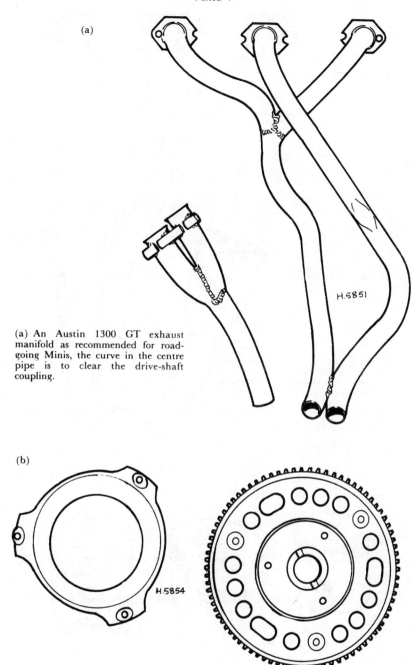

(a)

(a) An Austin 1300 GT exhaust manifold as recommended for road-going Minis, the curve in the centre pipe is to clear the drive-shaft coupling.

H.5851

(b)

H.5854

(b) A special Tuning ultra light steel flywheel and lightweight pressure plate.

PLATE VI

(a)

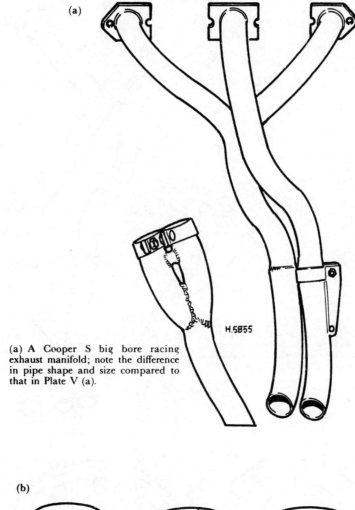

H.5855

(a) A Cooper S big bore racing exhaust manifold; note the difference in pipe shape and size compared to that in Plate V (a).

(b)

(b) **Three generations of 850 racing Mini pistons as used by the Authors.** *Left:* Standard Mini type, shortened and machined flat. *Centre:* Modified motorcycle piston for 62mm-stroke engine. *Right:* Specially made high-crown piston for ultra short stroke 850.

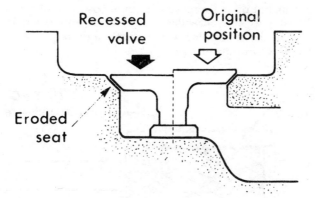

Fig. 7:5. Valve recession caused by erosion of the seat in the cylinder head. This must be corrected by grinding the roof of the head away and recutting the seat.

grade. A surprising amount of metal can be removed with 50 grit emery cloth run at high speed, so take care.

Modification of ports and passages

The inlet ports should receive attention next and to do this it is necessary to drift the valve guides down, out of the port, until they are below the level of the guide boss. The boss can then be ground away to streamline it as shown in fig. 7:7, and the guides may be tapered slightly at the ends but do not shorten them or excessive wear and oil burning may result. The inside corner of the port should be nicely radiused and the whole interior smoothed and then polished. The easiest tool for this is a piece of $\frac{1}{4}$in. diameter rod about 3in. long, split with a 1in. saw cut at one end. Emery cloth is wrapped round this and is used in the electric drill. The restricted part of the port between the pushrod holes can be enlarged with advantage when oversize valves are to be fitted, though it is not a good idea to open it out to as large a size as possible; this spoils the mid-range power to some extent. Suitable sizes are shown in figs. 7:9-11. If by accident a hole is made through into one of the pushrod holes, the best scheme of repair is to drill the pushrod hole out oversize and drive a piece of tight fitting steel tubing down it, sealing the ends with Araldite. See fig. 7:12.

When oversize valves are fitted, the port can be enlarged to suit the valve either by careful grinding with a fairly large round stone or by cutting with a flycutter in an arbor registered in the valve guide. In either case it is necessary to use a valve seat cutter to cut the new seat.

There is little point in highly polishing the exhaust ports but they can be smoothed. The inner corner of the exhaust port should be given a generous radius but do not remove the guide boss. On all the heads, the centre exhaust port can be widened somewhat and the ports can be matched to fit the manifold; any enlargement required should be continued well down into the head.

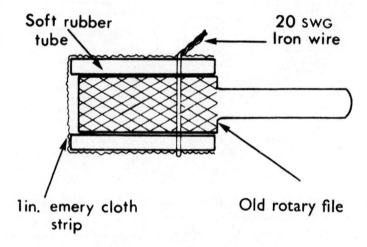

Soft rubber tube

20 SWG Iron wire

1in. emery cloth strip

Old rotary file

Fig. 7:6. A convenient tool for polishing combustion chambers.

The inlet ports should be carefully matched to the manifold. The heads used on 998 Coopers, 1275 GTs and all the Cooper S types have a register machined into the mouth of the inlet port to take locating rings. These should be retained unless twin $1\frac{1}{2}$in. bore carburetters are to be used. Care is required when polishing these ports not to grind away the edge of the register and thus leave a step when the locating ring is fitted.

If a head with registers is to be used with a manifold not having them, a very short piece of tubing should be pressed or fixed with Araldite, into the register in the head. This tube must be cut off flush with the manifold gasket face and polished into the port. This method is preferable to enlarging the port to the size of the register and then opening out the end of the manifold to fit because a bulge which hinders gas flow would be left at the joint. If the manifold is of a type which does not locate on rings or on its studs it should be dowelled on as described below for $1\frac{1}{2}$in. bore carburetters.

If $1\frac{1}{2}$in. carburetters are to be used, the steel tube may be discarded and the port opened out to a diameter of $1\frac{3}{8}$in. at the manifold joint face, thus completely removing the register. The standard inlet manifold should then be enlarged to give a gradual taper from $1\frac{1}{2}$in. bore at the carburetter end to $1\frac{3}{8}$in. bore at the cylinder head end. It is important, when this has been done, to dowel the manifold and head face together or correct alignment of the manifold and passages cannot be ensured.

The modification is shown in fig. 7:14. To dowel these together, the manifold should be drilled with a $\frac{3}{32}$ in. drill in the positions shown in fig. 7:15. It should then be bolted to the head in the correct position while

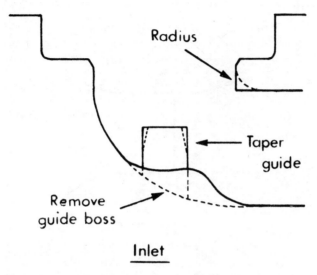

Fig. 7:7. Modification of the inlet ports behind the valves to improve gas flow. The guide may be tapered but must not be shortened.

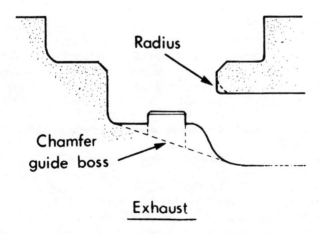

Fig. 7:8. Modification of the exhaust port below the valve to improve gas flow.

these drillings are continued through into the head for about $\frac{7}{16}$ in. The manifold is then removed and tapped to take 2BA bolts whose heads are cut off to leave about $\frac{3}{32}$ in. of shank protruding from the manifold face. The pilot holes in the head are then enlarged to $\frac{7}{16}$ in. diameter. Be sure to get the manifold on the right way up.

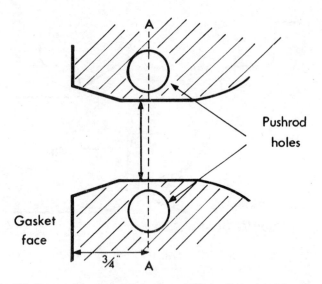

Fig. 7:9. Cross-section through inlet port of Mini cylinder head, between pushrod holes.

Valve seats

Once the combustion chambers and ports are polished, the valve seats should receive attention. The exhausts should have good pit-free seats of $\frac{3}{32}$ to $\frac{1}{8}$ in. wide. The inlets should be ground-in to give a seat all the way round and the width of this seat should be reduced by very carefully grinding away the inside of it, as shown in fig. 7:16. The finished seat width, after the grinding marks have been polished out, should be no more than $\frac{1}{32}$ in. The edges of the face on the inlet valve should be slightly radiused using a stone or a coarse emery while spinning the valve in a drill.

When the valve seats and faces are all finished off, the volumes of the combustion chambers must be checked and if necessary equalized. The volumes of all the chambers are measured by running in paraffin from a burette and the volumes are then equalized by removing metal from the smaller chambers to bring them up to the same size as the largest. When correcting a combustion chamber for size, metal should first be removed from any places in which it differs in shape from the others but if there are no obvious differences, a small amount will have to be taken off all over the roof of the chamber. The valves which are finally to be used in the head must be in position when the volumes are measured because variations in the thickness of the valve heads can significantly alter the volume. To measure the volumes, the head should be placed

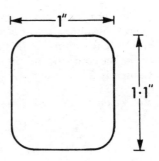

Fig. 7:10. Dimensions of the inlet port between the pushrod holes in the position shown at AA in Fig. 7:9. for 850 and 998 Minis.

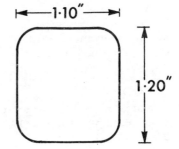

Fig. 7:11. Dimensions of the inlet port between the pushrod holes in the position shown at AA in Fig. 7:9. for 1275 GT and S type Coopers:

upside down on the bench, with a set of old sparking plugs in position.

The valves are then placed in position with a smear of grease round their seats. A piece of Perspex large enough to cover one combustion chamber, with a small hole ($\frac{1}{16}$ in.) in the middle, is stuck to the face of the head with a thin layer of grease and the chamber filled to the bottom of the hole in the Perspex with a measured quantity of paraffin carefully run in from a burette. The volumes should be within 0·2–0·3cc of each other when balancing is finished.

Calculation of compression ratio

When the volume of the combustion chamber has been found, the compression ratio must be calculated and the amount of metal, which has to be machined from the face to achieve the desired compression ratio, calculated. Compression ratio is calculated as follows:

$$CR = \frac{\text{Vol. of cylinder (V) plus Vol. of combustion space (v)}}{\text{Vol. of combustion space (v)}}$$

or

$$CR = \frac{V \text{ plus } v}{v}$$

Standard Minis have concave piston crowns which add to the volume of the combustion space and so does the volume created by the depth of the gasket. The volume of this additional combustion space has to be found before the compression ratio can be calculated. The total combustion space volume is found thus:

$$\text{Vol. of one cylinder} = \frac{848}{4} = 212\text{cc}$$

$$CR = 8{\cdot}3{:}1$$

$$\therefore \quad 8{\cdot}3 = \frac{212+v}{v}$$

$$\therefore \quad 212 = 8{\cdot}3v-v$$

$$\therefore \quad v = \frac{212}{7{\cdot}3} = 29\text{cc}$$

but as the cylinder head volume is 25cc (approx.) then the remaining space (contained by the gasket and the concave piston crown) = 4cc.

$$\therefore \quad CR = \frac{212 + \text{head vol.} + 4}{\text{head vol.} + 4}$$

The area of the combustion chamber is about 19cm^2 and thus removal of, for example, 0·060in. (1·52mm) reduces the volume by $19 \times 0{\cdot}152 = 2{\cdot}9$cc.

The new CR is therefore:

$$\begin{aligned} \text{Head vol. } 25{-}2{\cdot}9 &= 22{\cdot}1 \\ + \text{ remaining space} &= 26{\cdot}1 \end{aligned}$$

$$\frac{212+26{\cdot}1}{26{\cdot}1} = 9{\cdot}14{:}1$$

The compression ratio may be raised to about 9:1 without needing 100 octane fuel though this is preferable for ratios above that. Ratios of 9·5 to 10·1 are feasible if the engine is in good condition but for road use it is not practicable to go much higher.

Machining the cylinder head weakens the casting and, as all the castings vary, it is impossible to lay down a fixed maximum amount of metal that can safely be machined off. Some heads will stand removal of as much as 0·125in. without distorting enough to give gasket trouble but others will lift at the ends, when tightened down, and blow gaskets. Careful overtightening sometimes helps, 45lb ft on the centre studs and

48lb ft on the four end ones, but the studs must be in good condition or they may break. If Austin 1300 studs, which are high-tensile, are used they may be tightened to 50lb ft. Special gaskets such as the competition ones, part no. C–AEA 647 for 850 and 998cc Minis and C–AHT 188 for the 1275 GT and Cooper S, can cure the trouble sometimes and it is

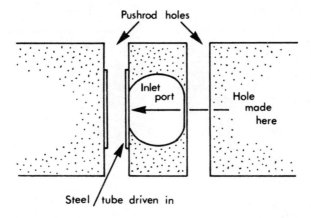

Fig. 7:12. Repair of pushrod hole after perforation during modification.

worth a try. The use of Araldite as a gasket cement is also effective and the head can still be removed fairly easily, especially if the Araldite is only applied thinly around the trouble spots. The 1275 heads are much stiffer than the smaller Mini ones and it is unlikely that much trouble will be experienced with these. If the head can be seen to be distorted, when checked with a straight edge across the face, it must be lightly skimmed to correct it. The top of the block must also be checked for truth and it is advisable to remove the head studs and lightly countersink the tops of the stud holes to ensure that the top threads do not pull up and stand proud of the block face.

Modification of rocker-shaft oil feed when machining the head

All the heads except the Cooper S types and 1275 GT have an oil feed to No.1 rocker post drilled downwards between the rocker-post studs, and the depth of this hole must be checked. Insert a pointed length of stiff wire down the hole as far as it will possibly go and mark the depth of the hole on the wire, then compare this length with the thickness of the head. (Standard heads are $2\frac{3}{4}$in. deep ± about 0·005in.).

Normally the drilling stops at about $\frac{1}{16}$in. short of the face and it is safe

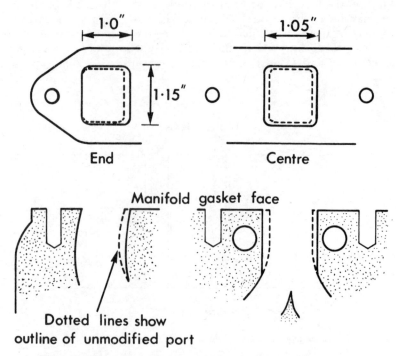

Fig. 7:13. Cross-section of exhaust passages showing how they may be enlarged.

to remove at least 0·060in. but on no account must the head be machined so that the face comes nearer to the drilling than around $\frac{3}{16}$in. or there is a danger that it may break through and the rocker-shaft oil will pour into No. 1 cylinder. If it is not possible to remove sufficient metal without coming too close to the drilling, the oil-feed must be altered as follows: (see also fig. 7:17).

Machine about 0·020in. less than is finally required from the face and drill down the vertical oil hole right through the head face. Mark the position of the transverse drilling which runs from the brass plug in the corner of the head to the vertical drilling to the rockers. This drilling must then be grooved out across the head face with a milling machine or a rotary burr to leave an open 'trench' large enough to take a piece of 'Bundy' tubing. The vertical drilling is opened out to $\frac{1}{4}$in. diameter to a depth of about $\frac{3}{4}$in. and a piece of 'Bundy' tubing, bent through an angle of 90 degrees at one end, is pushed into the drilling and laid in the 'trench'. This tube is brazed into position and the 'trench' filled up flush with the head surface with brazing metal. The head face is then machined to the required final thickness, the open end of the Bundy tube

Remove metal to dotted lines when using 1½" carburetters

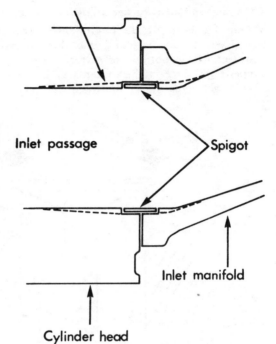

Fig. 7:14. Modification to twin carburetter inlet manifold and cylinder head when using 1½in. carburetters.

Inlet passage

Spigot

Inlet manifold

Cylinder head

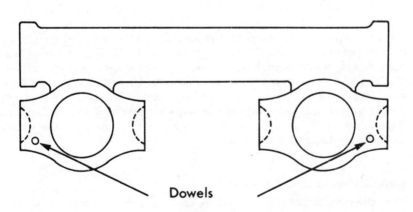

Dowels

Fig. 7:15. Position of inlet manifold locating dowels used with modification shown in Fig. 7:14.

closed with a brass plug and the oil-feed hole, which enters the head from the cylinder block, is redrilled.

Obtaining sufficient rocker adjustment after machining

When reassembling an engine after the cylinder head has been machined, it may be found that there is insufficient valve rocker adjustment left to obtain the correct tappet clearance. In this case, the tappet screw hole in the rocker may be counter-sunk, as shown in fig. 7:18 to get some more adjustment. It may then be necessary to grind

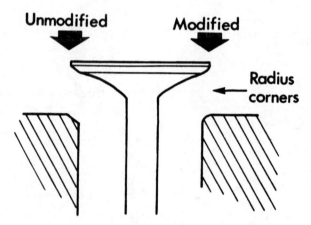

Fig. 7:16. Modification of inlet valve seats to improve flow past valve at low lift.

away the top of the push rod to stop it fouling the rocker and metal may be removed from this to the extent shown in fig. 7:18. These modifications should enable normal tappet clearance to be obtained even with as much as 0·120in. removed from the head face. Unless longer valves have been fitted packing pieces should not be placed under the rocker posts to obtain adjustment, as it alters the working angle of the rocker and imparts excessive side thrust on the valve stems, wearing out the guides and possibly bending the valves.

Identification of cylinder heads

The following notes on modifications applicable to each type of cylinder head should be used in conjunction with table 7:V which gives the identity marks of all B L 'A' type heads that are likely to be encountered by the potential Mini tuner.

850 and 998 Mini heads 2A629 and 12A1458 Stage A tune

The combustion chambers should be modified as shown in fig. 7:1 and the inlet ports streamlined below the valve as shown in fig. 7:7. The restricted section of the inlet port between the pushrod holes should be

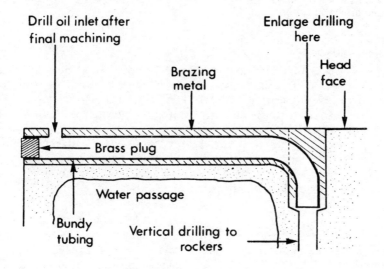

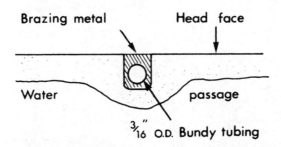

Fig. 7:17. Modification of rocker shaft oil-feed passage, when large amounts of metal have been machined from the cylinder-head.

enlarged to 1in. diameter and be blended smoothly with the rest of the inside of the port. The corner of the exhaust port should be radiused as shown in fig. 7:8. Mini Cooper exhaust valves may be used with some advantage as they are identical except that the material is improved to give longer life.

Stage D, 850cc and C, 998cc

In this case the combustion chamber should be modified as shown in fig. 7:2. The $1\frac{7}{32}$in. diameter inlet valves from the Austin/Morris 1100 are the best choice at this point, and the throat of the port must be enlarged to accommodate them. The size of the inlet passage given in fig. 7:10 must be obtained by carefully grinding out the circular hole to a squarish shape.

Stage D, 998cc

When a 998cc engine is modified to stage D or beyond, it will benefit from the use of 998 Mini Cooper $1\frac{7}{32}$in. diameter inlet valves. The port throat may be enlarged a little further still but be careful not to break into the pushrod hole. If this does happen the pushrod must be sleeved as already described, see fig. 7:12.

It is a good proposition to use the 12G295 Cooper head, modifying it as outlined for 998cc Coopers as an alternative to bringing the Mini head up to this specification. The Cooper head involves much less work as it is a better proportioned casting.

Mini Cooper 997 12G185, Stage A

The combustion chamber outline shown in fig. 7:2 is suitable, together with the port throat modified to the size shown in fig. 7:10. If a 997 is to be

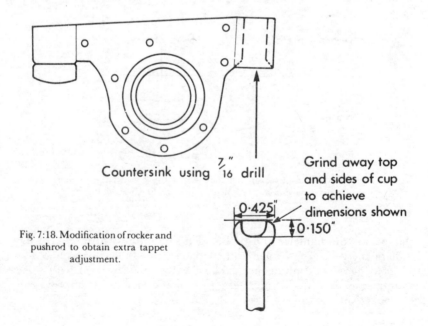

Countersink using $\frac{7}{16}$" drill

Grind away top and sides of cup to achieve dimensions shown

0·425"

0·150"

Fig. 7:18. Modification of rocker and pushrod to obtain extra tappet adjustment.

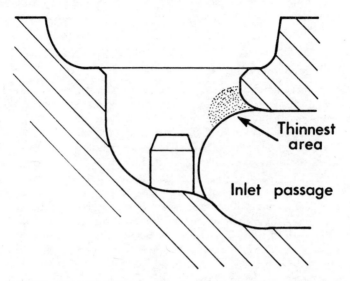

Fig. 7:19. The 1275 (12G 940) inlet port showing the 'nose' between the inlet valves where it is easy to break into the water passage.

modified beyond stage A, use of the $1\frac{7}{12}$ in. diameter 998cc Cooper inlet valves will be worthwhile.

998cc Cooper head 12G295

This is the best of the 'non 1300' type cylinder heads and requires less modification. The combustion chambers are quite good in standard form but they should be compared with the outline shown in fig. 7:3. The inlet ports should be at least as large as those shown in fig. 7:10 and the exhaust ports should be matched to the gasket and widened as in fig. 7:13. If a 998 Mini or Cooper is being tuned to Stage D (table 7:III) it is beneficial to use larger valves. The exhaust valve can be increased to $1\frac{1}{16}$ in. diameter by using the Mini oversize exhaust valve made by Tranco. Some specialists can also supply inlet valves of $1\frac{1}{4}$ in. diameter.

An alternative to these is to use the 1275 GT valves which are larger still. The exhaust being 1·15in. and the inlet 1·31in. diameter. If these valves are used it is also necessary to fit the 1300 type of cotter and stem seal. Because these valves are longer than the normal Cooper type, it is necessary to check that the fitted length of the spring is not too great. This check is explained below in the section covering valve springs. Inlet valves larger than 1·31in. diameter are unlikely to show an improvement except on an engine in racing trim.

It will be noticed that these heads have steps in the inlet pushrod holes to leave slightly more thickness in the side of the port. This allows a port width of 1⅛in. without breaking through provided that the hole is truly central.

1275 GT head 12G940 (9 stud)

The combustion chambers of these heads should be modified to the shape shown in fig. 7:4 taking great care not to go beyond the gasket line. The port below the inlet valve should be modified as shown in fig. 7:7. Great care is necessary with these heads, especially when larger inlet valves are fitted, as it is quite easy to make a hole through to the water passage at the point shown in fig. 7:19. This ruins the head as it is almost impossible to weld up a hole in this position. The inlet passage can be enlarged to the size shown in fig. 7:11 at the point where it passes between the pushrod holes and the exhaust ports can be enlarged as shown in fig. 7:13. Where larger valves are required, see table 7:IV, use the 1·401in. diameter 1300 GT valve and enlarge the inlet port to the size shown in fig. 7:11. Use of larger valves than this is normally restricted to competition cars as it shows little or no improvement with the engine in road trim. If the engine is modified to stage B or beyond (see table 7:IV) it is a good idea to fit the two extra studs found on the 1300 GT and Cooper S. The two extra holes must be drilled in the head and the stud holes drilled and tapped into the block.

Obviously the holes must be drilled in exactly the right position or there is a danger of drilling into a port or water passage. The simplest way to avoid this is by using a second head of the 11-stud type as a drilling jig. It needs only to be placed on top of the head to be drilled and retained in position by putting valves down the guides so that they dowell the upper head to the lower one. The holes can then be started in the lower head with a drill that fits the hole. When the holes have been started, remove the pattern head and finish the drilling. Do not use a smaller pilot drill but go straight through full size using a reasonably accurate drilling machine and a sharp drill. The cylinder head should be used as a jig when the tapping holes are drilled in the block. It is simplest to make both holes with a ⅜in. UNC thread. Short head studs can be used which need not be of the high tensile 1300 type as the stud nuts must not be tightened to more than 25–30lb ft torque. The stud hole above the water pump will break through the water jacket when drilled so it is essential to remove the water pump when this is being done. Cut any excess thread off this stud to prevent it protruding into the jacket and fouling the water pump impellor.

Cooper S head AEG165

The modification of these heads is substantially the same as for the 12G940 types. They are fitted with larger exhaust valves however and the edges of the valves nearly touch each other. This lack of space makes the heads liable to cracking between the valves. Very careful inspection is required to see these cracks in the early stages of development. A crack is not immediately serious but eventually it starts to burn the valve seat away. A skilled welder can sometimes make an effective repair using special cold electric arc electrodes. It can clearly be seen however that valve seat inserts cannot be fitted in such a restricted space. Obviously it is unwise to spend much time modifying a cracked head.

At stage A tune, table 7:III, the inlet valve guide bosses need not be cut right away and the bumps which will be found on the upper inside corners of the inlet passage may be retained. Beyond this state of tune the guide boss should be cut back as in fig. 7:7 and the inlet passage bumps removed. The inlet port itself should be enlarged as detailed in fig. 7:11. The exhaust ports should receive attention as with other heads and widening to suit the gasket is carried out as in fig. 7:13.

Most of these 'S' type heads were fitted with Hidural bronze valve guides which wear at a rather high rate. The valve stems also wear on the older type of valve which are of Nimonic alloy material. The later valves, although still made of the very expensive Nimonic alloy, have hard chrome plated stems to reduce wear. These plated valves may be run in a cast iron guide but the earlier type should only be used in Hidural guides.

The valves may be identified as they have their part numbers stamped at the top of the stem, they are AEA 764 and 765 for the early type and AEA 593 and 594 for the plated type. Hidural guides are now only available as a special tuning part and cannot be obtained from British Leyland Agents not keeping special tuning parts unless they are ordered specially. In some 'S' heads, especially old ones which have had the inlet guide bosses cut away, the Hidural guides become rather loose. To correct this circlips can be fitted as described in chapter 8 on page 183.

Valve springs

Selection of suitable valve springs is important if the best results are to be obtained. There is no point in using very heavy springs when the engine does not require them, they will only wear out the valve gear and absorb power which is thus wasted.

The 850 and 998 Minis have valve springs which do not allow engine speeds much in excess of 5,800 rev/min. The simplest solution with these engines is to fit standard Cooper 'S' outer springs. This will permit quite high enough engine speeds for a road Mini and it avoids the necessity of using Cooper double-spring type retainers and bottom seats which have registers on them to locate the inner spring.

The 997 and 998 Coopers have the Mini outer spring with a light inner one to raise the valve crash speed. Use of the normal inner spring together with 'S' type outers should be sufficient unless very large and heavy valves are fitted when both should be changed for the 'S' type. It is unhecessary to use competition springs on a road engine. The 'S' type Coopers will not get valve crash until around 7,500 rev/min with standard springs and this is enough except for competition cars. The 1275 GT is best fitted with double valve springs from the Austin 1300 GT or MG 1300 Mk II.

Where longer valves, such as the 1275 GT ones have been fitted to a Mini head, the position of the retainer relative to the head is altered. The reverse effect is obtained if old type Cooper S valves are fitted to a 1275 GT head. If for any reason the valve position or length has been altered the distance between the retainer and the spring seat in the head, usually referred to as the valve-spring 'fitted length', should be checked. In standard form they are Mini and Coopers 1·35in., Cooper S (AEG163 head) 1·35–1·40in. and 1275 GT 1·35in. If the distance is not within $\frac{1}{16}$in. of these figures it must be corrected, either by placing steel washers on the spring seat or by machining the spring seat recess deeper into the head as described in chapter 8.

Late Cooper S head 12G940

This head is identical to that used on the 1275 GT except that it has larger 1·4in. diameter inlet valves and 11-stud fixing. Modifications are exactly as for the 9-stud 12G940 in large-valve tune described earlier.

Swapping heads

Although all the stud positions are the same in all the Mini, 1100 and 1300 range, they are not fully interchangeable. All the non-1300 and non-'S' type heads will swap without mechanical difficulty but to put a 1300 head on to a 998 Cooper for instance is not a simple job. The main snag is that eleven of the water passages do not line up exactly and trouble may be experienced. It is quite an elaborate process to correct this and seldom worthwhile on a road car but the modification is covered in chapter 8 as it is often carried out on racing Mini engines.

THE INDUCTION SYSTEM

Modification of the induction system can give very worthwhile results on any Mini. Many alternative carburetter arrangements are available and, although it is impossible to make a critical assessment of all of them in the following section, it should be a helpful guide.

The 850 Mini—The standard carburetter

The standard 850 Mini is fitted with a 1¼in. bore SU carburetter type HS2, mounted on a cast-iron combined inlet and exhaust manifold. When the car is being mildly tuned, up to stage C, this arrangement is perfectly satisfactory but the manifold should be carefully aligned with the head to ensure there are no steps at the joint. This is best done by making a gasket of stiff paper which exactly fits the head and then

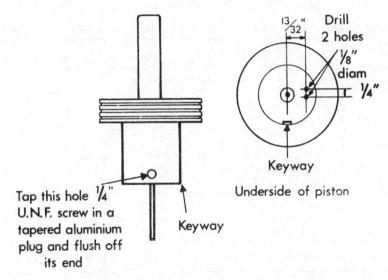

Fig. 7:20. Details of modification to SU carburetter piston for improved acceleration.

opening out the manifold to match the gasket exactly. The manifold aperture should never be of greater size than the head ports in the case of the inlet passages and never smaller in the case of the exhausts. It may sometimes be necessary to make a paper pattern of the manifold face and enlarge the head ports to suit but in all cases the aim must be a well fitting joint and a gradual change of section.

The inside of the manifold should be cleaned out as much as possible but it is not easy to get at all of it. Some people have gone to the lengths of sawing the manifold up, polishing the inside and then welding it back together but it is better to make another manifold of steel tubing if one is going to this extreme. The carburetter-to-manifold joint should be checked for alignment and the gaskets checked that they do not protrude inwards.

On modified engines, the carburetter can often be reset with advantage. The correct setting for a particular car can only be found by experiment but the following suggestions should be helpful.

At the expense of some increased intake noise, the air cleaner element can be removed and the carburetter fitted with the rich (M) needle. Alternatively the No. 2 or V 2 needles can be tried. Good results have been obtained, on some cars, using a carburetter piston modified as shown in fig. 7:20. A 'blue' damper spring should be used in place of the standard 'red' one and suitable needles are E 3 or E 3/1.

TABLE 7:VI

SUGGESTED NEEDLES FOR NON-STANDARD SU CARBURETTERS

Engine	Carburetters	Needle			Spring Colour
		Rich	Normal	Weak	
850cc	Single HS2 (modified) Twin HS2 Single H4 or HS4	AJ RLB	E3 or E3/1 AD RO or MME	HA AM	Red Blue Blue or Red
997/998cc	Twin HS2 Single H4 or HS4 Twin H4 or HS4	AH2 RO 7	GY or GZ AM or CU 6	EB AJ 5	Blue Red Blue
970 S	Twin H4 or HS4	MME	CP4	5	Blue
1071 S	Twin H4 or HS4	BG	MME	6	Blue
1275 S	Twin H4 or HS4	BG	MME	6	Blue
1275 GT	Single HS6 Twin H4 or HS4	MME	SS 7 or RLB	CP4 or 6	Red Blue
1098cc (1100)	Single HS2 Twin HS2 Single H4 or HS4 Twin H4 or HS4	H6 AH2 RO 7	AN GZ AM or CU 6 or CP4	EB EB AJ 5	Red Red Red Blue or Red with No. 5

Alternative single carburetters—850 and 998 Minis

For improved performance with a simple installation, a larger single carburetter may be used. The 1½in. bore H4SU will bolt straight on in place of the standard carburetter but the manifold must of course be enlarged to suit. It is better, however, if the carburetter stud holes in the manifold are brazed up and retapped ⅛in. higher. This not only helps by easing the flow into the manifold but gives extra clearance between the jet and bulkhead. If an unworn H4 is not obtainable (these are becoming rather rare) an HS4 type may be used. These are fitted to the Mini

Automatic and the 1300 saloons as well as the 1275 GT. If an adaptor plate is used, the HS4 can be used on the standard manifold but better results are obtained if the 1300 type manifold is also used. With this manifold it is obviously possible to fit the air cleaner assembly from the 1275 GT or Mini Automatic which keeps the induction noise within acceptable limits. The 1½in. 150 CD Stromberg carburetter can be obtained with an adaptor to fit the standard manifold. Results should be similar to the S U although a pancake gauze air cleaner is about all that can be accomodated.

1275 GT

An alternative to using twin 1½in. SUs on the 1275 GT is a single 1¾in. bore HS6 SU. This can be fitted to an enlarged standard manifold with an adaptor plate. The performance is better than with the standard carburetter if the engine is tuned to stage B of table 7:IV but it is unlikely to be superior to twin HS4 units. Suitable needles for this carburetter are given in table 7:VI.

Other possibilities

Several other makes of carburetter have been offered as an alternative to the standard SU. Some of these, including the small single-choke Dellorto and the 125CD Stromberg are merely replacements of the standard unit with another of substantially the same size but different design. Small gains in performance and economy are claimed but it would seem that the cost effectiveness of such a conversion does not compare favourably with the use of a larger than standard carburetter.

The Minnow and Fish or Reece-Fish type of carburetter has been used with great success on Mini 7 formula racers which are restricted to a single 1½in. carburetter. It is undoubtedly a power producer but has not won such universal acclaim for road conversions. The most probable reason for this is its cost compared to the alternatives, but it has also a reputation for icing up in cold damp weather although this is not an incurable fault.

Twin carburetters

Probably the most popular induction modification for the Mini is fitting twin SU carburetters. Several specialists used to supply twin 1⅛in. bore SU carburetters on manifolds to suit the 850 Mini and these gave reasonable results. This size of carburetter is now obsolete and the 1¼in. HS2 SU is now widely used. These units are of course standard fitment on the Coopers and 'S' types. Many conversion specialists supply an additional carburetter with suitable manifold and linkage to duplicate the original. This is undoubtedly the cheapest way to obtain a good twin-carburetter set-up although the standard Cooper or Cooper S manifold and carburetters will fit. Twin 1¼in. bore carburetters are suitable for an 850 in almost any stage of road tune and for a 998 up to stage E of table 7:II. Beyond this point, benefit will be gained on anything except an 850 by going up in size to twin 1½in. bore carburetters. H4 SUs were once supplied by tuning firms as well as by British Leyland Special Tuning. They would fit an enlarged Cooper manifold to make a fairly simple conversion. Good H4 SUs are now something of a rarity and B L Special Tuning have gone over to HS4s which, because of their diagonally offset flanges, will not fit the Cooper manifold. Special Tuning can supply a suitable manifold as can some specialist suppliers of manifolds (see Appendix VII). The Austin 1300 GT is now fitted with a manifold with large square flanges which may be drilled and tapped to take HS4 carburetters instead of the normal HS2 type. B L Special Tuning market a kit which adds an extra carburetter to the 1¼in. HS4 fitted to the 1275 GT. It is also possible to obtain twin CD Stromberg carburetters on a manifold to suit a Mini. These should give similar results to the equivalent SUs, they are obtainable both in 125CD (1¼in. bore) and 150CD (1½in. bore) forms.

Twin-choke carburetters

A variety of twin-choke carburetters is at present on the market and may have a possible application on a road-going Mini. Progressive downdraught types which have a small primary choke for low-speed running and a larger secondary choke which comes into operation at about two-thirds of full throttle can be regarded as a substitute for twin 1¼in. SUs or Strombergs. The larger horizontal DCOE Weber and Dellorto types come into use as an alternative to the 1½in. twin carburetters. The advantage one type may have over another is not clearly marked but in general the Authors have found that twin-choke carburetters give marginally more mid-range torque than the SU but that the SU gives better top end and tends to be more economical.

Many of the early 'bolt-on' conversions employing small Weber carburetters gave poor results because the carburetter was supplied with settings suitable only for the engine for which it was originally imported. These did not suit the Mini and gave bad low speed power and a high fuel consumption. Properly jetted, this type of carburetter can give good results but as jetting is very difficult for those with no experience of this type of carburetter, it is best left to the experts. (See Appendix VII.) Simply altering the main jet size, to get the top end of the rev range right, is not good enough if a satisfactory overall performance is to be obtained.

Air silencers and cleaners

Although it is possible to run a road car in Britain with open carburetters without great harm coming to it, there is nothing to be gained
by so doing. The wire-gauze, pancake-type of air cleaner should be
regarded as the very minimum and if possible a more sophisticated
arrangement should be used.

Apart from dirt entering the carburetters, which necessitates frequent
cleaning, the noise caused by open carburetters can be very objectionable. Intake roar at certain engine speeds can lead to an extremely
unpleasant resonance inside the car which makes conversation difficult
and long journeys tiring. Some varieties of twin-choke carburetters are
particularly bad in this respect and commercial air silencers which will
go under a Mini bonnet are seldom available. Pancake type air filters do
little to reduce the noise but a properly designed filter-cum-silencer
system will eliminate it completely.

The air filter assembly, as used on the Automatic-transmission Minis,
is very suitable for engines fitted with single $1\frac{1}{2}$in. carburetters and it
should be possible to adapt this for most installations. Where twin $1\frac{1}{4}$in.
carburetters are used, the best arrangement is the one used on the 998cc
and S type Coopers. Twin $1\frac{1}{2}$in. carburetters take up much space and
some ingenuity is required to silence them. A large box mounted on the
carburetter intakes, with a large diameter flexible tube leading off it, is
a good start but the length and diameter of the tube can have a
considerable and unpredictable effect on the performance. A long small
tube can lead to a lag in response when the throttle is opened and a very
large tube can produce the most alarming flat spots. A large tube
tapering towards the outer end or two relatively small diameter pipes
(around $1\frac{3}{8}$in.) fitted direct to the box is a good arrangement to try. For
twin-choke carburetters, something along the lines of the cleaner used on
the Ford Cortina GT is best but the very limited space under a Mini
bonnet is a challenge to ingenuity.

The exhaust system

The exhaust system on the standard 850 and 998 Mini is of small
diameter with a baffle type silencer. It is however, quite efficient and
unless the silencer, because of manufacturing tolerances, is a particularly
obstructive one, fitting a straight-through type will do very little to
improve the performance. If it is desired to fit a straight-through silencer
to a standard Mini, the Servais type with stepped ends is quite suitable
and inexpensive. Some silencers with very large tailpipes, although
acceptable on a standard car, can be very noisy on a tuned one. Engines
with high compression ratios produce more noise than standard ones and
this should be remembered. A noisy exhaust may impress the girl friend

as you drive up but she will be less enthusiastic after sitting inside and listening to it for half an hour.

The standard cast-iron manifold is quite a good shape and it is hardly worth changing it for a tubular one unless this is of the type which joins the outer branches before combining with the centre-port branch.

The three into one type of manifold which is used on the Mini Coopers will not give much improvement over the standard cast-iron article. The main pipe of the Cooper exhaust system is too big for an 850. A pipe of 1⅜in. diameter is adequate for all but the most highly tuned cars and 1½in. diameter is big enough for these.

Manifolds of the extractor type described earlier and the long centre branch type, shown on plate V (a), will give a substantial increase in bottom-end and mid-range torque. Although the best of this type are fairly expensive it is not worth buying a badly designed cheap manifold and assuming that because it is tubular and of the three branch type it will be better than the standard one.

The Cooper and S types as mentioned above have a mass-produced three-branch manifold and can be improved upon by the use of the long centre-branch type. These may be obtained from British Leyland Special Tuning as a competition part for the Cooper S. The 970 or 1071cc 'S' manifold is best for the 997 and 998 Coopers as the 1275 type is slightly taller and can sometimes foul the gearchange. The 1275 type is otherwise quite satisfactory. The 1275 racing, big-bore, manifold can be used on a road car but it is expensive and difficult to fit, especially if the car has not got Hardy-Spicer solid inner drive-shaft couplings which give more room for the pipes. Possibly the cheapest effective manifold for any size of Mini is that used on the Austin 1300 GT. Although it is rather a strange shape, in order to clear the rubber driveshaft coupling, it works well. The slight loss of ground clearance with this manifold may be found inconvenient and if desired it can be shortened by about 1in. where it passes the drive shaft, a piece being cut out and the pipes re-welded. This manifold, coupled to a Mini Cooper main pipe and silencer, is also suitable for the 1275 GT. The GT has a rather small main pipe in its standard system and best results will not be realized if this is retained.

If it is desired to fit a tubular exhaust manifold while retaining the standard cast iron inlet manifold used on the 850, 998 and 1275 GT, it is possible to saw off the inlet portion and retain it. Alternatively the exhaust manifold may be sawn off the inlet pieces but they cannot be separated without destroying one half or the other.

Camshafts and valve gear

The cam followers, pushrods and rockers used on all the Mini range are adequate for the purposes of tuning for the road. Lightening of the pressed steel type of rocker is not possible to any significant extent and the use of lightweight valve gear does not confer any real advantage at speeds below about 7,500 rev/min. Valve gear for competition is covered in chapter 8.

It is, naturally, essential that the valve gear is in good condition and if a new camshaft is to be fitted, the cam followers should be carefully examined for signs of wear or pitting on the working face. Damaged followers can quickly wear out a camshaft, so replace any that are suspect. Some followers will wear much faster than others and an old set which has covered some thousands of miles without showing significant wear can be regarded as suitable for further use. If a tappet becomes noisy with the clearance correctly adjusted, wear on the bottom could be occuring and it should be removed and inspected.

Camshafts

A wide variety of camshafts is available for the Mini range. Apart from the camshafts available from British Leyland, many specialist firms can supply reground camshafts for almost any purpose. These give good results when the work has been properly carried out but reground camshafts of doubtful type or unknown origin are best avoided.

For road work, the cams available from B L are both good and inexpensive so these will be described.

Reference to table 7:VII shows the range with notes on identification. They are almost all available with either pin drive for the oil pump or 'spider' drive as used on the 1275 GT and the automatic transmission models. Identification is by means of the width of the cam lobes, turned raised rings between the first and second lobes, and the presence or absence of a fuel-pump cam between the second and third lobes. Exceptions exist amongst the racing cams but these are normally stamped with a number as well. The first in the series is the 2A297 used in all 850 and 998 Minis as well as the 948cc Morris Minor, Austin A40 etc. It is not essential to change it if only moderate tuning is to be carried out. It has a fuel pump cam, narrow ($\frac{3}{8}$in.) wide lobes and no rings. The next logical step, as indicated in tables 7:I and 7:II is the AEA630, generally known as the 1100 cam. This is used, in pin-drive form, in the Austin and Morris 1100, and the 998cc Mini Cooper. It has narrow lobes, a fuel-pump cam and two rings. Three other versions of this cam exist: the AEG148 which is a wide-lobe one produced for the early Cooper S; the 1100 Automatic type (spider drive); and the 1275 GT and Austin/Morris 1300 version. All have the same lift and timing. Although it is of conservative timing and lift, it works very well indeed and does not start to restrict the breathing of the engine seriously until quite high engine speeds. It is quite suitable for the 850 and 998 engines for almost all road use.

The later Cooper S used a modified version of AEG148, this is

TABLE 7:VII

BRITISH LEYLAND A-TYPE CAMSHAFTS

Part No	Normal use	Valve duration Inlet	Valve duration Exhaust	Pump drive	Lobe width	Marking	Fuel pump cam	Tappet clearance	Valve lift
8G712 2A297 2A571	Mini, A35, Morris Minor etc	230°	230°	Pin	⅜in.	-	Yes	0·012	0·285
12G165 AEA630	1100 & Sprite	230°	252°	Pin	⅜in.	2 rings	Yes	0·012	0·318
AEG148	Cooper S to 1966 & Sprite	230°	252°	Spider	½in.	-	No	0·012	0·318
AEG510	Cooper S 1966 onwards	240°	252°	Pin	½in.	1 ring	No	0·012	0·318
88G229 2A948 12A122	997 Cooper	252°	252°	Pin	⅜in.	1 ring	Yes	0·015	0·318
C-AEA 731	Half-race	268°	268°	Pin	⅜in.	3 rings	Yes	0·015	0·320
12A1065	Mini-Automatic	230°	230°	Spider	⅜in.	-	Yes	0·012	0·285
12G726	1100 Automatic	230°	252°	Spider	⅜in.	-	Yes	0·012	0·318
AEG522 AEG538	1275 GT & Sprite	230°	252°	Spider	½in.	-	Yes	0·072	0·318
C-AEG 567	Special tuning	252°	252°	Spider	½in.	AEG 567	No	0·015	0·318
C-AEG 542	Special tuning	240°	252°	Spider	½in.	AEG 543 1 ring	No	0·015	0·318

AEG510 and it differs from the 148 in having a longer exhaust period. It gives slightly more power at the top of the normal rev range but has less low speed torque. This is also a useful mild camshaft for road tuning. The old 997cc Mini Cooper used a camshaft with more inlet duration, the 88G229 or 2A948 as it used to be known. With this cam, while the engine remains perfectly tractable it gives little real power below 3,000 rev/min but will breathe well up to 7,000 rev/min. It is the last really practicable camshaft of the range. The C–AEA 731 'half-race' camshaft has very little application in a road-car as it produces only 1–2 b h p more than the 88G229 at 6,000 rev/min and its lack of low-speed torque makes the car awkward to drive in traffic. In addition to the above camshafts, various other combinations of lobe width and pump drive may be encountered but all with one of the cam profiles already described. Apart from these all the other BL camshafts are for competition and are described in chapter 8.

Checking valve-to-block clearance

When a camshaft of higher than standard lift is fitted to an engine, other than the 'S' and GT types, that has had a lot of metal removed from the head face, it is essential to check that the exhaust valves, when at full lift, do not foul the cylinder block. The simplest way to check this is by measurement, although the clearance can be ascertained by placing small pieces of Plasticine on the block then replacing the head and turning the engine over so that the valves compress them. To check by measurement, first look up the valve-lift of the camshaft in use. For all the B L camshafts concerned this is given in the table 7:VII. The distance from the exhaust valve head to the cylinder head joint face is then measured. Normally an accurate steel rule can be read to within 0·025in. and one of these, together with a straight edge placed across the head to read off against, will suffice. If clearance is close, a depth micrometer or similar more accurate method is preferable. The depth in the head must never be less than the valve lift; the thickness of the gasket can only be regarded as the very minimum working clearance. If it is found that there is insufficient room, semi-circular pockets will have to be machined into the block underneath the exhaust valves. They can be made using hand grinding tools or with a cutter, made from an old valve as shown

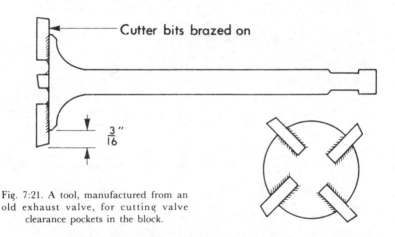

Fig. 7:21. A tool, manufactured from an old exhaust valve, for cutting valve clearance pockets in the block.

in fig. 7:21. In use, the cutter is placed in position in the valve guide of the head which is then bolted down to the cylinder block. The block is then placed on a drilling machine and the top of the cutter stem gripped in the chuck. It is fed down at a slow speed and feed to cut the pocket. Do not cut a deeper recess than is necessary and do not go down so far as to expose the top piston ring at t d c. There is no danger of either valve hitting the piston, unless a racing camshaft has been fitted or the valve timing is incorrect.

Clutch, crankshaft and block

Provided that all the parts are in good condition, nothing need be done to the block, crankshaft and clutch when only moderate tuning is carried out. The following details will help achieve reliability with higher-powered engines.

The clutch

All the standard clutches will transmit some extra power without slip but an 850 or a 998 Elf or Hornet coil-spring clutch may need stronger springs if the engine is tuned to stage 'D'. The 997 Cooper springs are suitable for these clutches. The later Minis (post mid 1964) are fitted with diaphragm spring clutches and these should be adequate for the job. Various strengths of springs are available and these are colour-coded with a paint spot to show the type. The colour code is as follows: starting with the lightest spring, brown, blue, green, white and orange (competition). The 'green' spring is now standard on all models.

It is possible, if machining facilities are available, to machine the centre of the coil-spring type flywheel to take a diaphragm spring and cover plate. The modification is shown in fig. 7:22. It may be necessary,

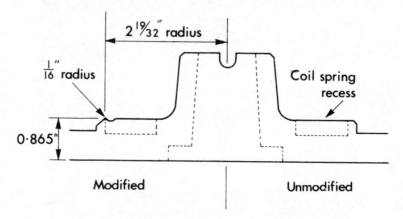

Fig. 7:22. Modification to coil-spring-clutch type flywheel to allow use of a diaphragm spring.

after modification of some flywheels, to place a packing washer behind the clutch-release thrust bearing to ensure that the clutch can be fully disengaged. If the clutch release arm is removed from the cover and the nuts on the release rod are taken off, the rod may be removed complete with the bearing. The bearing is withdrawn from the rod and any necessary packing washer fitted between the shoulder on the rod and the bearing.

The standard driven plate should be adequate for most purposes and there is little point in fitting a competition-type bonded plate unless the clutch is used very hard. Bonded plates are fitted with a special lining material which will withstand high loads and temperatures but it is advisable to use a heavy pressure spring to avoid slip.

The crankshaft

Although by no means a weak component, the 850 and 998 Mini crankshafts are not indestructible if driven at very high rev/min. These crankshafts together with the 1098cc (1100) type all have a torsional vibration period at around 6,000 rev/min and if they are run at speeds in excess of this their life cannot be guaranteed. Although some examples of these crankshafts seem to stand up to high rev/min indefinitely, breakage is by no means unknown on a tuned engine. The 1100 crankshaft tends to bend at very high speeds and this tilts the connecting rods, they will then hammer their gudgeon pins against the retaining circlips, eventually breaking them. This fact should be borne in mind when over-revving a Mini fitted with an 1100 engine. The 1275 GT is stronger and not likely to give much trouble on a road car while the Cooper S type crankshafts are virtually indestructible.

Two things can be done to minimize the risk of breakage of the standard crankshaft. These are dynamic balancing of the complete crank/clutch assembly to reduce any untoward vibration and Tufftriding, a process which hardens the surface of the crankshaft and increases its fatigue life. Many firms now advertise a quick and inexpensive balancing service and the cost of balancing a crankshaft after it is removed from the block should not exceed £10. Balancing the connecting rods and equalizing the weights of the pistons will also aid smoothness at high speed. Tufftriding is also carried out by a few firms who advertise in the sporting motoring press and it is not expensive for Mini parts.

British Leyland Special Tuning make special, strong, hardened crankshafts for the 850 and 998 which are extremely reliable.

'S' type duplex timing sprockets and chain can be fitted to all the Mini engines provided that the two bolts which retain the bottom of the front plate are replaced with countersunk screws, recessed into the plate (see page 188). These duplex parts are much more durable than the single-row chain which has limited life at high rev/min because of the torsional vibration of the crankshaft which is very destructive. The vibration damper from the 1100 can be used on the 850 and 998 if a Cooper engine-mounting bracket is fitted. This damper is a Metalastic iron and rubber type which has the fan-belt pulley machined onto it and it helps preserve both the timing chain and crankshaft.

The flywheel

Lightening the flywheel is hardly a necessary modification unless competition work is envisaged. If it is carried out, it should not be overdone or the engine will lose some of its low-speed flexibility and smoothness. The work is best left to experts as haphazard lightening of flywheels can be extremely dangerous. About ⅛in. can be machined off the face for road use and more details are given in chapter 8.

The cylinder block

There are no modifications to the cylinder block which are essential for a moderately tuned engine. All the standard pistons are adequately strong and nothing will be gained by changing them. On the 850 block, only the front camshaft bearing is fitted with a liner and, if a high-lift camshaft is used, some wear of the centre and rear bearings will occur. It is prudent therefore to have these bearings line bored and fitted with liners as used on the other blocks; the cost is around £7.

Increasing the capacity is a very satisfactory way of obtaining increased power output. Nowadays it is less practical to bore out an 850 which can be enlarged to about 950cc. There are so many 1100 engines available secondhand that it is a better proposition to rebuild one of these. It can be made to fit on to any Mini gearbox but some cutting out of the casing to clear the 1100 big ends is necessary on early Mini boxes. The early Mini small-crank flywheel will not fit but the later type are plentiful secondhand. The 1100 can be bored to about 1220cc when Hillman Imp pistons may be used but this is the maximum size that can be achieved cheaply. Some tuners have stretched the 'S' engine to around 1450cc but it is an expensive conversion and not every block can be successfully modified to this extent. Special crankshafts are also used for engines of this size.

The gearbox and final drive

Modification of the gearbox is quite expensive and not very worthwhile on a road-car. Alternative gears are available for some boxes but not the early ones. All the boxes which have 'B' type gears, can be converted. These are most easily identified by examination of the third-motion-shaft thrust between second and third gears. Early boxes have a phosphor-bronze thrust washer but the later 'B' types have a hard steel one, integral with the shaft. The 'three-speed-synchromesh' boxes can be fitted with gears from the Cooper S which have closer ratios and the all-synchromesh boxes can use the closer ratios from the Austin 1300 GT. The competition close-ratio gears which are produced for both types of box are now only available in straight-cut form. These, although stronger, are somewhat noisier than the normal helical type. Kits to

convert the gearboxes to close-ratio straight-cut gears are available from
B L Special Tuning for about £30. Details of stripping and rebuilding
gearboxes are given in chapter 4.

Alteration of the final-drive ratio is a cheaper and more popular
modification. It is unlikely for road use that anyone would wish to use
a lower gearing (higher numerical ratio) final drive than the 3·765:1
gears used in the 850 Mini. The lower gears available are mainly
intended for competition use and are covered in chapter 8. Two alternative higher final drives are available from B L. These are the
3·647:1 type used in the 1300 saloon and the 3·444:1 set used in the later
Cooper 'S' types. In the last few years the 998, Clubman, and 1275 GT
have apparently been produced with any one of these gearings and some
early 1275 GT models were turned out with a 4·133:1 ratio. There is no
simple way of finding out which is fitted to a particular car and reference
to the driver's handbook is not a reliable guide. Tachometer and
speedometer readings are seldom sufficiently accurate to help so that
counting the teeth on the gears is the only certain method.

An 850 when moderately tuned will pull the 3·444:1 gear but it will
spoil the top gear acceleration slightly. If the car is driven frequently on
motorways the 10% increase in cruising speed at the same engine
rev/min is both quieter and more economical. Any 998 could use the
3·444:1 ratio as can the 1275 GT but make sure it has not already got
one before you buy new gears. Swapping the gears is not a very
complicated job. They can be changed without removing the engine
from the gearbox if a long 1½in. AF box spanner or deep socket are
available to undo the third-motion-shaft nut. The speedometer will
obviously read incorrectly if the gearing is changed, the error is
proportional to the change in gearing. It is possible to have the
speedometer recalibrated and Smiths Motor Accessories Ltd can do this
if they are given details of the gearing and tyre size.

Limited-slip differentials

The competition-type limited-slip differential has a rather unpredictable
effect on the handling on bumpy surfaces and it is only really at its best
when the car is driven at racing speeds. Even though it improves traction
on slippery surfaces, it is unsuitable for regular use on the road.

The ignition system

The ignition system used on all Minis is quite suitable for high performance, if it is in good condition. Special high-voltage coils are unlikely
to show much improvement over the standard coil and, provided that the
distributor and plug caps are in good condition with no 'tracking' marks

on their insides or outsides, these and the suppressor-type leads are satisfactory. The distributor fitted to the van has a modified advance curve and a restricted amount of maximum advance to allow the engine to run on a lower grade of fuel than the normal saloon.

If a van engine is being modified it will be improved slightly by using a saloon-type distributor. Alternatively, the cam-stop in the van type can be shortened on the end where it touches the stop peg to allow 16 degrees of cam movement instead of 12 degrees. Saloon-type bobweight springs should also be used. Although the vacuum advance is different, this has no effect on the full-throttle performance.

When the compression ratio has been increased by a significant amount, the ignition timing can often be retarded by one or two degrees with advantage. This is because the flame speed in the combustion chamber is higher with a high compression ratio and thus less time is required to achieve complete combustion. Fitting a camshaft with more overlap, however, raises the engine speeds at which maximum power and torque are obtained. This gives a reduction in the time available for complete burning of the charge and so a more advanced ignition setting may be required. One or two degrees is again a suitable amount to try. Experiment is the only way (apart from the use of a test bed or rolling road) by which the optimum ignition timing can be achieved. The setting which gives the best mid range acceleration in third and top gear up a gentle incline is the best. Acceleration times between the same two speeds must be carefully measured with a stop watch and the ignition settings altered by one degree for each test.

It is obvious that the ignition timing must be very carefully set to achieve good results and whilst a variation of up to 5 degrees may not make an appreciable difference on a low-compression engine, this sort of inaccuracy can be damaging to a tuned engine.

In some cases where high compression ratios are used, the vacuum advance unit can produce excessive advance at light throttle openings which will cause undesirable pinking. This pinking occurs under conditions of moderate load and small throttle openings and will disappear as soon as the throttle is opened wider. Permanently disconnecting the vacuum unit and blocking the vacuum take-off on the carburetter will result in greatly improved flexibility under these conditions. The alternative is to use a Cooper 'S' type distributor which has no vacuum advance control.

The 1275 GT has a distributor which only allows 12 degrees of cam movement and some owners have found, especially with tuned cars, that use of the Cooper S distributor with its greater amount of advance is an advantage. Alternatively the GT distributor may be modified by filing about $\frac{3}{4}$ in. off the end of the cam stop of the centrifugal advance mechanism.

Spark plugs

The grade of spark plug used depends to a great degree upon the extent to which the engine is modified. Driving conditions however affect the requirement and for tuned engines a compromise is sometimes necessary. The compression ratio is the most important factor in plug choice. As a general guide, an engine with up to about 9·5:1 ratio may be run on the standard plug, ratios of up to 10:1 need a plug about one grade harder while above this a plug two grades harder is advisable. The standard conventional plug is Champion N5, the next choice being N4 or N3.

Where extended nose plugs are used the Champion N9Y is standard and the N7Y and N6Y are suitable steps. The conventional type of plug is in general less sensitive than an extended-nose type to overheating if too soft (hot running) for the engine but it is more prone to fouling if too hard (cold running).

If an extended-nose type of plug is used in an engine upon which the ignition timing was decided using a conventional plug, the timing may require alteration. Because of the more central position of the spark plug gap, the mixture burning time is reduced and less ignition advance is required. Up to 5 degrees retardation may be found necessary in some cases.

If much high-speed motorway type driving is usual, plug life and performance may be improved by using a plug one grade harder than would be suitable for normal motoring. Conversely a car used mostly for town driving may benefit from a softer than usual choice.

CHAPTER 8

MODIFICATION OF THE ENGINE
FOR COMPETITION USE

This section is intended to assist owners who wish to use a Mini for
serious competition work where a highly modified engine is desirable.
Many of the modifications described are aimed at improving the
reliability of the engine under the sort of conditions of continuous strain
encountered when racing; for whereas a sprint, driving test or club rally
will not harm a well-tuned road-car without these modifications, if much
serious racing or sprinting is to be done they may well help to avoid a
very expensive season.

Three sizes of engine will be covered, 850cc, 1000cc and 1300cc as
these are the current racing class limits.

Cylinder heads

Only the 12G940 casting is now being modified for serious racing use.
This is because the old 'S' head is obsolete and the 12G940 can do a
better job than any of the others without the problems of warpage and
oilway breakthrough associated with other heads. For those on a limited
budget the use of the other types may be necessary but compromise
solutions will not be covered in detail.

850cc heads

It is debatable whether the 850 requires inlet valves as large as 1·4in.,
especially when it is being used in stock block form (standard bore and
stroke). The Authors' preference at the time of writing is to use the head
in Austin 1300 form and fit inlet valves of about 1·35in. diameter. The
exhaust valves being left standard at 1·156in. diameter. The extra two
stud holes should of course be drilled as described in chapter 7. The
combustion chamber shape is good in standard form provided it is
cleaned up as shown in fig. 7:4.

The inlet ports should be modified, again as described in chapter 7
(fig. 7:7), the narrow portion being enlarged to the size shown in fig.
7:11. The exhaust ports should also be enlarged as shown in fig. 7:13 but,
for racing, most of the exhaust-valve-guide boss can be ground away as
is done for the inlet ports. Phosphor bronze valve guides are obtainable
through BL Special Tuning department and these help to cool the valve

Plate VII

(a)

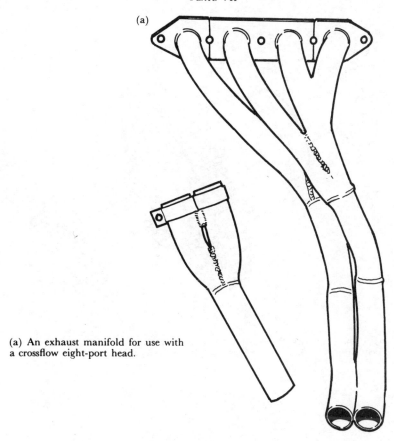

(a) An exhaust manifold for use with a crossflow eight-port head.

(b)

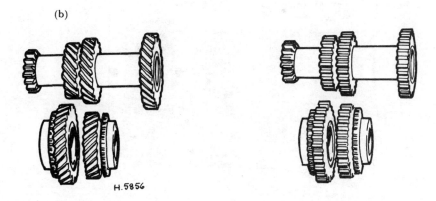

H.5856

(b) Mini gear clusters showing, *left*, the standard helical type and, *right*, the competition straight-cut close-ratio variety.

PLATE VIII

(a)

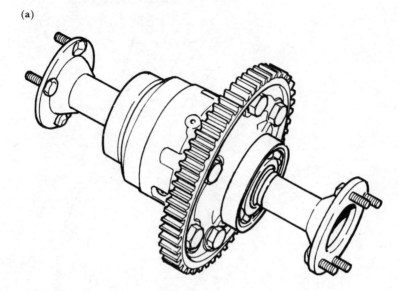

(a) A Mini Salisbury 'Powr-Lok' differential assembly as used for racing. It is fitted with a 4.6:1 ratio straight-cut final drive wheel.

(b)

H.5857

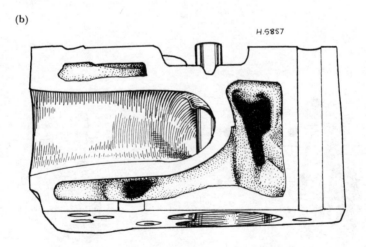

(b) A sectioned, modified 12G 940 cylinder head casting showing the inlet port and water passages. The closeness of the water passages to the inlet port can be seen.

stems and reduce friction but they are not absolutely essential. If bronze guides are used, it is advisable to fit retaining circlips to them to make sure that they do not move. To do this, their final position is ascertained and a groove is turned in the guide on the level of the spring seat as shown in fig. 8:1. A wire circlip, which can be cut from a suitable sized

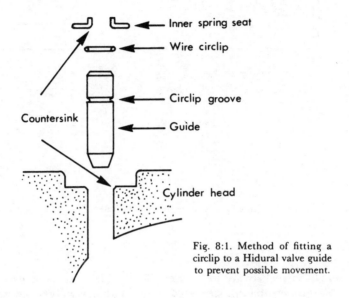

Fig. 8:1. Method of fitting a circlip to a Hidural valve guide to prevent possible movement.

coil spring is sprung into the groove before the guides are driven into the head. If normal lower inner-spring seats are used these should be lightly countersunk on their undersides so that they sit over the circlip. Either the 1300 GT or the old Cooper S valves may be used. The standard 1300 valves are not considered suitable as breakage of these has been known. Inlet and exhaust valves of both types can be lightened by thinning down their heads and the inlet valve will have to be reduced in diameter by 0·050in. The 1300 GT valves are slightly longer than the 'S' type valves and will probably provide sufficient room for the valve spring. Either the B L competition double springs or Terrys VS595 type are suitable and the fitted length should be between 1·37 and 1·40in. If there is not sufficient room, the spring seat in the head will have to be lowered. A cutter of the type shown in fig. 8:2 will do this job quite easily, especially if it can be used in a slow-speed (400 rev/min or less) drilling machine.

Before fitting guide circlips as described earlier, assemble the valves with caps, cotters, etc. into the head and measure the amount they can be pushed down before the cap (spring retainer) touches the top of the guide. This distance must be at least 0·425in. and possibly more if

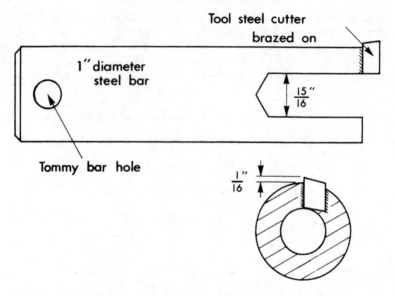

Fig. 8:2. A simply made cutter for lowering the valve spring seats in the head.

high-lift rockers are to be used. The guide must be driven through the head until sufficient clearance exists. With new valves and guides it is not essential to use stem oil seals but remember, if they are used, to allow room for these as well. It is not wise to use seals on the exhaust valves on a racer, any oil escaping here will merely cool and lubricate the valve stem. When machining the head for an 850, the remarks about valve-to-block clearance on page 175 should be noted. Cutaways in the block will be required, unless the engine is an ultra short-stroke type (see page 192) and they should be made as deep as possible, down to the top of the top ring at t d c. This cutaway seldom exceeds 0·250in. depth and as a safe working clearance at full lift with an AEA 648 camshaft (0·394in. valve lift) is about 0·050in. and the gasket is about 0·030in. thick, the head must not be machined to leave less than 0·170in. between the joint face and the exhaust valve. It will be found that a compression ratio of above 13:1 is almost impossible to achieve but get as near to this figure as possible. Using the head as described, there is no danger of the inlet valve touching the block, or the piston provided it is not of the raised crown type.

The head modified as above seems to give good results on formula Mini-Seven and free formula in standard, short and ultra short types. Theoretically, the ultra short stroke 850 should be able to make use of slightly larger inlet valves (1·4in. diameter) but the Authors' tests have failed to prove this conclusively yet.

1000cc heads

The same head is again used for both 998cc and 970 'S' short stroke 1000cc engines. The easiest casting to start with is the 1300 GT type as it is already machined to accept 1·4in. inlet valves which are probably about the optimum size, although some tuners use the large-valve head described below for 1300cc engines. The head should be relieved round the inlet valve as shown in fig. 8:3 and the port throat can be enlarged to the size shown in fig. 8:4. When carrying out this enlargement of the

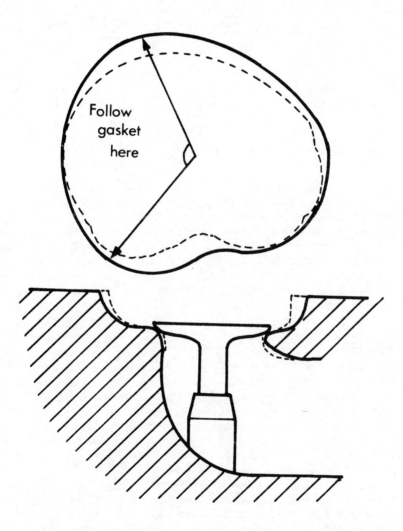

Fig. 8:3. Modified combustion chamber shape for Cooper S in racing tune.

port it is easy to break through into the pushrod holes. This is not serious and it should be corrected by driving in a short piece of steel tube, of such size that it is an interference fit in the pushrod hole (see page 162).

With the 998cc block, all the preceding remarks about valve cutaways in the block apply; the 970cc 'S' block does not suffer from this problem as the valves will go down the bore. It is obviously possible to machine the head to such an extent on one of these engines that the valves approach the piston. In this case the compression ratio would be very

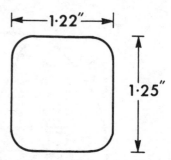

Fig. 8:4. Maximum dimensions of Cooper S inlet port at point between pushrod holes.

high if flat pistons were in use but it is worth remembering. The first valve to hit the piston (assuming of course that the valve timing is correct) is the inlet. This occurs at about 10 degrees after t d c on the induction stroke with the 970cc engine. The exhaust valve sometimes marks the piston where it has touched but this phenomenon is caused by valve float rather than insufficient clearance. If it is found that, at minimum, the inlet valve is closer than about 0·035in. from the piston, a shallow recess should be machined into the piston crown to allow sufficient room.

1300cc heads

The 1300cc engine uses either a head modified as described for the 1000cc engines or one identical except for the addition of larger inlet valves. These can now be obtained from British Leyland Special Tuning as well as other specialist Mini tuners. They are generally no larger than 1·47in. diameter which is about the largest inlet valve that can be accommodated in the head without touching the exhaust valve. When these valves are being fitted, care must be taken not to make a hole through in the position shown in fig. 7:19.

The 1300cc engine benefits from the use of high-lift rockers, chiefly because of the extra valve acceleration they impart. If these are being used, and with some types the lift can be as high as 0·460in., extra room will be needed for the valve spring to prevent coil binding and the guide may need positioning further down in the head.

The eight port heads

B L have produced several different types of crossflow, eight-port cylinder heads for Minis. These have ranged from the early cast-iron type with a flat face and combustion chambers formed in the pistons, through the cast-iron type with combustion chambers, to the present aluminium-alloy head.

Various induction systems have been used. The early ones used by the works had Lucas fuel injection; both twin Weber and quadruple Amal carburetters have been tried. Current trends seem to favour four Amals on the alloy head but it is still debatable whether, on the circuit, the eight-port head gives any real advantage over the best five-port engines.

As most of the heads have been supplied ready polished, modification is not covered. One feature common to all crossflow Mini heads is the cost. This obviously does not stop at the head alone since the carburetters, exhaust and camshaft must be changed to suit it. The crossflow heads have their valves arranged in a different order so that a special transposed-valve camshaft must be used.

Camshafts and valve gear

Apart from the eight-port type camshafts, B L produce three different basic types of camshaft for competition. These are generally known as the 649, part No. C–AEA648, the sprint C–AEA597, and super sprint C–AEA595.

The C–AEA648 has a pin-type oil-pump drive but under part No. C–AEA529 it is available with spider pump drive. The 597 and 595 cams are only available in spider drive form. The most popular of these camshafts is the C–AEA648 but the sprint type is gaining favour. The super sprint seems to give little real advantage although experiments with valve size, exhaust, and carburation arrangements may yield improvements in the future. For serious competition use where the highest power is required, intermediate camshafts, sometimes known as 'half-race', are to be avoided. Often they fall into the no man's land of poor road performance and mediocre competition performance.

All the racing camshafts suffer from a fairly high rate of wear. This does not ruin them for competition purposes but they are not at their best after a season's use. When using racing-type camshafts on the Mini, always use the Cooper S type spring retainers at the top of the valve. These are much stronger than the ordinary ones which will stretch and split, eventually allowing the cotters to pull right through, dropping the valve down the cylinder with dire results. They are identified by a 'W' stamped on them.

Valve rocker clearance with all the B L racing camshafts should be set at 0·015in. Slightly loose valve clearances are quite acceptable but tight ones waste power and upset the breathing.

Camshaft bearings

If a racing camshaft is used in an 850 block, which has not had liners fitted to the centre and rear camshaft bearings, the results will be disastrous. The block will wear very quickly allowing the camshaft to flex which ruins the valve timing and breaks the oil pump drive. Most reputable engine reconditioning firms will bore out the block and fit the camshaft liners used on the Cooper. The cost is about £7 including the bearings.

Timing gears

The best way to avoid timing-chain trouble is to use the duplex chain and sprockets used on the Cooper S. These parts will fit straight onto any Mini provided that the two hexagon bolts which hold the endplate of the engine to the front main bearing cap are replaced with countersunk-head setscrews. The front plate must be countersunk enough to allow the head to go down flush with the plate. Brake-drum retaining screws are suitable but as it is impossible to use the normal lockwasher to secure the screws they must be locked in position by centre punching the edge of their heads.

A lightweight camshaft sprocket is available from B L, alternatively the standard one may be drilled with six holes instead of the normal two. Some metal may also be turned off the boss and the centre may be thinned down but do not reduce the width of the boss or the teeth.

Tappets, pushrods and rockers

The cast-iron tappets used in all Minis are satisfactory for competition use provided that they are inspected regularly for signs of cracking and wear on the working face. They can be lightened somewhat by boring the inside of the tappet out to $\frac{11}{16}$in. diameter, this size can be continued downwards for a distance of $1\frac{1}{8}$in. from the top of the tappet. The pushrods can be lightened slightly by grinding the top and bottom ends as shown in fig. 8:5 and they must be checked for truth by rolling them along on two knife edges and observing if the rod is out of true. Rolling the pushrod along on a bench is not good enough because the ends are not sufficiently uniform to allow an accurate assessment to be made. Light alloy pushrods are not really a great advantage because they are necessarily made larger in diameter than the steel ones. This means that they have a tendency to foul the head, especially when a high-lift camshaft is used giving large rocker angles.

The pressed-steel type rockers should not be lightened and for this reason the forged ones used on earlier 'A' type engines and on the Cooper S are to be preferred. These can be lightened by grinding the tip down to the same width as the valve stem and by grinding the excess metal away from the adjusting screw end. The late type Cooper S had lightened rockers, fitted as a standard part (AEG 425) and these can of course be used on any Mini. On no account should the stressed areas be lightened or breakage may occur. The rocker screws should be checked for length and any excess trimmed off.

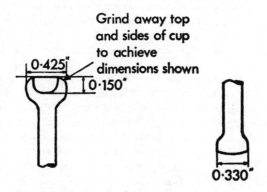

Fig. 8:5. Modification of pushrod ends to reduce weight.

Current production cars now have a stronger rocker shaft than early models. This shaft has its locating bolt in the second post instead of the end one which has the oil feed. This stronger shaft should be used together with modified or new type first and second posts. Be sure, when assembling this shaft, that the No. 1 post has an oil drilling in it to feed the rocker shaft.

The cylinder block

The 'S' type blocks need no modification for competition use. The bearing caps are of high tensile SG iron, the retaining studs are of high quality and the connecting rods and big end bolts very strong. Likewise, the crankshafts are of nitrided EN 40 B steel and virtually unbreakable. All that should be done is to check the height to which the pistons come at t d c and if necessary surface grind the face of the block to leave a clearance of 0·007–0·010in. between the top and the piston crown.

Austin 1300 high-tensile head studs should be used in the nine main positions but these are not required in the end bolt and stud holes. It may be found that the normal 'ovalized' self-locking type of main bearing cap nut is not satisfactory for use more than a very few times as the threads strip. Replacement of these with plain $\frac{7}{16}$UNF nuts (as found in steering swivel kits) is more satisfactory. It is not necessary to lock them provided they are carefully torqued down to about 70lb ft. The 850 and 998 block assemblies are by no means as satisfactory and some work is required to achieve reliability.

Starting at the top, it is found that when the 12G940 head is used eleven of the water passages in the block do not line up perfectly with those in the head. These are all the water holes except the three large ones in the rear, centre, of the block. To achieve 100 per cent gasket reliability the holes must be moved to the correct position. This is done, in the Authors' workshop, by drilling the holes out oversize, leaving a step at the bottom of the holes, and driving in interference-fit steel plugs. The block is then surface ground and the holes redrilled, somewhat smaller than before ($\frac{7}{32}$in. diameter) in the correct position using the competition gasket C–AHT 188 as a pattern. It will be found that one of the corner holes need not be redrilled at all.

The centre main bearing cap is insufficiently strong for a racing 850 or 998 and must either be replaced by a steel one or reinforced. If a steel cap is decided upon, it is a fairly expensive modification, the block must have its bearing housing line bored afterwards. As bearings are not obtainable for the Mini with oversize housings the caps are usually faced off to give an oval housing and the housings rebored to standard size. This modification raises the crankshaft centre line in the block slightly so leave surface grinding of the face until the caps have been fitted.

Reinforcement of the standard centre main bearing cap is generally done by machining the bottom of the bearing cap off until it is flat and level with the ends where the bolts sit. A piece of steel, the same width as the cap and about 1in. thick is machined perfectly flat on one side and drilled with holes matching the cap. Long studs are then used to bolt the cap and bar down to the block.

Crankshaft and connecting rods

The standard 850 and 998 crankshafts can be used for racing but will almost certainly break eventually. For reliability's sake either use the B L competition parts which are reasonably priced or get a standard sized crankshaft Tufftrided.

The 850 and 998 connecting rods are quite strong and not a really weak link. The pinch-bolt 850 rods should have their pinch-bolts renewed, but, provided that the threads in the rod eye are in good condition, they are not a source of trouble. Big-end bolt breakage is not unknown but the rather expensive double-hexagon cap screws supplied by Cosworth Engineering for Ford conrods seem to provide a satisfactory remedy. These are the right size and length for the 850/998 rods and should be tightened to 46lb ft torque. Tab washers cannot be fitted and are not required on a bolt tightened to this degree. The rods should be balanced end to end as well as overall so that the centre of gravity of all four rods is in the same position.

Pistons

The pistons used in any of the Minis can be used for racing without much trouble. An extra 0·001–0·002in. of skirt clearance should be allowed to reduce friction. The split-skirt type of piston should be examined regularly for signs of cracking, which starts at the top of the split and goes upwards and then across the crown. The weights of the pistons should be equalized to within ⅛oz. Metal can be turned off the bottom of the skirts of the heaviest ones until all four are the same weight and it does not matter if they are not all the same length.

In the 850, the best piston is the Hepolite Powermax, it is of solid skirt type with a Dykes top ring. They are manufactered in both flat and raised crown pattern but using the head and valve sizes suggested, the Authors prefer the flat top type as clearance problems arise with the raised ones.

The 998 pistons should be of the competition solid-skirt type for preference. Standard 998 pistons have a small raised portion on the crowns, this should be machined flat to avoid inlet valve problems.

The standard 850 pistons can be used and are reasonably strong but if an engine is being built from scratch it is obviously better to use the competition type. A popular way of obtaining near-flat-top pistons for an 850 was to machine about 0·030in. from the top leaving a small dimple in the centre and then grind about 0·035in. from the top of the cylinder block. With the 12G940 head, however, which does not have the machining limitations of the 850 and Cooper heads, this scheme does not confer any advantage. It also reduces the possible depth of the exhaust valve cutaway, thus limiting the attainable compression ratio.

The Cooper S types should have the competition three-ring pistons which, unlike the standard four-ring type are not susceptible to breakage of the ring lands. These pistons can be obtained with either flat or concave crowns and in cast or forged material.

The best piston for the 970 S is the flat-crown type as this enables a high compression ratio to be obtained. With the 1300 engine, the dished crown pistons are generally felt to give the best results.

The choice between forged and cast material is not critical, the cast ones being cheaper but not quite as strong as the forged variety. Neither should give any trouble. Boring out the block to the class limit is a worthwhile modification to racing 'S' types. The extra 18cc gained on a 1275 S are worth about 1·5 bhp and, on a 970 S, nearly 30cc or 2·5 bhp.

Oil pumps

The standard oil pump is satisfactory, provided it is in as-new condition. A racing engine circulates a lot of oil and it is unfiltered when it passes through the pump. This tends to ruin the pump if there are any metal particles whatsoever in the gearbox and these are amazingly difficult to eliminate. A new pump is often required after running-in a new engine. If a spider drive camshaft is used, a spider type pump is obviously essential. This should be of the latest two bolt type, rather than the four bolt pattern which has insufficient capacity. If a Cooper S oil-pressure release-valve spring is fitted, a pressure of 75–80lb/in²should be obtained, which, combined with Vandervell or Powermax copper-lead bearings, eliminates any danger of bearing failure.

Short stroke engines

Short stroke varieties of all three sizes of Mini engine have been built. The most popular is the short stroke 850 which can be arrived at by several methods. The simplest and cheapest type is based on the 970 'S' crankshaft which has a stroke of 62mm compared with 68mm for the standard engine. This, with a bore of 66mm, gives an oversquare engine of just under 850cc. The crankshaft will not fit an 850 block unless the main bearings are bored to 2in. diameter and reduced in width. It will however fit the late type 1100cc Austin-Healey Sprite block which requires no modification except for sawing the sump seal portion off the rear main bearing cap. Norton motor cycle pistons with flat crowns and 1275 'S' connecting rods are used but the rods must have the small-end bushed to take the smaller gudgeon pin. The pistons also require the machining away of part of one gudgeon-pin boss because the rods do not fit centrally in the bore. Surprisingly, this offset of the small end does not seem to matter. Using 'S' type rods results in an engine that is very awkward to assemble. The pistons must be put in first, without rings, and the rods inserted from below, the gudgeon pins and circlips being fitted with the piston pushed partly out of the bottom of the bore. Finally it is pushed out of the top again and the rings are fitted.

The engine is very satisfactory, apart from a slight tendency towards piston cracking, but a life of around one season's club racing can be expected.

It is possible to build one of these engines using a 970 'S' block but very thick liners will be required and the cylinder bores come out in a less advantageous place regarding inlet valve position.

The other method of building an 850 is to de-stroke a 970 'S', using a steel-billet crankshaft of about 52mm stroke. The real difficulty is lack of really suitable pistons which need to be around 0·2in. taller than those used in the standard Cooper S. The Authors built what was probably the first of these ultra short stroke 850 engines in 1971 and it is obvious from the number now racing that an acceptable solution to the piston problem has been found. Such units are very expensive indeed and are no guarantee of success as some of them have never developed their full potential.

De-stroking the 1000 and 1300 units cannot be carried out to the same degree as there is insufficient metal in the Cooper S block to bore it any bigger than about 74mm and not all blocks will stand this amount. Some very successful 1300s have been built, based on steel billet crankshafts of about 75mm stroke and even though their capacity has been restricted to as little as 1250cc by boring difficulties they have produced better outputs because of the higher usable crankshaft speed.

CLUTCH AND TRANSFER GEARS

On an 850, these parts do not give much trouble but the more powerful, larger, engines need some modification to avoid complications.

Primary gears

The latest type of primary gears produced for the Mini and Cooper S have a steel-lined inner bush which prevents it 'walking' out of the gear and crumbling up against the thrust washer as happened with the older type. The outer bush is still unbacked and there have been a few cases of the thrust face, which forms the outer end, breaking up and getting into the clutch. Replacing the end part of this bush with a phosphor bronze thrust washer cures this problem and it seems to have a satisfactory life in spite of the lack of lubrication at this point.

The idler gear, below the crankshaft, can be troublesome on 1300cc engines as the needle bearings are not really strong enough and can break up. The early bearings of 1in. outside diameter, have been superceded by a 1⅛in. diameter bearing with bigger rollers. These are generally adequate for club racing but Jack Knight, the gear and component manufacturer, has produced a modification which employs a large double taper roller bearing, fitted into the centre of a special gear which makes a very workmanlike job. A complete set of straight-cut transfer gears is also produced which reduces the power loss through the gear train. The straight-cut primary gears are normally fitted with steel-backed bushes in both ends.

Flywheel and clutch

The best and strongest flywheel is the B L Special Tuning ultra lightweight steel type. They can be further lightened to a small degree by drilling ¾in. diameter holes round the periphery. B L also sell a lightened pressure plate in malleable cast iron which is safer than using a lightened Mini one. If the cost of the steel flywheel and the pressure plate is beyond the limit of the budget, lightening of the standard article is unavoidable.

The Mini flywheels may be lightened by turning ⅜in. off the back face, i.e. the spring face, not the pressure face. After this has been done, it is necessary to pack up the pressure plate driving straps by ⅜in. to make them lie in the same plane as before. To prevent any danger of overstressing the driving-strap bolts, packing pieces ¼in. thick by 1in. diameter should be used. These are set in a 1in. diameter recess, ⅜in. deep, machined round the bolt hole in the flywheel, as shown in fig. 8:6.

Coil-spring type clutches are best converted to the diaphragm-spring type as described on page 176. If the starter ring is worn unevenly, it should be renewed before further uneven wear throws it out of balance.

The lightening of any flywheel must be done carefully and of course it must be rebalanced afterwards, a burst flywheel can be very dangerous and remember that, on a right-hand drive car, the driver is sitting directly in line with it!

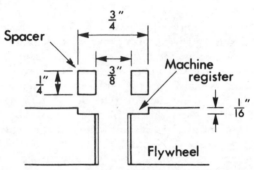

Fig. 8:6. Modification of clutch driving-strap bolt holes when the flywheel has been lightened.

The Mini pressure plate is not of such a good material as the Cooper S version and the 'S' type is the best one to modify. It may be thinned down by turning the back off until it is about ⅜in. thick. Also it may be cut away between the driving bosses as shown in plate V (b).

The gearbox

The ideal gearbox for competition is the remote-change type fitted with straight-cut, close-ratio gears. Either the three-speed-synchromesh or the all-synchromesh type can be converted with a straight-cut conversion kit available from B L Special Tuning. Any box with 'B' type gears, that is later than about 1966, can use the conversion for the three-speed-synchromesh gearbox but early boxes, with bronze-bushed third-motion-shafts, cannot be converted and are not really strong enough anyway.

The standard 'S' and Cooper gearboxes have closer ratios than the 850 and these close ratios are preferable. Some people prefer the three-speed-synchromesh box to the latest type because the gears are lighter and the change fractionally faster but the all-synchromesh type might be an advantage for hill climbs where first gear is frequently used. The Cooper and later Mini remote control can only be used on the very late 850 basic gearboxes with the long lever. Most of the long-lever 850 boxes have a differential housing different from the remote-change one and these housings are not interchangeable box-to-box. The Authors have not yet tried a remote control conversion which is positive enough for racing and these seem to be best avoided even if a remote-change box is not obtainable.

Some five-speed conversions have been produced for the Mini gearbox but the cost and lack of strength of the early versions prevented them gaining wide popularity. For an 850 or 1000 which, because of their narrow power bands would benefit most, the five-speed boxes are not really suitable because top gear is indirect and gives too high a top gear even with a very low final drive.

Final drive

For almost all competition use, a lower-than-standard final-drive gear is desirable. With a powerful 1000cc or 1300cc Mini, the best gearing depends to a great extent on the circuit, a ratio of 3·941:1 or even 3·77:1 being used on long fast circuits; while 4·13:1 or 4·27:1 gears are used on shorter, twistier ones, where a high top speed cannot be attained. An 850, because of its relatively small power output, cannot reach a top speed much in excess of 100 mile/h and there is no point in gearing it to reach 120.

Using racing tyres, a 4·35:1 final drive gives 98 mile/h at 7,500 rev/min and this is fairly suitable for longish circuits. The specialist concern, Jack Knight Developments, can supply gears of 4·6 or 4·8:1 which enable top gear to be used on tight circuits and this is an advantage. A 4·6:1 gear will give 100 mile/h at 8,000 rev/min and the majority of 850 engines will be almost as fast in a straight line with this gearing as with 4·35:1. The snag is that proprietary (*i.e.* non–B L) gears are about five times as expensive as the Special Tuning components.

Limited-slip differential

Except for special formulas which prohibit its use, a limited-slip differential is now almost essential for a competitive racing Mini. Two basic types have been used, the pawl type and the Powr-Lok type. The pawl type works on the ZF principle in which the output shafts have one internally and one externally ridged cam formed on them. These are positioned one inside the other and eight pawls, located by a steel cage, are held between them. The cage is driven by the final-drive gear and the pawls, engaging with the ridges on the output shafts transmit drive. When the pawls are not under high load, as occurs in a corner when power is not applied, one cam may turn faster than the other as the pawls ride up and down over the ridges. On full power, however, the pawls cannot ride up and down very fast because of the friction caused, so a lightly loaded wheel is prevented from spinning while the other is stationary.

The Salisbury Powr-Lok differential resembles a conventional unit but its sun wheels are connected to the differential carrier by metal-to-metal multiplate clutches. These clutches have a certain amount of preload which makes them grip the sun wheels even at rest. When power is applied to the unit, the star wheels force the sun wheels apart loading the clutches even more and locking them to the carrier thus preventing differential action.

The Powr-Lok is now the only one available from B L Special Tuning but Jack Knight is still manufacturing pawl differentials. The pawl differentials wear very quickly on a 1300 but not on an 850. It has some advantage in that it will accept the standard final-drive whereas the Powr-Lok has to have a specially machined gear which is more expensive. Both types are supplied with drive flanges to take Hardy-Spicer needle-roller inner driveshaft couplings which are longer lasting than rubber ones. Rubber ones do not last very long on a racing 1300 and repeated replacement is an expensive and inconvenient job. The Hardy-Spicer drive-shaft couplings will replace the inner sliding portion of any but the very early Mini driveshafts.

The induction system

There is a wide range of carburetters that could be used for racing on Minis but, in practice, only a few of the alternatives are used to any extent. The only restriction placed on the special saloon competitor is in Mini-Seven formula. Here, basically, a single carburetter choke of not more than 1½in. bore is allowed. All other classes are free and the most common choice is the 45DCOE Weber. This very adaptable carburetter can be fitted with chokes and jets suitable for 850, 1000, and 1300 Minis. It is normally fitted on a fairly long cast-aluminium inlet manifold which involves some cutting away of the bulkhead. Shorter manifolds, as used on old type Appendix J Group II cars, are not quite as efficient.

For best results, the carburetter should be mounted flexibly on the manifold. 'O' ring seals, and Thackeray type spring washers beneath the nuts are used to achieve this. Suitable settings to start experimenting with are given in Table 8:I. Apart from variation of these basic settings, the volume and rate of the accelerator-pump delivery can be altered as can the auxiliary venturi size. Fine tuning of the DCOE Weber is a fairly involved business as it is difficult to know which of the many variables is best altered to get the desired result. Experience of the job is the only way to achieve perfection but fortunately a racer only needs to be spot-on over a fairly narrow power band and much really difficult tuning of the low-speed range is unnecessary.

As a general guide, the following rule-of-thumb approach may be helpful to the raw beginner, but it does not hold true for all possible settings.

(1) Increasing the size of the main jet richens the mixture.

(2) Increasing the size of the air jet weakens the mixture.

(3) The effect of a variation of 10 units on the air jet has about half as much effect as the same variation of the main jet.

(4) Increasing the size of the pump jet richens the mixture at the top end of the rev range.

(5) If the engine fluffs and will not pick up cleanly when changing down to a lower gear, try either a bigger pump jet or a stronger pump spring.

(6) If the engine fluffs when changing up try a smaller pump jet or a small size of pump valve bleed.

(7) If trouble is experienced with fuel surge, the engine cutting out or misfiring on corners, try raising the float level to cure cutting out in a bend or lowering the float level to cure a misfire on the exit of a bend. Alter the level about 2mm at a time.

TABLE 8:1

SUGGESTED SETTINGS FOR WEBER 45DCOE CARBURETTER

Engine	Main	Air jet	Pump jet	Slow run jet	Choke
850cc	150	160	35	45F6	36mm
1000cc	165	170	45	50F6	38mm
1293cc	190	190	55	50F6	40mm
850cc Mini Seven using 1 choke	200	175	55 or drill out to equal 100	50F6	34–36mm

Note: All above settings assume:—

Emulsion tube F2
Auxiliary venturi 4·5
Pump-valve blank

Except:—
With Mini 7 using 55 pump jet, use 50 or 100 pump valve bleeds
With split (one choke per 2 cyls) twin DCOEs, use 50 pump valve bleeds
Float level   7mm – 9mm

Split Webers

An increasingly popular, if expensive, modification is to use two 45 DCOE Webers, one choke of each being used per port. The unused ones being blanked off. The idea is to take the 'S' bend out of the induction tract and allow slightly shorter manifolds to be used. It is not easy to accommodate one left- and one right-hand choke as the right-hand carburetter fouls the clutch master cylinder. The normal scheme is to cut away part of the left-hand side of the right-hand carburetter and use the right-hand choke for cylinders three and four while cylinders one and two are fed from the right-hand choke of the other carburetter which need not be sawn up. Special inlet stubs are required of course and some modification of the carburetter is necessary. The pump jet not in use must be plugged up and a bleed of about size 100 should be used in place of a plain pump valve. If the auxiliary venturi is put in the wrong way round it will block off the main fuel outlet and that is really all that needs to be done.

Twin SU carburetters of 1½in. bore were at one time widely used, but the superior mid-range torque given by the Weber made it more popular. Lately, some competitors, especially those using the very high revving 970 'S' unit, have turned to twin 1¾in. or even 2in. bore SUs.

TABLE 8:II

SU CARBURETTERS FOR RACING

Engine	Carburetter	Needle	Spring colour
850cc	Twin H4 or HS4	No 6	Red
1000cc	Twin H4 or HS4	CP4	Red
	Twin HS6	TS	Red
1275cc	Twin H4 or HS4	BG	Red
	Twin HS6	RR	Blue

These give more top end power than a 45DCOE and the small 'S' unit seems to be able to take advantage of this. B L Special Tuning now market an 1¾in. carburetter kit for the Mini engines which includes a manifold which will accept the four-stud type carburetter. Carburetters as large as this are unlikely to benefit an 850.

Mini-Seven formula

Originally the most common carburetter was the 1½in. SU but this is seldom used nowadays. The 1½in. bore Fish type carburetter is probably the most common and it is available in both semi-downdraught and downdraught forms. The Reece-Fish semi-downdraught type is the most popular and it is often used on a tubular-steel inlet manifold of the type produced by Janspeed.

Both the downdraught Minnow and the Reece-Fish carburetters are basically similar to each other. They are fixed-choke types but possess a very novel metering and atomization system, see plate III (b).

There are no jets or needles to change, as the mixture strength is controlled by three simple adjustments. Full-power mixture is controlled by a small Allen screw restricting the maximum amount of fuel that can pass to the spraying jets. Access to this screw is obtained by removing a screwed plug on the outside of the carburetter body, holding the throttle fully open and then inserting a small Allen key down the hole exposed by removal of the plug, to engage with the adjusting screw. Turning the adjuster clockwise weakens the mixture and turning it anticlockwise richens it. Alteration of the mixture should be made by turning the screw one flat of the Allen key at a time.

Mid-range mixture is controlled by the position of the throttle spindle and the position of the throttle butterfly. The amount of fuel passed is controlled by the position of the throttle spindle because one end of the spindle moves a fuel pick-up arm across a tapered groove which allows an increasing amount of fuel to pass to the spraying jets as the throttle is opened. The amount of air supplied in the middle range of engine speeds is controlled by the position in which the throttle butterfly is clamped onto the throttle spindle. It can thus be seen that by fixing the throttle spindle and loosening the butterfly clamping screw, the mixture can be adjusted. Opening the butterfly weakens the mixture and closing it richens it.

Slow-running mixture is adjusted by means of a knurled screw, on the outside of the carburetter, which bleeds air from one side of the butterfly to the other, when the throttle is closed.

Fuel injection

The eight-port head has made the use of fuel injection possible and both the Lucas and Tecalemit systems have been used. Club racing Minis have usually employed the Tecalemit system as it is cheaper and simpler. Even though fuel injection has theoretical advantages over carburetters, they have still been employed on eight-port heads. The main reason for this is probably that most private owners have not the time or experience to get the best out of fuel injection systems. They are certainly more difficult to tune and require more adjustment to compensate for temperature and atmospheric pressure changes than carburetters. In the

short time available for practice at club race meetings, only those with
sufficient knowledge of the job seem to get it right.

The exhaust system

To achieve good results, all Minis should be fitted with a long-centre-
branch type as described on page 172. The BL large-bore competition
manifold is rather big for an 850 but it is suitable for 1000 and 1300cc
engines. Many different tailpipe variations have been tried and no
particular arrangement seems to merit either recommendation or rejec-
tion. In general, however, use of a small tail pipe of $1\frac{3}{4}$in. diameter extending to the rear of the car will give reasonable results with any size of engine.
Some 1300cc engines have given better results using a pipe of about 60in.
length emerging in front of one rear wheel. The Authors have used pipes
as short as 36in. and of nearly 2in. bore on an 850 with good results.
Different types of exhaust manifold have been used by Downton and by
Richard Longman's successful tuning establishments. The Longman type
is a long three-into-one type which takes three separate pipes down past
the driveshaft and joins them all together just round the corner.
Downton have tried manifolds which join the outer pair of pipes just
beneath the driveshaft and then join the centre pipe to this one at some
distance down the tunnel. Short tail pipes are usually employed with
these manifolds, sometimes of megaphone pattern.

The eight-port head has, of course, four separate exhaust outlets for
which many variations of manifold have been produced. The most
common looks like a normal long-centre-branch type with two centre
pipes joined together the same distance from the head as the outer pair.
A four-into-one version could possibly show an improvement at high
rev/min but the difficulty of accommodating four primary pipes of sufficient
length would be considerable.

The ignition system

Some attention to the ignition system is necessary to ensure reliability at
high engine speeds, although the standard parts will work effectively up
to 8,000 rev/min if they are in perfect condition.

The plug leads should preferably be of the conventional wire-cored
type and the caps must be in good condition with no tracking marks on
them. The standard (non-Cooper) coil is alright but many people prefer
to fit one of the sports, high-voltage types to give a greater margin of
reliability. The Coopers are fitted with a higher-than-normal voltage coil
in standard form and this should be adequate. The distributor, as used
on the Cooper S, is very suitable for racing use on any Mini. The
advance curve is better suited to racing camshafts than that of the
normal Mini distributor and it has no vacuum advance mechanism. This
is an advantage because the vacuum advance control is an unnecessary

complication on a racing engine as it adds nothing to the power output, being purely an economy device.

The Cooper S contact-breaker assembly has a stronger spring than the standard Mini type and it prevents contact bounce at high engine speeds. This contact set should be used even if the standard distributor is retained.

The ignition timing may need considerable alteration from the standard setting to achieve optimum results. The best way to find the correct setting is to run the engine at full throttle on a test bed or rolling road at a speed of 5,000 to 6,000 rev/min and, keeping the engine speed constant by adjustment of the test equipment, alter the ignition timing to achieve the maximum torque reading.

If no test facilties are available, the only method is by road testing the car as described on page 180. The settings suggested in Table 8:III are a good start but the optimum figure for a particular engine may differ considerably from these. All the settings in Table 8:III apply to engines fitted with a Cooper S distributor and the C–AEA 648 camshaft.

TABLE 8:III

SUGGESTED IGNITION TIMING FOR RACING
USING COOPER S DISTRIBUTOR AND C-AEA 648 CAMSHAFT

Engine	Timing – static degrees before t d c
850 (68mm stroke)	10°
(62mm stroke)	13°
(52mm stroke)	15°
1000 (76mm stroke)	8°
(62mm stroke)	14°
1275 (82mm stroke)	5°

Spark plugs

A harder, cooler running, spark plug is needed for competition use and the grade depends on the type of competition and the state of tune of the engine.

Using too soft a plug will result in overheating of the electrodes which causes pre-ignition, rough running and loss of power. The plugs will have a burnt appearance whatever the mixture so that it will be impossible to judge the state of the carburation from the plug colour. Too hard a plug will suffer from persistent sooting or oiling up and will give a falsely 'rich' appearance to the deposit on the insulator.

For rallying, a plug as suggested for fast road work should be suitable and one harder than Champion N3 or N6Y is unlikely to be needed.

Racing engines should use a plug of the recessed electrode type such as Champion N62R or N57R. Extended nose plugs can be troublesome in Mini engines with very shallow combustion chambers as the piston could touch the earth electrode thus closing the gap. Most racing engines, with compression ratios of 12:1 or above, will probably need an N57R although for sprints, especially in cold weather, a softer plug like the N62R should be adequate and less prone to fouling.

Even though a racer's engine will usually start up perfectly well on racing plugs, use of soft plugs such as a set of N5 type is a good idea for cold starting. Using these, the engine does not have to be revved to keep the plugs clean when stone cold and if the day is cold and the engine a little awkward to start, a set of soft plugs will save wetting the racing ones. Plugs are very easy to change on a Mini and this precaution will save the need for frequent cleaning of racing plugs which should be avoided if possible.

THE COOLING SYSTEM

Radiators

Most road- and rally-cars will be kept adequately cool if the late 'S' type radiator is used which has 16 gills per inch of matrix instead of 13 used originally. Some competitors have added the radiator element from an old heater, mounted at the front, to gain extra cooling. It is usually piped between the heater offtake in the head and the bottom hose. For club racing, the ideal system is a front-mounted radiator, either of the normal or crossflow type. This does away with the need for a fan thus saving valuable power. A fan can absorb up to 3 b h p at high revs and this should not be wasted just cooling the engine.

A 1300 engine may well need a specially-made front-mounted radiator but, for the smaller sizes of engine, a normal Mini radiator can be employed. It can be used upright, as normal, or on its side in crossflow form. If the filler neck is unsoldered and the hole blanked off, the standard outlets may be used when the radiator is laid on its side. The normal bottom outlet becomes the top hose connection and the old top one is connected to the water pump by a rather long and tortuous pipe. A small header tank employing the cap and neck removed from the radiator should be placed as high as possible and connected between the top of the radiator and the thermostat outlet on the head.

Thermostats and the by-pass hose

The by-pass hose serves to allow circulation of water between the block and head when the thermostat is closed. To obtain maximum efficiency from the cooling system, the thermostat should be removed and the by-pass passage blocked off with a thermostat blanking sleeve which fits in its place. An alternative to this sleeve is to weld up the ends of the by-pass hose connections in the head and water pump. This avoids the necessity of fiddling with the hose every time the head is removed.

When a thermostat is not used there is some danger of overcooling in cold weather so bear this in mind and have some provision for blanking off part of the radiator matrix to get the running temperature up to about 80°C.

Water pumps

Two types of water pump are fitted to the Mini. The latest, high-capacity type is obviously the best for any racer that may have cooling problems. This pump is supplied under Unipart No. GWP 102 and has a larger impellor and a bigger bore inlet pipe than the older type. If this pump is fitted to an old block it may be necessary to grind or turn a small amount of metal from the end of the impellor to reduce both its length and diameter by about $\frac{1}{16}$ in. If this is not done there is some danger that the impellor will foul the inside of the block. Trying the pump in the block will soon indicate whether sufficient clearance exists. It is also helpful to grind a smooth, tapered entry into the inlet pipe of the pump. Check that the heater take-off pipe in the bottom hose (if fitted) does not protrude into the bore of the hose so obstructing the flow and do not use long pieces of convoluted rubber hose, which, because of their internal knobblyness tend to hinder smooth flow of coolant.

Oil coolers

An oil cooler is advisable for any competition Mini and essential for one that will be used for more than two or three minutes at a time. Probably the best cooler to use is the large 13 row Cooper S type. This comes in a kit from B L Special Tuning complete with hoses and adaptors. It fits in place of the pipe between the oil filter housing and the cylinder block. Without a cooler, severe loss of pressure will be experienced when driving at racing speeds if the oil temperature becomes excessive.

ANCILLARY EQUIPMENT

Generator

If the engine is run at speeds in excess of 6,000 rev/min for prolonged periods, there is a danger that the generator armature will disintegrate. To avoid this, the large generator pulley C–AEA 535 should be used together with the long fan belt C–AEA 756. The load on the generator bracket is reduced if the coil is removed from the generator; it may be remounted on the wing valance in front of the control box.

Oil breathers

To comply with regulations for race meetings, all the engine breather pipes must end in a catch tank, unless the engine has provision, such as positive crankcase ventilation, for collecting its own breather fumes.

Usually, connecting the breather outlets to a conveniently placed quart tin with ½in. bore plastic tubing does the job adequately.

Some engines will however blow a large quantity of oil out of the breathers at high engine speeds and some modification of the system is necessary. As most of the oil loss seems to come from the tappet-cover breather, one solution is to blank this off and then add an extra large breather, of at least 1in. diameter, to the rocker cover which is connected to the catch tank through a large hose.

Oil surge

Most racing Minis suffer from oil surge to a certain extent when sharp right hand corners are taken at racing speeds. This is caused by centrifugal force which throws the oil away from the pick-up pipe and allows the pump to suck air instead of oil.

The first emergency step towards curing this is to overfill the engine with oil to the level of the X in the MAX on the dipstick. This may effect a cure but if the engine burns oil or blows it out into the catch tank, the level may drop far enough during a race to cause loss of pressure on corners. A better proposition, therefore, is to alter the oil pick-up tube to collect oil from the centre of the transmission casing rather than from one corner. A suitable method is to remove the gauze oil strainer and weld a length of pipe on to the bottom of the pick-up pipe at right angles, so that it passes through the web in the casing and can collect oil from the centre of the case. A strainer must be incorporated in the end but this is simply done by cutting the 'bottom' of the horizontal tube away for about two inches and brazing a piece of gauze onto it to cover the resulting hole.

CHAPTER 9

PREPARING A MINI FOR COMPETITION

Modification of the engine and improvement of the brakes and suspension have already been dealt with in chapters 8 and 6 so all that remains is to outline the work involved in preparing the rest of the car. As the layout of the controls and interior and exterior decor are very much personal things, few hard and fast rules will be given. This chapter will indicate what must be done, what should be done and what can be done.

It is clearly impossible to list all the various formulae and different F I A and R A C rules governing all the aspects of competition use. These rules change from year to year anyway and thus would soon become valueless if repeated here.

Basically, however, club-level competition, as distinct from National and International competitions, are run for cars with no restrictions as regards modification so long as the car complies with the R A C vehicle regulations. Some clubs run standard-car classes in sprints, driving tests and hill climbs and several clubs run races for 850 Minis complying with the Mini-Seven Formula. This is a popular class for 850 Minis with certain modification restrictions. The regulations for this class can be obtained from the Mini-Seven Club or the Seven Fifty Motor Club secretaries. (Addresses in R A C Motor Sport Year Book).

The onus is clearly on the competitor to ensure that his car complies with the R A C vehicle regulations and the additional regulations applicable to the event he is entering, most of which are listed in the R A C Motor Sport Year Book that every driver gets when he takes out a competition licence. These requirements should be closely studied.

It is amazing how many people turn up at their first meeting and are failed at scrutineering because of inadequate attention to or misinterpretation of the regulations. This chapter is intended to help the would-be competitor avoid these pitfalls as well as to make his car safe and reliable.

WHAT MUST BE DONE

General competition

The bulkhead, between the engine and the interior of the car, must be fireproof. This means that the hole in the bulkhead, behind the speedometer, should be covered with a piece of steel or aluminium sheet with no holes in it except those necessary to let the speedometer cable and wiring through.

If the car is fitted with Perspex windows, they must be at least $\frac{3}{16}$ in. (4mm) thick.

A bonnet strap must be fitted on the outside of the bonnet in such a way that any official can see that it is properly fastened.

Wheel-spacers must not be more than 1in. thick and they must have at least as large a flat surface, for the wheel to bolt up to, as the brake drum or hub. Only one-piece studs are allowed. The type of stud extension that screws onto the existing stud is not allowed. The tyre treads must not protrude beyond the outside of the bodywork (see chapter 6, page 142), even if the policeman lets you get away with it, the scrutineer won't.

Races and speed events

Without listing all the requirements, the most common pitfalls are covered here.

Windscreens: A laminated-glass or Perspex windscreen must be used for races but it is not necessary for speed events. Normal Mini screens are of toughened glass which will not do. Laminated windscreens have the word 'laminated' etched onto them near the screen-maker's name and the scrutineer will look for this.

Mirrors: A rear-view mirror must be fitted and if it is inside the car, the edges must be bound with insulation tape or something similar unless it is one of the late Mini mirrors which have a plastic surround.

Fireproofing: The boot of the Mini must be sealed off from the inside of the car to prevent the passage of flame or liquid. The areas that require sealing are the sides of the rear parcel shelf, the holes in the middle of it, the sides of the rear seat backrest, above the wheel arches, and the hole in the middle of the rear seat backrest which is normally covered by a piece of cardboard. These holes are best covered with pieces of aluminium sheet, riveted to the parcel shelf and seat backrest. The gaps at the edges can then be filled in with fibreglass mat and resin. If the scrutineer can see any sign of daylight coming through into the boot from the inside of the car he will not pass it. If plastic fuel pipes are led through the inside of the car they must be covered with solid metal or fibreglass ducting.

Catch tanks: A catch tank of at least 1 litre (2 pints) capacity must be fitted, for all events except autocross, to collect any oil blown out of the engine breathers (see chapter 8, page 204).

Ignition switch: The ignition switch must be clearly marked ON and OFF in letters large enough to be easily seen by someone who doesn't know where they are. If the driver can't reach the switch when wearing a seat belt, either move it or extend the key with a loop of stiff wire soldered on or a strip of aluminium bolted to it.

While dealing with ignition, make sure that the battery is securely fixed in position and cannot get free in the event of the car rolling over.

Throttle return spring: At least one throttle return spring per carburetter must be fitted so as to act directly on the throttle spindle. Minis comply with this in standard form but an extra return spring which will operate in the event of the main one breaking, is better.

Crash helmets and licences: One final point while covering essential requirements: crash helmets must comply with BSI specification No. 1869 or 2495 or carry the approval mark of an equivalent national institution. Check up on this, a BSI kite mark alone is not enough, it must have the correct number as well.

A competition licence valid for the event must be presented and, for races, an RAC medical certificate card, filled in and signed by a doctor.

WHAT SHOULD BE DONE

Several points, although not mandatory, are worth careful attention. These apply especially to races but they should be considered in the light of any type of competition.

Seat belts: By far the best type of belt is a good full harness securely anchored. The protection afforded by a lap and diagonal type belt in a car which is somersaulting is not really adequate, there is still a chance of the driver being flung half out of the car and then having the car roll over on him. Although one or two people have been thrown out and had miraculous escapes from saloon cars, ninety nine times in a hundred it is far safer to remain inside until everything has stopped.

Seats: If possible, the driving seat should be fixed permanently to the floor. Lugs welded onto the seat legs and bolted through the floor with large washers placed beneath the floor will stop it tipping forward or coming adrift, should one of the front mountings break. A special racing bucket seat is advantageous as it helps the driver to maintain a comfortable position during violent manoeuvres. It should have a strong frame, though; some light fibreglass seats, although ideal if fitted onto a stout tubular frame, are useless if they are only bolted down through the bottom, as it is sometimes done. If the seat breaks loose it is much more difficult to stay in it.

Roll-over bars: In the last two years, the fitting of roll-over bars inside racing saloons has become increasingly popular. In a Mini, the form this usually takes is a stout tubular steel hoop bolted to the bottoms of the rear parcel pockets and just clearing the roof with a strut fixed to the middle of it at roof level going down to a plate bolted to the rear parcel shelf. In the event of a severe roll over, this will prevent the roof being squashed down on top of the driver, which reduces the chance of injury and enables him to escape faster. Roll-over bars for the Mini can be purchased for about £10 (John Aley Racing).

Fire extinguishers: Racing saloons are more likely to catch fire than a normal road car for several reasons. Among these are the open car-buretter intakes; the valve timing, which allows liquid fuel to be ejected from the intakes at low speeds, and the very high temperatures reached by the exhaust system. With these facts in mind, it is obvious that a fire extinguisher is a very valuable accessory. A small carburetter fire, if extinguished after a few seconds, could be little more than a dangerous incident, but if left to burn for one or two minutes, might ruin a £50 carburetter or even the complete car. Be sure to buy an extinguisher suitable for petrol fires and then mount it where it is easily reached. Learn how to use it so that you do not have to waste time reading the instructions while the fire is blazing merrily away.

Flame resistant overalls: Several types of flame resistant overalls are now available and the best of these are the permanently flame-proof Nomex and Protex variety. Although these are expensive, they do represent the best practical form of protection for the driver of a racing car. For maximum protection, underwear, socks and gloves of the same material should be used. Face masks, made in these materials, are a sensible precaution because they reduce the risk of lung scorching if the driver becomes trapped in a blazing car.

Although there have not been many cases of saloon car drivers being badly burned, the few instances show that it is a possible hazard and not one to be dismissed lightly.

WHAT CAN BE DONE

Controls and instrumentation

For the competition driver, the standard layout of controls and instruments leaves much to be desired. The first thing that should receive attention, is the control layout. Most drivers prefer to rake the steering column downwards at a greater angle using one of the commercially available rake adjusters. When fitting these always make sure that the rack-securing 'U' bolts are slackened before lowering the column. No strain must be imposed on the pinion shaft.

Steering wheels: Most drivers prefer a slightly smaller steering wheel when driving on tarmac circuits. For very rough events, such as autocross, it is debatable whether the heavy standard wheel is not better as it absorbs some of the shocks. If a smaller wheel is chosen for a racer, do not make the mistake of using one too small. A Mini with a limited-slip differential can require a considerable steering effort and, as this often must be applied with one hand, a wheel of 13in. diameter must be regarded as a minimum size.

The type is purely a matter for the driver to decide but be sure that the wheel chosen has a continuous metal ring built into the rim. This reduces the chances of the wheel breaking in an accident.

Pedals: The positions of the clutch and brake pedals suit most people and all that needs to be done to these is to ensure that the pedal rubbers are in good condition and firmly fixed. They can be glued on with Bostik or similar adhesive to prevent any chance of movement. The position of the throttle pedal often requires alteration.

The pedal should be bent into a position where the driver can easily achieve 'heel-and-toe' operation of the throttle and brake. The pedal should be set with the driver wearing the shoes in which he will race, since the type of shoe can make a considerable difference to the best position for the pedal. Some drivers may find that extending the pedal downwards by riveting on a piece of metal, or fitting a commercial throttle-pedal extension, is a great help. A stop should be fitted beneath the pedal to prevent it being pushed down further than is required to obtain full throttle.

Gear levers: The gear lever on the Cooper is easily reached by most people and rarely requires alteration. A small screw-on extension is all that is ever needed. The 850 lever is, however, extremely difficult to reach if the driver's seat is moved back as far as is desirable for good control and weight distribution. Remote linkages usually seem to have a certain amount of lost motion which is very undesirable in a competition car. Probably the best solution is to heat the lever just about a foot from the bottom and bend it downwards a little and then make a light tubular extension piece and weld it on to the top. This is much stronger than screwing on a long extension. If the extension is screwed on, the thread on top of the gear lever is sure to break off at a most inconvenient time.

Instruments: Three essential instruments are a tachometer, and accurate oil-pressure and water-temperature gauges. The capilliary-tube type of oil and water gauges are preferable, and accurate, 270 degree scale, instruments are available at quite reasonable prices. The electronic impulse type of tachometer is probably the most widely used variety and it is sufficiently accurate for most purposes. A 0–8,000 rev/min model will cover most contingencies except racing when a 0–10,000 rev/min model could be needed. The price is almost the same for either. Mounting is again a matter for the driver to decide upon but the tachometer should be placed in such a way that it can be seen whatever the position of the hands on the steering wheel.

Lightening

Bodywork lightening can pay considerable dividends for a relatively small outlay. A one cwt reduction in the weight of a Mini increases the power-to-weight ratio by 8%. This is equivalent to about 5 b h p on an 850 racer or nearly 9 on a 1275 S. This is obviously worthwhile for racing.

For most classes of competition, there is no restriction on lightening and most club-racing special saloons have one-piece fibreglass fronts, Perspex windows and sometimes Perspex windscreens. Fibreglass boot lids and doors are also widely used. Lightening beyond the straight replacement of non-structural panels needs careful thought if strength and rigidity are not to be lost. The rear seat and parcel tray do quite a lot to stiffen the rear of the car and replacing these with thin aluminium sheet can impair the handling. Likewise, fitting a fibreglass roof panel without making provision for putting back some of the structural rigidity can lead to a very flexible and potentially dangerous motor car. The floor, especially in the front foot wells, contributes a great deal to the strength of the car and should not be altered without very careful thought.

An increasingly popular modification is to replace the rear suspension with a lightweight beam axle which certainly saves weight but, as with any radical modification of the car, it must be thoroughly thought out and carefully executed. A look around the paddock at any club race meeting will show many ideas on the subject and they should all be considered, although some may have obvious defects. The golden rule is: if in doubt, either find out from someone who knows or leave it alone.

Lightweight fuel tanks moved to the centre of the boot are both weight-saving and safer as, if the filler is moved inside, it is less vulnerable in the event of an accident. Do make sure that the tank is securely fitted. A vent pipe should be led outside the car, fairly high up to minimize spillage of fuel. A couple of holes in the boot floor to prevent spilt fuel collecting in the spare-wheel well is a wise modification.

Racing tyres

The choice of tyre construction, tread pattern and rubber composition has been shown to be extremely important when trying to achieve the best possible performance in competition.

As the power output of the engines has increased and faster laps are attained so more and more demand is placed upon the tyres.

To satisfy this demand, special racing tyres have been developed for the Mini by both the Dunlop company and by Firestones.

The first Mini tyres produced especially for competition were based on the Dunlop C41 pattern but with a nylon casing substituted and moulded in a special rubber compound.

With the demand for such tyres obviously expanding, Dunlop then developed the first true Mini racing tyre with a special tread pattern, these were the CR48 500 L10 and were moulded in an all-weather rubber compound coded 'green-spot'. At the same time a few tyres were produced in a softer compound for wet-weather use coded 'yellow-spot'.

By this time Mini racing was becoming very popular and soon a new tyre the CR 65 MkII 500 L10 appeared, first in 'green-spot' rubber as an all-weather tyre and then in a softer rubber coded 'white-spot'.

Later this tyre was to become available in three other rubber mixes mainly for intermediate or wet weather, these in order of reducing 'hardness' were the 184 compound, the 350 and 376.

A smooth treaded tyre with star-shaped indentations was produced for dry use called CR 70 and this was moulded in green or white spot rubber compounds, the mix recommended depending mostly upon tyre running temperatures achieved by the particular vehicle.

At about this time the Firestone company produced their Mini racing tyre, the Super Sports Indy, a 600 × 19·3 × 10 tyre in 118 compound, which proved very successful both on the 1300 racers and on smaller-engined models.

To improve the adhesion of their tyres still further and to keep tyre temperatures down on the very powerful 1300 S types, a new wider 'dry' tyre was then produced by Dunlops called the CR 81 with a D22 construction. These were first made as 450·700·10 for the normal racing wheels used at that time, but as wider wheels became available a 450·900·10 was produced to suit. Both sizes were moulded in 232 compound.

For special use on single seaters and ultra light cars, a low pressure version of the CR 81 was also produced in D34 construction, this could be run at 30–35p s i as opposed to the more normal 45–50p s i used in the D22 tyre.

With the development of low profile tyres the numbering system changed from 450·700·10 to 150·500·10 and from 450·900·10 to 185·500·10, the newer tyres being produced in 232 and 376 rubber but still basically CR 81.

Developments by the Cooper Car Co. using 12 inch wheels required the production of an ultra low-profile tyre for use on Minis. This was the CR 84 MkII, 375·800·12 in D22 construction, and was tried in 232, 184, and 350 rubber compounds: later this tyre was renumbered 155·500·12.

In 1972 the slick tyres were developed for the 1300 S made in a D15 construction and numbered 160·490·10 Slick, the rubber compound most favoured being 388. These are very wide, very low-profile tyres giving exceptional road holding and handling. Firestones at this time brought out their new Mini tyre, the Super Sports GP, slightly wider than the Indy at 6·5 × 19·3 × 10 but now moulded in IB 19 rubber although some were produced in IB 24.

In order to take advantage of the tyre development work being undertaken for single-seater cars with 13 inch wheels, some racing Minis are being fitted with 13 inch wheels and are using 180·500·13 Slick tyres for the front wheels and 160·500·13 Slicks for the rear. These are produced by Dunlop in 376 compound at present but will obviously change as new developments become available.

Racing tyres have a very light construction and are carefully balanced during manufacture but it is important to recheck the wheel balance whenever new tyres are fitted. While these racing tyres produce very high adhesion and performance on the race track they are quite unsuitable for use on the road where the necessary high pressures would give rise to a very bumpy ride and the tyre construction makes them sensitive to gulleys in the road surface and raised white lines, causing the car to wander. For this reason it is now illegal to use any racing tyre on the road.

Getting to the event

Obviously a rally car will be driven to the starting point and there is no problem about transporting it: for other events, however, driving to the venue can be an unnecessary evil. An out-and-out racer, even if registered and insured for road use, should not be driven to a circuit if it can be avoided. The racing life of the valve gear and other highly stressed parts will be reduced and anyway most club racers are unpleasant to drive in traffic as well as uncomfortable. Most people will take along a second car to carry tools, spare wheels, petrol, mechanics, popsies etc. and this may well be used to tow the racer. A trailer is undoubtedly the best solution as there is no wear on any part of the car and it can be brought home again, even if damaged. Towing on a solid bar is better than using a rope but even then it is a rotten job steering the towed car on a long journey. Building a trailer for a Mini is not a very complicated job. A look round the paddock at a race meeting shows what can be done quite cheaply and a Mini can be towed behind almost anything, provided it is heavier than the combined weight of racer and trailer.

When lashing the car down onto a trailer, tie down the wheels or hubs rather than the sub-frames. This allows the car to move freely on its springs and prevents body movement from slackening or breaking the ropes. The trailer should be loaded so that it is slightly nose heavy, a weight of around 80lb on the towing hitch is best for most tow cars.

Rally equipment

The foregoing section has dealt mainly with cars that are to be used for racing and speed events where everything that is not absolutely essential is removed. For serious rallying, even at club event level, a certain amount of extra equipment is desirable.

A sump guard is a very practical extra, desirable for events which may include an occasional diversion down a rough road and essential for timed sections on rough private tracks where much damage could be caused by striking rocks or tree stumps with the sump. For light work, several firms sell guards which protect the front of the sump and some of the underside quite adequately.

For the serious type of event where much fast, rough going is expected, a much stronger guard is needed. The type that covers the whole of the sump and has an extension reaching rearwards to protect the gearchange and front of the exhaust is a necessity. Skids welded on to the exhaust pipe and silencer to prevent the front and rear of the silencer from catching on protruding obstacles are also essential. Obviously the exhaust system should be mounted as high up as possible.

Many enthusiasts move the brake pipes, starter cable, fuel pipe and hydrolastic pipes inside the car to avoid damage on rough tracks. The pipes can conveniently be led through, beneath the rear seat and out again at the front, in a position where they are protected by the sump guard.

If a Mini is being prepared for rallying it is well worth checking that all the welds on the sub-frames are properly made. The front tie-rod brackets on the front sub-frame must be welded on all round as these are especially vulnerable. Seat mountings take a great deal of punishment on a rally car and the front anchorages may well need reinforcement as the captive nuts sometimes pull out of the seat crossmember. Extra securing straps for the fuel tank are advised. One which passes round the tank from front to back, about halfway up, bolted through the rear seat and the boot-opening channel, should suffice. Needless to say, all electrical connections must be securely made and the wires must be well supported to avoid breakage. Crimped-on terminals are better than soldered ones, provided that they are properly made, using the correct sized terminal for the wire. Waterproofing the ignition circuit is another essential. Rubber covers for coil, distributor and plugs, together with splash guards behind the grille are effective. Sealing the holes where the leads enter the cap, coil and plug covers with silicone grease also keeps out the water.

Extra lamps are usually a must for the night rally enthusiast. Fitting is covered in chapter 10 but, for rally use, remember that spot lamps must be wired up so that they are extinguished when the headlamps are dipped. A useful lamp bracket is available from British Leyland Special Tuning (part no. C–AJJ 3318) which, by the removal of one bolt, hinges forward to enable the grille to be removed for servicing without disturbing the adjustment of the lamp.

A useful modification for a Mini which is fitted with a lot of electrical extras is to replace the standard generator with an alternator which has a much higher current output. An alternator kit can be obtained from British Leyland Special Tuning (part no. C–AJJ 3332). It is complete with all the necessary parts and wiring, and output should cope with several auxiliary lamps as well as map lights and electrically heated screens.

The choice of navigational equipment must rest with the navigator and the requirements will vary slightly between events. The golden rule is to keep everything as simple as possible. Average speed calculators such as the Halda Speedpilot are not often needed for club rallies but they can be useful if average-speed sections are included. One thing to remember is that changing from standard to low-profile tyres can alter the effective final-drive ratio enough to upset average-speed instruments and the odometer.

Make sure that everything inside the car is tied down so that lights, pencils, romers etc. do not end up on the floor at the first big bump. It is a wise precaution to carry a few spares such as bulbs, spark plugs, a throttle cable and a fan belt but if serious trouble is encountered it doesn't matter how long it takes to fix as you will be out of the running anyway.

Extra fuel tank capacity is very useful on a Mini used for rallying. One tankful doesn't go very far on a 1275 S that is being thrashed round country lanes in the lower gears. An extra fuel tank, fitted in the right hand side of the luggage boot is an optional extra on the Cooper S. These tanks may be obtained separately and can be fitted into any Mini provided that a hole is first cut in the right hand side of the boot for the filler neck. They can be obtained through any B L agent complete with all necessary straps, brackets, bolts and pipework.

CHAPTER 10

INSTALLATION AND MAINTENANCE OF ELECTRICAL ACCESSORIES

Before attempting to fit any electrical accessories to a vehicle, it is wise to learn a little about the wiring and electrical systems commonly used.

During the early days of the motor industry, when electrical systems were first fitted, all vehicles incorporated a two-wire system between the component and the battery, much the same as the domestic lighting systems used today. However, when the economics of construction became a major factor, it was realized that if one terminal of the battery were connected to the frame of the vehicle it was only necessary to connect the components also to the frame of the vehicle and one length of wire could be eliminated. This is called the earth-return system.

The first cars produced with this system had the negative terminal of the battery connected to the frame and thus all components were fitted with a negative earth; unfortunately this system produced excessive corrosion of the battery terminals. On the other hand it was found that if the ignition were changed to positive-earth it required 10 % less voltage than if it were negative, to produce the same spark. British car manufacturers therefore changed to a positive-earth system, whilst many Continental and American manufacturers retained the negative-earth systems.

Recently, with the increase in Continental trade it has become important for motor vehicles to be more standardized and many British companies, including British Leyland, have reverted to negative-earth systems. Improved materials used for battery construction have reduced the corrosion to controllable proportions and modifications to coil construction enable the high tension circuit to be positively earthed even with a negative-earth system.

When fitting accessories or working on the electrical system, always check that the earth polarity is correct for the component. This is especially important for radios or instruments incorporating transistors.

Identification of wires by colour code

So that the wires in each circuit can be easily identified, even when they are all bound together in a wiring loom, a colour-coding system is used.

The most common system is for feed wires to carry a main colour only; switch wires have the main colour with a second tracer colour (identifying the sub-circuit) as well. Earth wires are almost always black; where components are switched or controlled on the earth side, *i.e.* the switch is in the return line, like the horn or self-parking windscreen wipers, the wire usually has a black tracer line.

There are seven common basic colours:

Brown	– Battery and generator circuits
White	– Ignition circuit
Blue	– Headlamp circuit
Red	– Side and tail circuit
Green	– Auxiliary circuits fed through the ignition switch and protected by fuse-terminal 4
Purple	– Circuits protected by fuse-terminal 2 but not wired through the ignition switch
Black	– Earth circuits

Selection of wire size

When wiring new accessories into an electrical system it is important to select the correct size wire for the job. First determine the amperes which the component will take; if the unit to be fitted is rated in watts, divide this figure by the voltage of the system (12) and the result is the amperes of current which the wire must carry safely.

If this figure is less than 6, 14/0·010 cable will be sufficient, if it is more than 6 but less than 18 then 28/0·012 cable is satisfactory.

For the main power supplies from the generator 44/0·012 cable is normally used, this has a current capacity of 28 amperes. The main leads from the battery to the starter motor are of course larger still, being usually 61/0·036.

Fuses

While considering the current being carried to the component, it is worth checking the fuses which protect that particular circuit, or considering fitting a separate in-line fuse.

The fuses used in motor vehicles differ from the domestic fuses normally encountered in that they will blow when the current reaches their rated value and their continuous capacity is approximately half this; domestic fuses on the other hand will carry their rated current continuously and only blow when this figure is approximately doubled.

Fuses are colour-coded for ease of identification as follows:

Colour Code of Fuse Ratings

Red printing on yellow paper	5 amps
Green printing on black paper	10 amps
Black printing on light brown paper	15 amps
Black printing on pink paper	25 amps
Black printing on white paper	35 amps
Purple printing on yellow paper	50 amps
Yellow printing on red paper	60 amps

Alternators

It is possible, when a large number of electrical accessories has been fitted, that under some conditions the d c generator normally fitted will not be capable of supplying sufficient power to keep the battery fully charged.

Most d c generators have a cut-in speed of about 1,100 rev/min which is somewhat higher than the engine tickover speed. In the slow traffic conditions often experienced during winter (when auxiliary equipment is used to the full) the low engine speeds and high discharge rate do not give the generator much chance to charge the battery. Under these conditions a higher charging rate at low engine speed is very desirable.

An alternative system, which is now a standard fitment on several of the more expensive British cars, incorporates an a c generator or alternator. Most leading car electrical manufacturers now offer alternator conversion kits, those fitted to B L vehicles being supplied normally by Lucas.

Part of the control equipment required for the alternator is built into the end of the unit but an electronic voltage regulator unit (*e.g.* model 4TR consisting of transistors, diodes, a thermistor, resistors and capacitors) is normally mounted separately and connected to the field circuit of the alternator. At zero or very low engine speeds, the semi-conductor characteristics of the diodes prevent battery current from flowing through the output windings, so that a cut-out relay is unnecessary. A field-energizing relay (*e.g.* model 6RA) and a warning light control unit (*e.g.* model 3AW) complete the control equipment.

Because alternator equipment incorporates semi-conductor devices, extreme care must be taken when fitting or servicing the equipment and manufacturers' instructions must be followed punctiliously. Transistors and diodes are highly sensitive to polarity and an incorrect connection, however brief, will ruin them. If in doubt, have the equipment checked by a competent service engineer. The following points must always be observed:

(1) Make sure that the battery earth polarity and the earth polarity of the alternator are the same and that all intermediate connections are of correct polarity.

(2) Never allow the alternator main-output cable to short to the vehicle body in any way; it is 'live' with respect to the body as long as the battery terminals are connected.

(3) Never run the alternator on open-circuit (*i.e.* with the alternator-to-battery main cable disconnected) with the rotor field-winding energized.

(4) It is advisable, when an alternator is fitted, to disconnect the battery terminals from the vehicle before connecting a battery charger but in any case ensure that the polarity is correct.

Ammeter

When extra electrical equipment has been fitted, an ammeter provides an excellent check on power consumption and the generator charging rate; it may thus prevent exhausting the battery. Disconnect the battery terminals before starting to fit an ammeter, which should then be connected, in series, in the main feed wire between the terminal on the starter solenoid and the control box. If the vehicle has a 'key start' with the solenoid mounted on the engine, the main feed wire is the thicker of the two brown wires connected to the solenoid. On early vehicles, where the starter switch is mounted beneath the floor, the main feed wire is the thick brown wire connected to the front terminal marked A on the control box. The extra wires used to connect up the instrument must be of no less a current-carrying capacity than that already fitted, as it has to carry the full load for all the equipment (except the starter).

Check that the electrical connections have been securely made and are properly insulated, then reconnect the battery. Check the circuit by starting the engine and accelerating, the needle should move towards the + or charging side, if it does not but moves the other way, the connections on the meter are incorrect and should be reversed.

Headlamps and sidelamps

All production Minis incorporated the sidelamps in the headlamp unit until the Wolseley and Riley variants appeared; on these models, separate sidelamps were fitted beneath the headlamps and incorporated in the indicator lamp housing.

The headlamps of all these early models were semi-sealed pre-focus units consisting of an integral reflector and lens. The headlamp bulbs were inserted into the back of the reflector and located accurately in position by a flange. The sidelamp bulbs were inserted through another hole in the reflector.

Although this pattern produced adequate lighting, the units were very susceptible to water ingress and the reflectors rapidly deteriorated. Also with the production of faster versions of the Mini, an improved lamp unit was necessary.

A 'sealed-beam' lamp-unit was produced especially for the Mini range. These units consist of a combined reflector and light unit manufactured entirely of glass. The reflector surface being a thin layer of aluminium deposited on the inside of the envelope rather like the construction of a mirror.

The main and dipped beam filaments are sealed into the assembly and the whole unit operates like a large bulb. A clear patch left in the reflector allows the light from a sidelamp bulb, positioned behind the unit, to show through the front lens.

The advantages of the sealed beam unit over the previous arrangements are: that the filament can be of stronger construction and can be positioned very accurately relative to the focal point of the reflector; as the unit is completely sealed it is not subject to corrosion and the reflecting surface retains a high finish; whereas in a bulb the outer surface of the filament vaporizes in use and the tungsten is deposited over the inner surfaces causing blackening, with a 'sealed-beam' unit the much larger internal surface area allows the tungsten to be more diffusely deposited and thus cause far less blackening.

A kit of adapting connectors is available to convert the older Minis to 'sealed-beam' units and these can.be fitted reasonably quickly and simply. All in all, this is a highly recommended conversion.

An alternative conversion for the old semi-sealed units is to replace the existing bulbs with quartz-halogen type but this is only worthwhile if the reflecting surface is in perfect condition and even then the light output appears to be little better than 'sealed-beam' units.

If expense is no object, the 'sealed-beam' headlamp unit can be replaced by quartz-halogen 'sealed-beam' units, these give a higher output for a given wattage but are quite an expensive conversion.

Headlamp-flasher switch

If it is desired to fit a switch with which to flash the headlights, it may be simply accomplished as follows:

Obtain a switch which is suitable for switching 8–10 amps at 12 volts, this may be of the normal on/off type or better, one which returns to the off position when released.

On the dip switch will be found four spade terminals and three wires connected to them. Of these wires, the plain blue one is the main power input from the lighting switch. The blue and red is the output wire from the dip switch to the dipped-beam filaments and the blue and white wire is the output to the main-beam filaments.

The spade connections may be arranged so that the spare one is also connected to the main beam circuit and a suitable cable run from here via the headlamp flasher switch to another source of power, preferably to the A4 connection on the fuse box, thus completing the circuit so that the flasher will only work when the ignition is switched on.

Driving lamps

With the improvements in design and efficiency being incorporated into the headlamp units now used on production models, extra lights for normal driving are less necessary than at one time. However, if long-range driving-lamps are to be fitted, it is well worth investing in the more expensive but very much more efficient quartz-halogen lamps now obtainable. These lamps are now used almost universally where efficient, high-output lighting is required, and are to be found on almost every vehicle used for competitions at night.

Many drivers find it convenient to have the wiring of a long-range driving lamp so arranged that the lamp goes out when the headlamps are dipped.

On cars with a floor-mounted dip switch, this can easily be done by connecting up the lamp-switch feed wire to the same terminal of the dip switch as the headlamp main-beam feed wire. This is the blue and white wire.

On cars with a column-mounted dip switch, it is rather more difficult to arrange the connections and it is necessary either to solder a connection into the switch wiring on the steering column or to run a wire back from the snap connector where the feed wire is split to serve the two light units.

When fitting extra lights, it should be remembered that the distance from the bulb centre to the ground is required by law to be at least 24in. unless the lamp is used only in fog or falling snow.

When driving in foggy conditions at night, the biggest problem for the driver is the amount of light which is scattered and reflected back by the water particles in the fog. Less light is reflected when on dipped beam because the beams are directed downwards and the lens is designed to give a fairly sharp cut-off of light at the top of the beam.

Foglamps are designed to reduce the amount of reflected light even further by incorporating even sharper cut-off while still illuminating the road in front with a wide flat beam.

Very many varieties of foglamp are available, some being better designed than others. Some models incorporate a dimmer switch to reduce the light output if so desired. An examination of the published beam patterns for the lamps will give a good indication of the better models but only use in foggy conditions will prove their value.

High-intensity rear lamps

In recent years there has been a series of multiple-vehicle accidents in foggy conditions, especially on motorways.

Where a line of vehicles is travelling too fast for the prevailing conditions and the vehicles are too close together, in order to keep the tail-lights of the vehicle in front in sight, an accident or sudden braking for a thick fog patch results in a chain reaction back down the line and a series of collisions.

In an attempt to avoid this situation developing, lamp manufacturers have recently produced a high-intensity red rear lamp which can be switched on in foggy conditions giving following vehicles an earlier view and encouraging them to follow at a greater distance.

Hazard warning devices

One accessory which has been fitted to many Continental cars and most British export models for some time is a hazard warning device.

In the event of an accident or breakdown at night, when it is essential to leave the vehicle parked on the roadway, this unit, which is connected into the existing direction indicator circuit via a non load-sensitive flasher unit, flashes all four direction indicator lights simultaneously. The feed wire for this system is normally independent of the ignition switch and will operate regardless of whether the ignition switch and direction indicator switch are on or off.

Because the flasher unit used is not load-sensitive, it will still operate if one or more bulbs have been damaged in the accident. It should be remembered that this flasher unit cannot be interchanged with the standard load-sensitive type.

Reversing lamps

A variety of reversing lights is also available in many shapes, sizes and power outputs, although by law this should not exceed 24 watts; they must also have a warning light fitted unless an automatic switch is interconnected with the gear-change mechanism so that the lamp lights up only when reverse is engaged.

These switches are available from British Leyland Agents and are fitted in place of the plug which retains the reverse detent plunger. This is located on the front of the gearbox at the radiator end of the engine.

Wiring additional lamps

Additional lights fitted to the Mini should normally be connected to the power supply via the ignition switch to prevent them being left on when the vehicle is parked, they should also be in circuit with the 35 amp fuse. A terminal is provided on the fuse block on the wing valance; this is on the bottom fuse. On the wiring diagram it is marked 4.

Flashing direction indicators

The direction indicator system used is reasonably reliable and should not give more trouble than the occasional replacement of bulbs. However, other problems do sometimes crop up and they are usually not too difficult to solve.

To comply with Ministry regulations, the lights should flash between 60 and 120 times per minute and the ratio between time on and off should be about 50:50.

The bulbs fitted are rated at 21 watts and as the flasher unit is load-sensitive, wrong or faulty bulbs will produce the wrong flashing speed. If the lamps fail to illuminate or flash, check that the fuel gauge and windscreen wipers operate: if neither function then probably the fuse, between terminals 3 and 4 of the fuse block, has blown or there is a fault in the cable or connections between the fuse and the unit.

Look at the fuse to see that the wire is intact and also ensure that the fuse holders are clean; these are often corroded, resulting in mysterious electrical failures!

1)   If the fuse is blown, switch everything off and fit a new fuse; switch on the ignition and if the fuse blows immediately, suspect the fuel gauge. Otherwise switch the accessories controlled by that fuse on and off in turn. If the fuse blows again, then the circuit just switched was faulty and should be thoroughly checked. Otherwise the circuits will now be functioning correctly.

2)   If the fuse is not blown, the flasher unit may be faulty or the cable or connections in the circuit may be faulty.

Remove the feed wire from the flasher unit and connect it to the output wires from the unit. All the indicator lamps should light: if they do then the flasher unit is faulty. If one or more fail to light, then the individual circuits should be checked, if all fail to light then the feed is faulty.

Windscreen wipers

When driving in light rain or on damp roads after a recent shower it is not unusual to find that the amount of water falling on the screen is sufficient to obscure the vision but insufficient to require more than one or two sweeps of the wipers every minute to clear the screen. A useful accessory for these conditions is an intermittent windscreen wiper system. These systems have a built-in electronic delay which switches the wipers on at regular intervals and off again after one or two sweeps. Components to install such systems are available from several electrical equipment manufacturers; one relatively inexpensive alternative, tried by the Authors on several vehicles fitted with self-parking wipers and more adaptable to those with no foot-operated dip switch, is to fit a foot-operated wiper switch.

Because the windscreen wipers are self-parking, it is only necessary to energize the circuit briefly and they will complete one sweep. This can be simply arranged by running a second wire from the terminal on the wiper motor which is connected to the switch on the dash panel, down to a push button switch on the floor. The circuit is activated by an earth return so that only one wire is necessary, the other terminal of the switch should be linked to earth on the floor, pressing the switch will earth the circuit and set the wipers in motion for one sweep. Heavy duty micro switches such as are available from WD surplus stores have been found to be very efficient for this purpose but any simple push button as used for electric door bells would probably be satisfactory.

This arrangement cannot be fitted, however, to recent models having a permanent magnet type wiper motor (identified by its cylindrical shape) as the wiring circuit is unsuitable.

Power outlet sockets

One more extra which may be easily fitted and find considerable use is a power socket. This may simply be a jack-plug socket, wired to the live connection on the back of the ignition switch, into which can be fitted wander lead-lights, parking lights or any other portable electrical item used. It may also be used as a simple input connection for a battery charger.

Radios

Probably one of the most popular accessories used today is a radio; these can range from a battery-operated portable used occasionally in the car, to a sophisticated VHF set with self-seeking tuning, multiple speakers and a built-in cassette tape player.

Even when a portable radio is used, an external aerial is often necessary to obtain satisfactory reception. Usually radio aerials are mounted on the nearside wing, approximately $2\frac{3}{4}$in. out from the nearside bonnet edge. A grommet is provided, adjacent to the windscreen-wiper motor in the wing valance, through which to run the aerial lead; from here it may be led into the interior via a hole drilled in the bulkhead, adjacent to the fuel pipe bracket and fitted with a rubber grommet. This is already provided on some models.

The normal position for fitting the speaker for a fixed car radio varies; if fitted to the Countryman, van or pick-up, the speaker is usually mounted in the trim above the parcel tray on the left-hand side. The backing of the trim is already cut away at the rear to facilitate this and an expanded-metal grille for the speaker is usually fitted with the radio.

On the saloons, the speaker is normally fitted beneath the rear parcel shelf. When fitted in this position, the connecting wire is led along beside the exhaust-pipe tunnel (beneath the floor covering) to the rear seat; with the seat cushion removed, a hole is drilled in the seat pan about 5in. to the rear of the front edge, on the centre line of the car. This hole should be fitted with a rubber grommet and the lead passed through to the rear squab just in front of the petrol tank where a ¾in. diameter hole is already provided, through which the lead runs to the rear parcel shelf, being retained in the luggage compartment by the existing cable clips.

The metal panel of the rear parcel shelf is provided with two large holes beneath which the speaker is mounted. There are also four small holes for the mounting bolts.

On some models, the underside of the parcel shelf is covered with felt silencing material. This must of course be cut away before fitting the speaker. Also cut away the sections of the interior trim visible through the two large holes and pierce the trim for the four mounting bolts.

Finally for good radio reception, it is important to have the electrical system correctly suppressed. The spark plugs should be fitted with suppressor caps if they are not already fitted with the suppressor leads provided on recent models. The distributor incorporates a built-in resistor in the main h t lead.

Capacitors of 1 uF should also be connected to the following points: One to the SW lead of the ignition coil and earthed to the coil mounting bolt. One to the output lead of the generator (the thicker of the two leads) and earthed to the generator mounting bolt. One capacitor should be connected to the power supply lead of the petrol pump and the earth lead connected both to the earth terminal of the petrol pump and to the pump-mounting bracket.

For efficient suppression, it is essential to clean down to the bare metal at each earth connection. Also an extra earth should be provided on the windscreen wiper motor. An earthing lead should be connected from the small cheesehead screw, on the terminal end plate of the motor, to the car body; a small hole is provided in the gusset plate immediately in front of the wiper motor for this purpose.

The power supply lead to the radio should include an in-line fuse and be connected to the A1 terminal on the voltage control box.

APPENDIX I

MINI PRODUCTION MODELS

August 24th 1959—June, 1973

Introduction Date	Model	
24 August 1959	Basic Saloon De Luxe Saloon	Austin and Morris models
April 1960	5 cwt Van	
Sept. 1960	Countryman Traveller	Early models had fuel tank and battery inside at rear
April 1961	Countryman Traveller	All steel body Export only at first
June 1961	5 cwt Pickup	
Sept. 1961	Mini Super de Luxe	Extra instruments, duo-tone paintwork and Mini Cooper trim
Sept. 1961	Mini Cooper	997cc, twin carburetters and disc brakes
Oct. 1961	Riley Elf Wolseley Hornet	Different front grilles, extended boots and extra sound deadening together with better trim than Super de Luxe
Oct. 1962	Super de Luxe replaced de Luxe	Extra instruments retained but not the Mini Cooper type seats and duo-tone paintwork of first Super de Luxe. Baulk ring synchromesh gearbox introduced
March 1963	Riley Elf Mk II Wolseley Hornet Mk II	998cc engine and improved brakes
March 1963	Mini Moke	
April 1963	Mini Cooper S 1071cc	Improved Mini Cooper with engine developed from B M C Formula Junior racing engine
January 1964	Mini Cooper 998cc	Replaced 997cc model

225

March 1964	Mini Cooper S 970cc & 1275cc	
Sept. 1964	Saloons	Hydrolastic suspension on all models except van and countryman. Riley Elf/Wolseley Hornet Mk II type front brakes fitted to all models except Coopers
Oct. 1965	Austin/Morris Mini	Automatic transmission introduced as optional extra
March 1967	Riley Elf Mk III Wolseley Hornet Mk III	Remote gearchange and improved ventilation
Oct. 1967	Mini Mk II	Revised front grille, larger rear window, 998cc engine and improved brakes
Oct. 1969	Mini Clubman	Body re-styled at front to slightly longer and squarer shape. 998cc engine. Windows changed to wind-up type.
	1275 GT	Incorporates Clubman body with different interior trim. 1275cc engine with single carburetter as fitted to BL 1300 models. $4\frac{1}{2}$J Rostyle wheels fitted.
	BL Mini Saloon	Mechanical SU fuel pumps fitted. Wind-up windows. Austin/Morris names discontinued.

APPENDIX II

GENERAL DATA

850 MINIS, ELF MK I and HORNET MK I
ENGINE

Type	8MB
Number of cylinders	4
Bore	2·478in. (62·94mm)
Stroke	2·687in. (68·26mm)
Capacity	51·7in³ (848cc)
Firing order	1, 3, 4, 2
Compression ratio	8·3:1
Capacity of combustion chamber (valves fitted)	1·49in³ (24·5cc)
Valve operation	Overhead by push-rod
B m e p	128lb/in² (9kg/cm²) at 2,900 rev/min
Torque	44lb ft (6·08kg m) at 2,900 rev/min
Compression pressure	150lb/in² (10·5kg/cm²)
Oversize bore: 1st	+0·010in. (0·254mm)
Max.	+0·040in. (1·016mm)

Crankshaft

Main journal diameter	1·7505 to 1·751in. (44·46 to 44·47mm)
Minimum regrind diameter	1·7105in. (43·45mm)
Crankpin journal diameter	1·6254 to 1·6259in. (41·28 to 41·29mm)
Crankpin minimum regrind diam.	1·5854in. (40·27mm)

Main bearings

Number and type	3 shell type
Material	Steel-backed white metal
Length	1·187in. (30·16mm)
End clearance	0·002 to 0·003in. (0·051 to 0·076mm)
End-thrust	Taken on centre main bearing
Running clearance	0·0005 to 0·002in. (0·013 to 0·051mm)

Connecting rods

Length between centres	5·75in. (146·05mm)

Big-end bearings

Material	Steel-backed lead-bronze with lead-indium-plated surface, or steel-backed copper-lead with lead-tin-plated surface
Bearing side clearance	0·008 to 0·012in. (0·203 to 0·305mm)
Bearing diametrical clearance	0·001 to 0·0025in. (0·025 to 0·063mm)

Pistons

Type	Split skirt
Clearances: Bottom of skirt	0·0006 to 0·0012in. (0·015 to 0·030mm)
Top of skirt	0·0026 to 0·0032in. (0·066 to 0·081mm)
Oversizes	+0·010in., +0·020in., +0·030in., +0·040in., (0·254mm, 0·508mm, 0·762mm, 1·016mm)

Piston rings

Compression: Top ring	Plain
Second and third rings	Tapered
Width	0·069 to 0·070in. (1·75 to 1·78mm)
Thickness	0·095 to 0·101in. (2·41 to 2·56mm)
Fitted gap	0·007 to 0·012in. (0·178 to 0·305mm)
Clearance in groove	0·0015 to 0·0035in. (0·038 to 0·089mm)
Oil control type	Slotted scraper
Width	0·124 to 0·125in. (3·15 to 3·175mm)
Thickness	0·095 to 0·101in. (2·41 to 2·56mm)
Fitted gap	0·007 to 0·012in. (0·178 to 0·305mm)
Clearance in groove	0·0015 to 0·0035in. (0·038 to 0·089mm)

Gudgeon pin

Type	Clamped in little-end
Fit in piston	Hand push-fit
Diameter (outer)	0·624in. (15·86mm)

Valves and valve gear

Valves

Seat angle: Inlet	45°
Exhaust	45°
Head diameter: Inlet	1·093 to 1·098in. (27·76 to 27·89mm)
Exhaust	1·000 to 1·005in. (25·40 to 25·53mm)
Stem diameter: Inlet	0·2793 to 0·2798in. (7·096 to 7·109mm)
Exhaust	0·2788 to 0·2793in. (7·081 to 7·096mm)
Valve lift	0·285in. (7·24mm)
Valve stem/guide clearance:	
Inlet	0·0015 to 0·0025in. (0·038 to 0·064mm)
Exhaust	0·002 to 0·003in. (0·051 to 0·076mm)
Valve rocker clearance: Running	0·012in. (0·305mm) cold
Timing	0·019in. (0·48mm)

Timing marks

Timing marks	Dimples on timing wheels, marks on flywheel
Chain pitch and number of pitches	$\frac{3}{8}$in. (9·525mm) 52

Inlet valve: Opens	5″ b t d c	⎫ With 0·019in. (0·48mm)
Closes	45° a b d c	⎪ valve rocker clearance
Exhaust valve: Opens	40° b b d c	⎬ (for checking purposes
Closes	10° a t d c	⎭ only)

Valve rocker bush bore (reamed)	0·5630 to 0·5635in. (14·30 to 14·312mm)

Valve guides

Length: Inlet and exhaust	1·687in. (42·86mm)
Diameter:	
Outside: Inlet and exhaust	0·469in. (11·91mm)
Inside: Inlet and exhaust	0·2813 to 0·2818in. (7·145 to 7·257mm)

Valve springs

Length: Inlet and exhaust	1·625in. (41·27mm)
Number of working coils	$4\frac{1}{2}$
Pressure: Inlet and exhaust	
Valve open	70lb (31·8kg)
Valve closed	37·5lb (17·027kg)

Tappets

Type	Barrel type
Diameter	0·812in. (20·64mm)
Length	1·5in. (38·10mm)

Camshaft

Journal diameters:	Front	1·6655 to 1·666in. (42·304 to 42·316mm)
	Centre	1·62275 to 1·62325in. (41·218 to 41·231mm)
	Rear	1·3725 to 1·3735in. (34·862 to 34·887mm)

End-float 0·003 to 0·007in. (0·076 to 0·178mm)
Bearings: Type: Front White-metal-lined, steel-backed
     Centre and rear Plain (running in block)
Inside diameter (reamed in position) 1·667 to 1·6675in. (42·342 to 42·355mm)
Clearance: Front 0·001 to 0·002in. (0·025 to 0·051mm)
    Centre and rear 0·00125 to 0·00275in. (0·0317 to 0·0698mm)

Engine lubrication system
Oil pump
Type Hobourn Eaton, Burman or C M C
Relief pressure valve opens 60lb/in² (4·2kg/cm²)
Relief valve spring: Free length 2⅘in. (72·63mm)
      Fitted length 2³⁄₃₂in. (54·77mm)

Oil filter

Type Full-flow
Capacity 1 pint (1·2 US pints, 0·57 litre)
Oil pressure
Normal running 60lb/in² (4·22kg/cm²)
Idling (minimum) 15lb/in² (1·05kg/cm²)

Fuel system

Carburetter

Make and type SU Type HS2
Diameter 1¼in. (31·75mm)
Jet 0·090in. (2·29mm)
Needle Standard EB. Rich M. Weak GG.

Air cleaner

Type Paper element

Fuel pump

Make and type:	Early cars	SU electric PD
	Later cars	SU electric SP: AUF
Delivery rate:	PD type	45 pints/h (25·5 litres/h)
	SP, AUF, type	56 pints/h (32 litres/h)
Delivery pressure:	PD type	2 to 3lb/in² (0·14 to 0·21kg/cm²)
	SP, AUF, type	2½ to 3lb/in² (0·17 to 0·21kg/cm²)

1970 and later cars SU mechanical

Cooling system
Thermostat setting
Normal 82°C (180°F)
Cold climates 87°C (188°F)
Hot climates 74°C (165°F)

Ignition system
Spark plugs Champion N5
Size 14mm. ¾in. (19mm) reach
Plug gap 0·025in. (0·625mm)
Coil LA12
Resistance at 20°C (68°F):
Primary winding 3·2 to 3·4 ohms (cold)

Distributor: Early type   DM2
             Later type   25D4
Distributor contact points gap   0·014 to 0·016in. (0·36 to 0·40mm)

Distributor test data:	*Premium fuel distributor*	*Regular (commercial) fuel distributor*
Automatic advance commences at	500 rev/min (engine	1,250 rev/min (engine)
Maximum advance	30–34° at	22–26° at
Vacuum advance:	3,400 rev/min	5,000 rev/min
Commences	7in. (17·7cm) Hg	
Ends	10° at 13in. (33cm) Hg	16° at 11in. (28cm) Hg
	rev/min	*rev/min*
Decelerating check	24° to 28° at 2,500	22° to 26° at 5,000
	21° to 25° at 2,000	15° to 19° at 3,900
	14° to 18° at 1,000	1° to 5° at 1,700
	4° to 11° at 800	
Static ignition timing	t d c	7° b t d c
Stroboscopic ignition timing	3° b t d c at 600 rev/min	10° b t d c at 600 rev/min

Clutch

Type	Single dry plate
Diameter	7·125in. (180·9mm)
Facing material	Wound yarn
Pressure springs	6 (or 1 diaphragm spring)
Colour: Coil springs	Red spot
Diaphragm spring	Brown or green spot
Damper springs	Nil

Gearbox

Number of forward speeds	4
Synchromesh	Second, third and fourth gears
Ratios: Top	1·0:1
Third	1·412:1
Second	2·172:1
First	3·627:1
Reverse	3·627:1
Overall ratios: Top	3·765:1
Third	5·317:1
Second	8·176:1
First	13·657:1
Reverse	13·657:1
Speedometer	6/17

Steering

Type	Rack and pinion
Steering-wheel turns—lock to lock	2⅓
Mini Mk II and later cars	2¾
Steering-wheel diameter	15¾in. (40cm)

Camber angle	1° positive to 3° positive	
Castor angle	3°	
King pin inclination	9° 30′	With vehicle
Toe-out	1⁄16in. (1·59mm)	in an unladen
Lock angle of outer front wheel with inner wheel at 20°	18½°	condition

Final drive

Ratio 3·765:1

Electrical equipment

System	12 volt, positive earth, late cars negative
Charging system	Compensated voltage control
Battery	Lucas BLT7A, BLTZ7A, BT7A, BTZ7A
Capacity: BLT7A, BLTZ7A	34 amp/h at 20h rate
BT7A, BTZ7A	43 amp/h at 20h rate
Starter motor	Lucas M35G
Generator	Lucas C40
Control box	Lucas RB106/2
Cut-out: Cut-in voltage	12·7 to 13·3
Drop-off voltage	8·5 to 11·0
Reverse current	5·0 amps (max)

Regulator (at 3,000 rev/min generator speed):
Open-circuit setting at 20"C (68"F) 14·7—15·3 volts
For ambient temperatures other than 20°C (68°F) the following allowances should be made to the above setting:
For every 10°C (18°F) above 20°C (68°F) subtract 0·1 volt.
For every 10°C (18°F) below 20°C (68°F) add 0·1 volt.

Brakes

Type	Lockheed hydraulic, single leading shoe
Drum size	7in. (17·8cm) diameter
Lining dimensions: Front or rear	6·75in × 1·25in. (17·14cm × 3·17cm)
Lining area: Front or rear	33·75in^2 (217·7cm^2)
Lining material	DON 202

Type	Lockheed hydraulic, two leading shoe
Drum size	7in. (17·8cm) diameter
Lining dimensions: Front	6·75in. × 1·5in. (17·14 × 3·8cm)
Lining area total	40·5in^2 (261·29cm^2)

Wheels

Type: Ventilated disc   3·50B × 10

Tyres

Size	
Standard	5·20-10 tubeless
Optional (Radial ply)	145-10 tubeless

Tyre pressures

Standard: Normal load	Front 24lb/in^2 (1·7kg/cm^2)
	Rear 22lb/in^2 (1·55kg/cm^2)
Full load	Front and rear 24lb/in^2 (1·7kg/cm^2)
Optional (radial ply) all loads	Front 28lb/in^2 (1·97kg/cm^2)
	Rear 26lb/in^2 (1·83kg/cm^2)

MINI AUTOMATIC

The following information is applicable to the Mini Automatic and should be used in conjunction with the preceding specification for the Mini saloon.

ENGINE

Type	8AH
Compression ratio	9:1
Torque	44lb ft (6·08kg m) at 2,500 rev/min
Engine idle speed (approx.)	650 rev/min
B h p	39 at 5,250 rev/min

Lubrication system

Oil pump

Type	Hobourn Eaton

Oil filter

Type	Full-flow
Capacity	1 pint (1·2 US pints, 0·57 litre)

Oil pressure

Normal running speed and temperature	60lb/in^2 (4·22kg/cm^2)
Idling (minimum) at normal running temperature	15lb/in^2 (1·05kg/cm^2)

Fuel system

Carburetter

Make and type	SU type HS4
Diameter	1½in. (38·1mm)
Needle	AN (Standard), EB (Weak), H6 (Rich)

Ignition system

Distributor	Lucas 25D4
Serial number	HC 41134A
Timing marks	Dimples on timing wheels, marks on converter
Timing: Static	3° b t d c
Stroboscopic	6° b t d c at 600 rev/min

Final drive

Ratio	3·76:1

AUTOMATIC TRANSMISSION

Ratios:	Top	1·0:1
	Third	1·46:1
	Second	1·845:1
	First	2·69:1
	Reverse	2·69:1
Overall ratios:	Top	3·76:1
	Third	5·49:1
	Second	6·94:1
	First	10·11:1
	Reverse	10·11:1
Speedometer		7/17

Torque converter

Type	3-element
Ratio	2:1 maximum
Converter output gear ratio	1·15:1
End float	0·0035 to 0·0065in. (0·089 to 0·164mm)

998cc MINIS, RILEY ELF MK II & III, WOLSELEY HORNET MK II & III, CLUBMAN

ENGINE

Type	9WR, 99H
Number of cylinders	4
Bore	2·543in. (64·588mm)
Stroke	3·00in. (76·2mm)
Capacity	60·96in³ (998cc)
Compression ratio	8·3:1
B m e p	130lb/in² (9·14kg/cm²) at 2,700 rev/min
Torque	52lb ft (7·28kg m) at 2,700 rev/min
Oversize bores: 1st	+0·010in. (0·254mm)
2nd	+0·020in. (0·508mm)

Crankshaft

Main bearings	
Material	Steel-backed copper-lead; thin wall
Running clearance	0·001 to 0·0027in. (0·025 to 0·069mm)

Connecting rods

Big-end bearings	
Material	Steel-backed copper-lead; thin wall
Bearing length	0·875in. (22·22mm)

Pistons

Type	Solid skirt
Clearance: Bottom of skirt (pressure face)	0·0005 to 0·0011in. (0·013 to 0·028mm)
Oversizes: 1st	+0·010in. (0·254mm)
2nd	+0·020in. (0·508mm)

Piston rings

Compression: Top	Plain, chrome-faced
Second and third	Tapered
Width	0·0620 to 0·0625in. (1·574 to 1·588mm)
Thickness (all rings)	0·106 to 0·112in. (2·692 to 2·835mm)

Gudgeon pin

Type	Fully floating, with circlip location
Fit	Hand push fit

Valves and valve gear

Valves	
Throat diameter: Inlet	0·969in. (24·61mm)
Exhaust	0·908in. (23·06mm)
Valve lift	0·28in. (7·14mm)

Camshaft

Journal diameters:	Front	1·6655 to 1·666in. (42·304 to 42·316mm)
	Centre	1·62275 to 1·62325in. (41·218 to 41·231mm)
	Rear	1·3725 to 1·3735in. (34·862 to 34·887mm)
End-float		0·003 to 0·007in. (0·076 to 0·178mm)
Bearings: number and type		3. Steel-backed white metal

Inside diameter (reamed in position):

Front	1·667 to 1·6675in. (42·342 to 42·355mm)
Centre	1·6245 to 1·6255in. (41·261 to 41·287mm)
Rear	1·3748 to 1·3755in. (34·914 to 34·937mm)
Running clearance	0·001 to 0·002in. (0·025 to 0·051mm)

Fuel system

Carburetter	SU
Needle	Standard GX. Rich M. Weak GG.

Ignition system

Timing	5° b t d c (91-octane [research method] fuel and above)
Distributor	Lucas. Type 25D4
Automatic advance commences	600 rev/min
Maximum advance (crankshaft degrees)	26° at 5,600 rev/min
Vacuum advance (crankshaft degrees	14° at 11in. (279·4mm) Hg
Decelerating check (crankshaft degrees	24° at 5,000 rev/min 18° at 3,400 rev/min 8° at 1,300 rev/min

Clutch

Pressure springs—colour

Coil	Black enamel with white spot
Diaphragm	Green

Brakes

Type	Lockheed hydraulic; two-leading shoe
Lining dimensions	6·75 × 1·5in. (17·14 × 3·8cm)
Lining area (total)	40·5in² (261·29cm²)
Lining material	DON 202

MINI-COOPER 997cc

ENGINE

Type	9F
Number of cylinders	4
Bore	2·458in. (62·43mm)
Stroke	3·20in. (81·28mm)
Capacity	60·87in³ (997cc)
Compression ratio: High compression	9:1
Low compression	8·3:1
B m e p: High compression	134lb/in² (9·42kg/cm²) at 3,500 rev/min
Low compression	129lb/in² (9·07kg/cm²) at 3,500 rev/min
Torque: High compression	54lb ft (7·46kg m) at 3,600 rev/min
Low compression	53lb ft (7·32kg m) at 3,500 rev/min

Crankshaft

Main bearings	
Material	Steel-backed, copper-lead, thin wall
Length	1·0625in. (26·99mm)
Running clearance	0·001 to 0·0027in. (0·025 to 0·069mm)

Connecting rods

Big-end bearings	
Material	Steel-backed copper-lead; thin wall
Bearing length	0·875in. (22·22mm)

Pistons

Type	Solid skirt
Clearance: Bottom of skirt (pressure face)	0·0016 to 0·0022in. (0·041 to 0·056mm)

Piston rings

Compression: Top	Plain, chrome-faced
Second and third	Tapered
Width	0·0615 to 0·0625in. (1·563 to 1·588mm)

Valves and valve gear

Valves:

Head diameter: Inlet	1·156in. (29·4mm)
Exhaust	1·000in. (25·40mm)
Throat diameter: Inlet	1·0312in. (26·2mm)
Exhaust	0·908in. (23·06mm)
Valve lift	0·312in. (7·92mm)
Inlet valve: Opens	16° b t d c
Closes	56° a b d c
Exhaust valve: Opens	51° b b d c
Closes	21° a t d c

With 0·019in. (0·48mm) valve rocker clearance (for checking purposes only)

Valve springs

Free length: Inlet and exhaust	1·750in. (44·45mm)
Number of working coils	4½
Pressure: Inlet and exhaust:	
Valve open	90lb (40·8kg)
Valve closed	55lb (24·9kg)

Camshaft

Journal diameters: Front	1·6655 to 1·666in. (42·303 to 42·316mm)
Centre	1·62275 to 1·62325in. (41·218 to 41·231mm)
Rear	1·3725 to 1·3735in. (34·862 to 34·887mm)
End float	0·003 to 0·007in. (0·076 to 0·178mm)
Bearings: Number and type	3. Steel-backed white metal
Inside diameter (reamed in position):	
Front	1·667 to 1·6675in. (42·342 to 42·355mm)
Centre	1·6245 to 1·6255in. (41·261 to 41·287mm)
Rear	1·3748 to 1·3755in. (34·914 to 34·937mm)

Engine lubrication system

Oil pump

Type	Hobourn Eaton
Relief pressure valve operates	70lb/in² (4·92kg/cm²)
Relief valve spring: Free length	2$\frac{39}{64}$ in. (66·28mm)
Fitted length	2$\frac{5}{32}$ in. (54·77mm)

Oil pressure

Normal running	70lb/in² (4·92kg/cm²)
Idling (minimum)	15lb/in² (1·05kg/cm²)

Fuel system

Carburetters

Make and type	Twin SU type HS2
Diameter	1¼in. (31·75mm)
Jet	0·090in. (2·29mm)
Needle	Standard GZ

Fuel pump

Make and type	SU electric type SP
Delivery rate	56 pints/h (67·2 US pts/h, 32 lit/h)
Delivery pressure	2½ to 3lb/in² (0·18 to 0·21kg/cm²)

Air cleaners

Type	Oil wetted gauze or paper element

Cooling system

Thermostat setting	83°C (180°F)

Ignition system

Coil	HA12
Timing: High compression	7° b t d c (premium fuel)
Low compression	5° b t d c (91 to 96 octane rating fuel, Research method)

Clutch

Pressure springs—colour	Black enamel with white spot

Gearbox

Ratios: Top	1·0:1
Third	1·357:1
Second	1·916:1
First	3·2:1
Reverse	3·2:1

	Standard	Available alternative
Overall ratios: Top	3·765:1	3·444:1
Third	5·11:1	4·674:1
Second	7·213:1	6·598:1
First	12·05:1	11·03:1
Reverse	12·05:1	11·03:1

Final drive

Ratio   3·765:1 standard; 3·444:1 optional

Brakes

Front
Type   Disc
Disc diameter   7in. (177·8mm)
Pad material   DA3
Rear
Lining material   DON 202

998cc MINI COOPER   To be used in conjunction with 997cc
                                            Mini Cooper data

ENGINE
Type   9FA
Number of cylinders   4
Bore   2·543in. (64·588mm)
Stroke   3·00in. (76·2mm)
Capacity   60·96in³ (998cc)
Compression ratio: High   9:1
                    Low   7·8:1
B m e p: High compression   142lb/in² (10kg/cm²) at 3,000 rev/min
          Low compression   135lb/in² (9·5kg/cm²) at 3,000 rev/min
Torque: High compression   57lb ft (7·881kg m) at 3,000 rev/min
          Low compression   56lb ft (7·74kg m) at 2,900 rev/min
Oversize bores: 1st   +0·010in. (0·254mm)
                 2nd   +0·020in. (0·508mm)

Crankshaft

Main bearings
Material   Steel-backed copper-lead or
                                            aluminium-tin; thin wall
Running clearance   0·001 to 0·0027in. (0·025 to
                                            0·069mm)
Connecting rods

Big-end bearings
Material   Steel-backed copper-lead or
                                            aluminium-tin; thin wall
Bearing length   0·875in. (22·22mm)

Pistons

Type   Solid skirt
Clearance: Bottom of skirt
  (pressure face)   0·0005 to 0·0011in. (0·013 to
                                            0·028mm)
Oversizes: 1st   +0·010in. (0·254mm)
            2nd   +0·020in. (0·508mm)
Piston rings

Compression: Top   Plain, chrome-faced
              Second and third   Tapered
Width   0·0620 to 0·0625in. (1·574 to
                                            1·588mm)
Thickness (all rings)   0·106 to 0·112in. (2·692 to
                                            2·835mm)

Gudgeon pin

Type	Fully floating, with circlip location
Fit in piston	0·0001in. (0·0025mm) tight to 0·00035in. (0·0089mm) slack
Fit in small end	0·0002in. (0·005mm) slack, to size
Diameter	0·6244in. (15·86mm) to 0·6257in. (15·867mm)

Valves and valve gear

Valves

Throat diameter:	Inlet	1·172in. (29·77mm)
	Exhaust	0·908in. (23·06mm)
Head diameter:	Inlet	1·219in. (30·86mm)
	Exhaust	1·00in. (25·4mm)
Valve lift		0·312in. (7·92mm)
Inlet valve:	Opens	5° b t d c
	Closes	45° a b d c
Exhaust valve:	Opens	51° b b d c
	Closes	21° a t d c

Valve springs

Free length:	Inner	1·672in. (42·47mm)
	Outer	1·75in. (44·45mm)
Pressure: Inner:	Valve closed	18lb (8·17kg)
	Valve open	30lb (13·6kg)
Outer:	Valve closed	55½lb (25·13kg)
	Valve open	88lb (39·9kg)

Fuel system
Carburetter

Needle	Standard GY
Spring	Blue

Ignition system

Coil	Lucas HA12
Resistance at 20°C (68°F) primary winding	3·1 to 3·5 ohms (cold)
Distributor	Lucas 25D4
Static ignition timing	
High compression	5° b t d c (98 octane fuel)
Low compression	5° b t d c (91 to 96 octane fuel)
Stroboscopic ignition timing:	7° b t d c at 600 rev/min
Maximum advance	30° to 34° at 6,600 rev/min
Decelerating check	30° to 34° at 6,600 rev/min
	20° to 24° at 4,000 rev/min
	12° to 16° at 1,800 rev/min
	1° to 5° at 800 rev/min

MINI-COOPER S

To be used in conjunction with the preceding specifications for the Mini Cooper.

ENGINE

Number of cylinders	4
Bore (all models)	2·780in. (70·6mm)

Stroke: 970cc	2·4375in. (61·91mm)
1071cc	2·687in. (68·26mm)
1275cc	3·2in. (81·33mm)
Cubic capacity: 970cc	59·1in³ (970cc)
1071cc	63·35in³ (1071cc)
1275cc	77·9in³ (1275cc)
Compression ratio: 970cc	10:1
1071cc	9·0:1
1275cc	9·75:1

Capacity of combustion chamber
(valves and spark plug fitted)   1·306in³ (21·4cc)

B m e p: 970cc	142lb/in² (9·98kg/cm²) at 4,500 rev/min
1071cc	143lb/in² (10·05kg/cm²) at 4,500 rev/min
1275cc	153lb/in² (10·76kg/cm²) at 3,000 rev/min
Torque: 970cc	57lb ft (7·88kg m) at 5,000 rev/min
1071cc	62lb ft (8·58kg m) at 4,500 rev/min
1275cc	79lb ft (10·92kg m) at 3,000 rev/min
Compression pressure	190 to 200lb/in² (13·36 to 14·07kg/cm²) at 500 rev/min

Crankshaft

Main journal diameter	2·0005 to 2·0010in. (50·81 to 50·82mm)
Minimum regrind diameter	1·9805 to 1·9810in. (50·30 to 50·31mm)

Main bearings

Material	Steel-backed copper-lead: thin wall
Length	1·000in. (25·4mm)
Running clearance	0·001 to 0·0027in. (0·025 to 0·068mm)

Connecting rods

Little-end bore diameter	0·8110 to 0·8115in. (20·60 to 20·61mm)

Pistons

Type	Solid skirt
Clearance:	
Bottom of skirt (pressure face)	0·0019 to 0·0025in. (0·048 to 0·063mm)
Top of skirt	0·0025 to 0·00283in. (0·063 to 0·072mm)

Piston rings

Compression:	
Top ring	Plain
Second and third ring	Tapered
Width	0·0459 to 0·0469in. (1·16 to 1·19mm)
Thickness	0·116 to 0·122in. (2·94 to 3·09mm)
Fitted gap	0·008 to 0·013in. (0·20 to 0·33mm)
Clearance in groove	0·0015 to 0·0035in. (0·04 to 0·09mm)
Oil control type	Slotted scraper
Width	0·1553 to 0·1563in. (3·94 to 3·96mm)
Thickness	0·116 to 0·122in. (2·94 to 3·09mm)
Fitted gap	0·008 to 0·013in. (0·20 to 0·33mm)
Clearance in groove	0·0015 to 0·0035in. (0·04 to 0·09mm)

Gudgeon pin

Type   Pressed in connecting rod
Fit in piston   Hand push-fit
Diameter (outer)   0·8123 to 0·8125in. (20·63 to 20·64mm)
Fit in connecting rod   0·0008 to 0·0015in. interference
                              (0·020 to 0·038mm)

Valves and valve gear

Valves

Head diameter: Inlet   1·401 to 1·406in. (35·58 to
                              35·71mm)

                Exhaust   1·214 to 1·219in. (30·83 to
                              30·96mm)
Valve lift   0·312in. nominal (7·92mm)
Valve rocker
clearance: Standard   0·012in. (0·30mm) cold
              Competition   0·015in. (0·38mm) cold
              Timing   0·021in. (0·53mm)
Valve timing:
  Early cars
Inlet valve: Opens   5° b t d c ⎫ With 0·021in. (0·53mm)
             Closes   45° a b d c ⎪ valve rocker clearance
Exhaust valve: Opens   51° b b d c ⎬ (for checking purposes
               Closes   21° a t d c ⎭ only)
  Post 1966 cars
Inlet valve: Opens   10° b t d c ⎫ With   0·021in.   (0·53mm)
             Closes   50° a b d c ⎪ valve rocker clearances (for
Exhaust valve: Opens   51° b b.d c ⎬ checking purposes only)
               Closes   21° a t d c ⎭

Valve springs

Free length: Inner   1·705in. (43·31mm)
              Outer   1·740in. (44·19mm)
Number of working coils: Inner 6¼
                         Outer 4¼
Pressure: Inner: Valve closed 26·6lb (12·065kg)
                  Valve open   46lb (20·865kg)
          Outer: Valve closed 49·6lb (22·498kg)
                  Valve open   94lb (42·638kg)

Camshaft

Journal diameter: Rear   1·3727 to 1·3735in. (34·87 to 34·88mm)
Inside diameter (reamed in
position): Rear   1·3745 to 1·3750in. (34·91 to 34·92mm)
Running clearance: Rear   0·001 to 0·0022in. (0·025 to 0·057mm)
Bearing length: Rear   0·765in ± 0·010in. (19·45 ± 0·25mm)

Engine lubrication system

Oil pressure (normal running) 75lb/in² (5·27kg/cm²)

Cooling system

Thermostat setting   82°C (180°F)

Ignition system

Spark plugs		Champion UN12Y or N9Y
Coil		HA12
Distributor		23D4
Timing (static):	970cc engine	12° b t d c
	1071cc engine	3° b t d c
	1275cc engine	2° b t d c
Timing:		
(stroboscopic):	970cc engine	14° b t d c at 600 rev/min
	1071cc engine	5° b t d c at 600 rev/min
	1275cc engine	4° b t d c at 600 rev/min
Centrifugal advance:	970cc	24° at 1,500 rev/min, 32° at 4,000 rev/min
	1071cc	15° at 1,500 rev/min, 23° at 4,000 rev/min
Maximum advance 1275cc		27° to 31° at 7,000 rev/min
Decelerating check 1275cc		22° at 4,000 rev/min
		11° to 15° at 2,000 rev/min
		14° at 1,500 rev/min
		0° to 2° at 600 rev/min

Fuel system

Carburetter needle	AN (970cc engine)
	H6 (1071cc engine)
	M (1275cc engine)

Clutch

Type		Single dry plate
Diameter		7·125in. (180·9mm)
Facing material:	Standard	Wound yarn, riveted
	Optional	Wound yarn, cemented and riveted
Pressure springs (coil):	Inner	6
	Outer	6
Colour (coil):	Inner	Green spot
	Outer	White spot
	(diaphragm)	Green spot

Gearbox

		Standard ratio	Optional close ratio
Normal helical gears			
Ratios:	Top	1·0:1	1·0:1
	Third	1·357:1	1·242:1
	Second	1·916:1	1·78:1
	First	3·200:1	2·57:1
	Reverse	3·200:1	2·57:1

		Standard ratio	Close ratio
Spur gears for racing use			
Ratios:	Top	1·0:1	1·0:1
	Third	1·307:1	1·255:1
	Second	1·875:1	1·722:1
	First	3·077:1	2·573:1
	Reverse	3·077:1	2·573:1

These gears can only be used in sets with the latest type of reverse and first-speed gear. They are not suitable for use with 22A377 reverse gear and 22G96 first-speed gear. They will fit the 850 gearbox after engine No. 815140.

Overall ratios: 3·765:1 standard   3·444:1 optional
                                   final drive   final drive
Standard: Top   3·765:1   3·444:1
            Third   5·109:1   4·674:1
            Second   7·213:1   6·599:1
            First   12·047:1   11·022:1
            Reverse   12·047:1   11·022:1

                                   3·765:1 standard   3·444:1 optional
                                   final drive   final drive
Optional: Top   3·765:1   3·444:1
            Third   4·68:1   4·28:1
            Second   6·7:1   6·13:1
            First   9·7:1   8·85:1
            Reverse   9·7:1   8·85:1

Final drive

Ratio   3·765:1; standard; 3·444:1 optional
Ratios also available using
  parts as follows:

Ratio	3·938:1	4·133:1	4·267:1	4·35:1
Final drive wheel	C-22G 340	22G 101	C-22G 370	C-22G 443
Final drive pinion	C-22G 69	22G 99	22G 99	22G 99

Road speed in top at 1,000 rev/min:
Ratio
   3·444:1   16·03
   3·765:1   14·7
   3·939:1   14·06
   4·133:1   13·4
   4·267:1   12·96
   4·35:1   12·42

Brakes

Type   Lockheed hydraulic with vacuum servo
Front: Type   Disc
       Disc diameter   7½in. (190·5mm)
       Pad material   DA6
       Minimum pad thickness   1/16in. (1·6mm)

Front hubs

Bearings   Timken taper roller

Wheels

Type: Ventilated disc   3·50B × 10 or 4·5J × 10

Tyres

Size: Standard   145-10SP, tubed, or 5·20-10C41 tubed
       Optional   500L-10, tubed

Tyre pressures (145-10SP and
  5·20-10C41 only):
    Front   28lb/in² (1·969kg/cm²)
    Rear   26lb/in² (1·828kg/cm²)

1275 GT

ENGINE

Type	12H
Number of cylinders	4
Bore	2·78in. (70·61mm)
Stroke	3·2in. (81·28mm)
Capacity	77·8in³ (1274·86cm³)
Firing order	1, 3, 4, 2
Valve operation	Overhead by push-rod
Compression ratio:	
High compression	8·8:1
Low compression	8·3:1

Crankshaft

Main journal diameter	2·0005 to 2·0010in. (50·81 to 50·82mm)
Crankpin journal diameter	1·7504 to 1·7509in. (44·45 to 44·47mm)
Crankshaft end thrust	Taken in thrust washers at centre main bearing
Crankshaft end-float	0·002 to 0·003in. (0·05 to 0·07mm)

Main bearings

Number and type	Three thin-wall; split shells copper-lead-indium
Material	VP3, lead-indium at NFM/3B
Length	0·975 to 0·985in. (24·76 to 25·02mm)
Diametrical clearance	0·001 to 0·0027in. (0·025 to 0·07mm)
Undersizes	0·020in. (0·51mm) and 0·040in. (1·02mm)

Connecting rods

Type	Horizontally split big end, plain small end
Length between centres	5·748 to 5·752in. (145·1 to 146mm)

Big-end bearings

Type and material	Thin wall; steel-backed, copper-lead-indium plated
Length	0·840 to 0·850in. (21·33 to 21·59mm)
Diametrical clearance	0·001 to 0·0025in. (0·02 to 0·06mm)
End float of crankpin	0·006 to 0·010in. (0·15 to 2·5mm)

Pistons

Type	Aluminium, solid skirt, dished crown
Clearance in cylinder:	
Top of skirt	0·0029 to 0·0037in. (0·07 to 0·09mm)
Bottom of skirt	0·0015 to 0·0021in. (0·04 to 0·05mm)

Number of rings	4 (3 compression, 1 oil control)
Width of ring grooves:	
Top, second, third	0·0484 to 0·0494in. (1·23 to 1·26mm)
Oil control	0·1578 to 0·1588in. (4·01 to 4·03mm)
Gudgeon pin bore	0·8125 to 0·8129in. (20·64 to 20·65mm)

Piston rings

Compression: Type:		
	Top	Internally chamfered chrome
	Second and third	Tapered cast iron
Width:	Top	
	Second and third	0·0615 to 0·0625in. (1·57 to 1·60mm)
Fitted gap:	Top	0·011 to 0·016in. (0·28 to 0·41mm)
	Second and third	0·008 to 0·013in. (0·20 to 0·33mm)
Ring-to-groove		
clearance:		
	Top	
	Second to third	0·0015 to 0·0035in. (0·04 to 0·09mm)
Oil control		
	Type	Duaflex 61
	Fitted gap: Rails	
	Side spring	0·012 to 0·028in. (0·30 to 0·70mm)

Gudgeon pin

Type	Pressed in connecting rod
Fit in piston	Hand push fit
Diameter (outer)	0·8123 to 0·8125in. (20·63 to 20·64mm)
Fit to connecting rod	0·0008 to 0·0015in. (0·02 to 0·04mm) interference

Camshaft

Journal diameters:	Front	1·6670 to 1·6675in. (42·34 to 42·35mm)
	Centre	1·62425 to 1·62475in. (41·25 to 41·37mm)
	Rear	1·3745 to 1·3750in. (34·91 to 34·92mm)
Bearing liner inside		
diameter:		
Unreamed after fitting:		
	Front	1·652in. (41·98mm)
	Centre	1·61in. (40·89mm)
	Rear	1·36in. (34·52mm)
Reamed after fitting:		
	Front	1·6670 to 1·6675in. (42·34 to 42·35mm)
	Centre	1·62425 to 1·62475in (41·25 to 41·37mm)
	Rear	1·3745 to 1·3750in. (34·91 to 34·92mm)
Bearings: Type		White-metal-lined, steel-backed
Diametrical clearance		0·001 to 0·002in. (0·02 to 0·05mm)
End-thrust		Taken on locating plate

End float	0·003 to 0·007in. (0·07 to 0·18mm)
Cam lift	0·318in. (8·07mm)
Drive	Duplex chain and gear from crankshaft
Timing chain	⅜in. (9·52mm) pitch × 52 pitches

Tappets

Type	Bucket
Outside diameter	0·81125 to 0·81175in. (20·60 to 20·62mm)
Length	1·495 to 1·505in. (37·97 to 38·23mm)

Rocker gear

Rocker shaft: Diameter	0·5615 to 0·5625in. (14·26 to 14·29mm)
Rocker arm: Bore	0·686 to 0·687in. (17·45mm)
Bush inside diameter	0·5630 to 0·5635in. (14·3 to 14·31mm)

Valves

Seat angle inlet and exhaust	45°
Head diameter:	
Inlet	1·307 to 1·312in. (33·20 to 33·21mm)
Exhaust	1·1515 to 1·1565in. (29·24 to 29·37mm)
Stem diameter: Inlet	0·2793 to 0·2798in. (7·09 to 7·11mm)
Exhaust	0·2788 to 0·2793in. (7·08 to 7·09mm)
Stem-to-guide clearance:	
Inlet and exhaust	0·0015 to 0·0025in. (0·04 to 0·08mm)
Valve lift: Inlet and exhaust	0·318in. (8·07mm)

Valve guides

Length: Inlet	1·6875in. (42·87mm)
Exhaust	1·8437in. (46·83mm)
Fitted height above seat:	
Exhaust ⎫	
Inlet ⎬	0·540in. (13·72mm)

Valve springs

Free length	1·95in. (49·13mm)
Fitted length	1·383in. (35·13mm)
Length at top of lift	1·065in. (27·05mm)
Load at fitted length	79·5lb (36·03kg)
Load at top of lift	124lb (56·3kg)
No. of working coils	4½

Valve timing

Timing marks	Dimples on timing gears
Rocker clearance: Running	0·012in. (0·305mm) cold
Timing	0·021in. (0·533mm)
Inlet valve: Opens	5° b t d c
Closes	45° b b d c
Exhaust valve:	
Opens	51° b b d c
Closes	21° a t d c

Lubrication system

Oil pump

Type	Internal gear, splined drive from camshaft
Oil pressure relief valve	60lb/in² (4·2kg/cm²)
Relief valve spring: Free length	2·86in. (72·64mm)
Fitted length	2·156in. (54·77mm)
Load at fitted length	13 to 14lb (5·90 to 6·35kg)

Oil filter

Type	Full-flow; renewable element
Capacity	1 pint (1·2 US pints, 0·57 litre) approx.

System pressure

Running	60lb/in² (4·2kg/cm²)
Idling	15lb/in² (1·05kg/cm²)

Ignition system

Coil	Lucas LA 12
Resistance at 20°C (68°F) primary winding	3·2 to 3·4 ohms
Consumption: Ignition switched on (contact points closed)	3·6 amps
Distributor	Lucas 25 D4
Rotation of rotor arm	Anti-clockwise
Cam closed period	60" ± 3"
Cam open period	30° ± 3°
Automatic advance	Centrifugal
Contact point gap setting	0·014 to 0·016in. (0·35 to 0·40mm)
Breaker spring tension	18 to 24oz (510 to 680·5gm)
Condenser capacity	0·18 to 0·24mF
Timing marks	Flywheel and pointer on clutch cover
Spark plugs	Champion N9Y
Size	14mm
Gap	0·024 to 0·026in. (0·62 to 0·66mm)

Ignition advance

Automatic advance commences	300 rev/min
Maximum advance	18 to 22° at 4,000 rev/min
Deceleration check (vacuum pipe disconnected)	11 to 15° at 2,800 rev/min
	6 to 10° at 2,000 rev/min
	4 to 8° at 1,600 rev/min

Static timing	8° b t d c
Stroboscopic timing	10° b t d c at 6,000 rev/min

Cooling system

Thermostat settings

Standard	82°C (180°F)
Cold countries	88°C (190°F)
Hot countries	74°C (165°F)

Fuel system

Fuel pump	SU Mechanical
Carburetter	SU type HS4
Choke diameter	1½in. (38·1mm)
Jet size	0·090in. (2·29mm)
Needles	(*see chapter 2*)

Gearbox

Number of forward speeds	4
Synchromesh	All four forward speeds
Ratios:	
Top	1·0:1
Third	1·43:1
Second	2·22:1
First	3·52:1
Reverse	3·54:1

ELECTRICAL

Starter motor	Lucas M35J
Generator	Lucas C40
Windscreen wiper	Lucas 14W

BRAKES As Cooper S see page 242.

APPENDIX III

TORQUE WRENCH SETTINGS

850 and 998cc Minis, Elfs and Hornets

Engine

Cylinder head stud nuts	40lb ft (5·5kg m)
Connecting rod big-end bolts	35lb ft (4·8kg m)
Main bearing setscrews	60lb ft (8·3kg m)
Flywheel centre-bolt	110 to 115lb ft (15·2 to 15·9kg m)
Gudgeon pin clamp screws	25lb ft (3·4kg m)
Rocker shaft bracket nuts	25lb ft (3·4kg m)
Transmission case to crankcase	6lb ft (0·8kg m)
Cylinder side cover: Early type	2lb ft (0·28kg m)
Deep pressed type	5lb ft (0·7kg m)
Timing cover—$\frac{1}{4}$in. UNF bolts	6lb ft (0·8kg m)
Timing cover—$\frac{5}{16}$in. UNF bolts	14lb ft (1·9kg m)
Water pump	17lb ft (2·3kg m)
Water outlet elbow	8lb ft (1·1kg m)
Oil filter	16lb ft (2·2kg m)
Oil pump	9lb ft (1·2kg m)
Manifold to cylinder head	15lb ft (2·1kg m)
Rocker cover	4lb ft (0·56kg m)
Crankshaft pulley nut	70lb ft (9·6kg m)

Gearbox

Transmission case stud.—$\frac{3}{8}$in. diam UNC	8lb ft (1·1kg m)
Transmission case studs—$\frac{15}{16}$in. diam. UNC	6lb ft (0·8kg m)
Transmission case stud nuts—$\frac{3}{8}$in. UNF	25lb ft (3·45kg m)
Transmission case stud nuts—$\frac{5}{16}$UNF	18lb ft (2·5kg m)
Bottom cover setscrews—$\frac{1}{4}$in. diam. UNF (change speed tower)	6lb ft (0·8kg m)
First motion shaft nut	150lb ft (20·7kg m)
Third motion shaft nut	150lb ft (20·7kg m)
Flywheel housing bolts and stud nuts	18lb ft (2·5 kg m)
Setscrew, driving strap to flywheel	16lb ft (2·2kg m)
Setscrew, clutch spring housing to pressure plate	16lb ft (2·2kg m)

Final drive

Driven gear to differential cage	60lb ft (8·3kg m)
Nut, driving flange to differential	60lb ft (8·3kg m) (and align to next split pin hole)
End cover bolts (differential housing)	18lb ft (2·5kg m)

Suspension and steering

Steering lever to hub bolts	35lb ft (4·8kg m)
Steering lever ball-joint nut	20 to 24lb ft (2·77 to 3·32kg m)
Steering knuckle ball-pin bottom nut	35 to 40lb ft (4·8 to 5·5kg m)
Steering knuckle ball-pin top nut	35 to 40lb ft (4·8 to 5·5kg m)
Steering knuckle ball-pin housing	70lb ft (9·6kg m)
Front hub nut (drive shaft)	60lb ft (8·3kg m)
Rear suspension stub axle nut	60lb ft (8·3kg m) (align next to slot)
Front suspension upper arm pivot-pin nut	26 to 28lb ft (3·6 to 3·87kg m)
Steering wheel nut	41lb ft (5·76kg m)
Road wheel nuts	38 to 43lb ft (5·25 to 5·94kg m)

Mini, Automatic Transmission

Converter centre bolt	110 to 115lb ft (15·2 to 15·9kg m)
Converter (six central bolts)	22 to 24lb ft (3·04 to 3·32kg m)
Converter drain plugs	22 to 24lb ft (3·04 to 3·32kg m)
Converter housing bolts	18lb ft (2·5kg m)
Differential driving flange securing bolts	40 to 45lb ft (5·53 to 6·62kg m)
Gear train bearing caps	12lb ft (1·66kg m)
Gear train carrier strap	12lb ft (1·66kg m)
Input shaft nut	70lb ft (9·6kg m)
Servo unit securing bolts	17lb ft (2·35kg m)
Top and reverse clutch hub nut	150lb ft (20·7kg m)
Transmission to engine securing nut	12lb ft (1·66kg m)
Valve block securing bolts	17lb ft (2·35kg m)
Valve block bolts (securing three sections)	7lb ft (0·97kg m)
$\frac{5}{16}$in. UNF bolts	18 to 20lb ft (2·5 to 2·77kg m)
$\frac{3}{8}$in. UNF bolts	30lb ft (4·15kg m)

Mini Cooper

As for 850 Mini except for:

Caliper retaining bolts	35 to 40lb ft (4·84 to 5·53kg m)
Steering lever ball joint	25 to 30lb ft (3·46 to 4·15kg m)

Mini Cooper S

As for Mini Cooper except for:

Ten cylinder-head nuts	42lb ft (5·81kg m)
One cylinder-head bolt	25lb ft (3·46kg m)
Connecting-rod big-end bolts	46lb ft (6·22kg m)
Main bearing setscrews (early type)	67lb ft (9·26kg m)
Main bearing nuts (later type)	57lb ft (7·88kg m)
Drive shaft nut	150lb ft (20·74kg m)

1275 GT

As for 850 Mini except for:

Caliper retaining bolts	35 to 40lb ft (4·84 to 5·53kg m)
Cylinder head nuts	50lb ft (6·91kg m)
Connecting-rod big-end bolts	31 to 35lb ft (4·3 to 4·8kg m)
Drive shaft nut	150lb ft (20.7kg m)

APPENDIX IV

GENERAL DIMENSIONS

Wheelbase	Mini Saloon, Elf/Hornet, Moke	6ft 8$\frac{3}{32}$in.	(2·036m)
	Van, Pick-up, Traveller, Countryman	7ft 0$\frac{5}{32}$in.	(2·138m)
Overall length	Mini Saloon	10ft 0$\frac{1}{4}$in.	(3·05m)
	Elf/Hornet	10ft 8$\frac{3}{4}$in.	(3·27m)
	Van, Traveller, Countryman	10ft 9$\frac{7}{8}$in.	(3·259m)
	Pick-up	10ft 10$\frac{1}{2}$in.	(3·315m)
	Moke	10ft 0in.	(3·04m)
	Clubman Saloon	10ft 4$\frac{23}{32}$in.	(3·16m)
	Clubman Estate	11ft 2$\frac{1}{32}$in.	(3·37m)
Overall width		4ft 7$\frac{1}{2}$in.	(1·41m)
	Moke	4ft 3$\frac{1}{2}$in.	(1·36m)
Overall height	Mini Saloon, Elf/Hornet	4ft 5in.	(1·35m)
	Van	4ft 6$\frac{1}{2}$in.	(1·38m)
	Traveller, Countryman, Pick-up	4ft 5$\frac{1}{2}$in.	(1·36m)
	Moke	4ft 8in.	(1·42m)
Ground clearance		6$\frac{5}{32}$in.	(15·63cm)
	Moke	6$\frac{1}{2}$in.	(16·2cm)
Turning circle	Mini Saloon, Elf/Hornet	31ft 7in.	(9·63m)
	Van, Pick-up, Traveller, Countryman	32ft 9in.	(9·893m)
	Moke	31ft 0in.	(9·4m)
	Clubman, Mini Saloon Mk II	28ft 6in.	(8·55m)
Track	Front	47$\frac{7}{16}$in.	(1·205m)
	Rear	45$\frac{7}{8}$in.	(1·164m)
	Mini Cooper S		
	Front: 3$\frac{1}{2}$in. rim	47$\frac{17}{32}$in.	(1·207m)
	4$\frac{1}{2}$in. rim	48$\frac{17}{32}$in.	(1·233m)
	Rear: 3$\frac{1}{2}$in. rim	46$\frac{5}{16}$in.	(1·176m)
	4$\frac{1}{2}$in. rim	47$\frac{5}{16}$in.	(1·202m)
Kerbside weight	Saloon (rubber suspension)	1,294lb	(587kg)
	(hydrolastic suspension)	1,398lb	(634·5kg)
	Mini Cooper (rubber suspension)	1,400lb	(635kg)
	(hydrolastic suspension)	1,433lb	(650kg)
	Mini Cooper S (rubber suspension)	1,411lb	(640kg)
	(hydrolastic suspension)	1,540lb	(698kg)
	Elf/Hornet	1,466lb	(668kg)
	Van	1,334lb	(605kg)
	Traveller/Countryman	1,456lb	(660kg)
	Pick-up	1,328lb	(603kg)
	Moke	1,240lb	(562kg)

Capacities

Transmission casing (incl. filter)	8½ pints	(10·2 US pints) (4·83 litres)
Cooling system	5¼ pints	(6·3 US pints) (3 litres)
With heater	6¼ pints	(7·5 US pints) (3·55 litres)

Fuel tank:

Mini Saloon, Elf/Hornet	5½ galls	(6·6 US gals) (25 litres)
Mini Cooper S (optional)	11 gals	(13·2 US gals) (50 litres)
Van, Pick-up	6 gals	(7·2 US gals) (27·3 litres)
Traveller/Countryman (early models)	6½ gals	(7·8 US gals) (29·6 litres)
(later models)	6 gals	(7·2 US gals) (27·3 litres)

APPENDIX V

ROUTINE MAINTENANCE

Weekly

Check oil level in engine/transmission. Top up if necessary.
Check water level in radiator. Top up if necessary.
Test tyre pressures, and regulate if necessary.
Check battery level, and top up if necessary.

3,000 miles (5,000km)
or 3 months optional inspection check

Engine	Top up carburetter piston damper.
	Check water level in radiator, and top up if necessary.
	Top up windscreen washer bottle.
Clutch	Check level of fluid in the supply tank, and top up if necessary.
Steering	Check the steering-column clamp bolt and tighten to the correct torque figure
Brakes	Check brakes and adjust if necessary.
	Make visual inspection of brake pipes and hoses.
	Check level of fluid in the supply tank and top up if necessary.
Electrical	Check battery and top up to correct level.
	Check headlight beam alignment.
Lubrication	Check oil level in engine/transmission unit. Top up if necessary or—
	Change oil in engine/transmission unit if using monograde or single-viscosity conventional lubricants.
	Lubricate all grease nipples.
Automatic transmission	Change the oil in the engine/automatic transmission unit.
	Fit new oil filter element.
Wheels and tyres	Check tyre pressures.

6,000 miles (10,000km) or 6 months service

Engine	Top up carburetter piston damper.
	Check fan belt tension.
	Check valve rocker clearances, and adjust if necessary.
	Check water level in radiator and top up if necessary.
	Top up windscreen washer bottle.

252

Ignition	Check contact-breaker points and adjust if necessary. Check functioning of the automatic advance mechanism. Lubricate distributor as necessary. Clean and adjust spark plugs.
Clutch	Check level of fluid in the supply tank and top up if necessary. Check clearance at return stop and adjust if necessary.
Steering	Check front wheel alignment and adjust if necessary. Check the steering-column clamp bolt and tighten to the correct torque figure.
Brakes	Check brakes and adjust if necessary. Make visual inspection of brake pipes and hoses. Check level of fluid in the supply tank and top up if necessary.
General	Check tightness of all nuts and bolts on universal joints and suspension etc.
Electrical	Check battery cell specific gravity readings and top up to correct level Check all lamps for correct functioning. Check headlight beam alignment.
Lubrication	Change oil in engine/transmission unit (Synchromesh and Automatic) and wipe magnetic drain plug. Lubricate generator bearing. Fit new oil filter element (Synchromesh and Automatic). Lubricate all grease nipples. Lubricate door locks and hinges.
Wheels and tyres	Check tyre pressures.

9,000 miles (15,000km) or 9 months service

Carry out the 3,000 miles (5,000km) or 3 months optional inspection.

12,000 miles (20,000km) or 12 months service

Engine	Top up carburetter piston damper. Check valve rocker clearances and adjust if necessary. Fit new air cleaner element. Check and adjust fan belt tension. Check radiator water level and top up if necessary. Top up windscreen washer bottle. Crankcase closed-breather system; change engine oil filler cap and clean crankcase breather valve.

Ignition   Check contact-breaker points, clean and adjust if
                    necessary.
                    Check functioning of the automatic advance system.
                    Lubricate distributor as necessary.
                    Fit new spark plugs.

Clutch   Check level of fluid in the supply tank and top up if
                    necessary.
                    Check clearance at return stop and adjust if necessary.

Steering   Check steering and suspension moving parts for wear.
                    Check front wheel alignment and adjust if necessary.
                    Check the steering column clamp bolt and tighten to
                    the correct torque figure.

Brakes   Check brakes and adjust if necessary.
                    Make visual inspection of brake pipes and hoses.
                    Check level of fluid in the supply tank and top up if
                    necessary.
                    Inspect and blow out brake linings and drums.

General   Check tightness of all nuts and bolts on universal joints
                    and suspension etc.

Electrical   Check battery cell specific gravity readings and top up to
                    correct level.
                    Check all lamps for correct functioning.
                    Check headlight beam alignment.

Lubrication   Change oil in engine/transmission unit (Synchromesh
                    and Automatic) and wipe magnetic drain plug.
                    Lubricate generator bearing.
                    Fit new oil filter element (Synchromesh and Automatic).
                    Lubricate water pump.
                    Lubricate door locks and hinges.
                    Lubricate all grease nipples.

Wheels and tyres Check tyre pressures.

APPENDIX VI

WIRING DIAGRAMS

The following wiring diagrams refer specifically to 1964 and subsequent vehicles. The wiring layout of Minis manufactured before then differs mainly in that they have an oil-pressure warning light instead of a pressure-gauge, no temperature gauge, and a floor-mounted starter switch instead of the ignition-key-operated solenoid now used. There is no roof light in these earlier models but instead there are lights on the parcel shelf and in each rear pocket. The cable colour code is basically the same on all models. (See next page).

Key to the Wiring diagrams illustrated on the following pages

1. Generator.
2. Control box.
3. 12-volt battery.
4. Starter-solenoid.
5. Starter motor.
6. Lighting switch.
7. Headlamp dipswitch.
8. R.H. headlamp.
9. L.H. headlamp.
10. Main-beam warning lamp.
11. R.H. sidelamp (in headlamp or flasher lamp).
12. L.H. sidelamp (in headlamp or flasher lamp).
13. Panel lamps switch.
14. Panel lamps.
15. Number-plate lamp (two for A/M/ADO15/W).
16. R.H. stop and tail lamp.
17. L.H. stop and tail lamp.
18. Stop lamp switch.
19. Fuse unit: 1-2, 35-amp.; 3-4, 35-amp.
20. Interior light.
21. R.H. door switch.
22. L.H. door switch.
23. Horn.
24. Horn-push.
25. Flasher unit.
26. Direction indicator switch.
27. Direction indicator warning lamp.
28. R.H. front flasher lamp.
29. L.H. front flasher lamp.
30. R.H. rear flasher lamp.
31. L.H. rear flasher lamp.
32. Heater switch.⎞ When
33. Heater motor.⎠ fitted.

34. Fuel gauge.
35. Fuel gauge tank unit.
36. Windscreen wiper switch.
37. Windscreen wiper motor.
38. Ignition/starter switch.
39. Ignition coil
40. Distributor.
41. Fuel pump.
42. Oil pressure switch.
43. Oil pressure warning lamp.
44. Ignition warning lamp.
45. Speedometer.
46. Temperature gauge.
47. Temperature gauge transmitter.
64. Bi-metal instrument voltage stabilizer.
67. Line fuse, 35 amp.
75. Automatic gearbox safety switch.
83. Induction heater and thermostat (when fitted).
84. Suction chamber heater (when fitted).
94. Oil filter switch.
95. Tachometer.
105. Oil filter warning lamp.
110. R.H. repeater flasher ⎞ when fitted
111. L.H. repeater flasher ⎠
115. Rear window-heater switch.
116. Rear window-heater element.
131. Starter inhibitor switch (automatic transmission models).
139. Connect to No. 6 for USA (alternative connection)
150. Rear window-heater warning light.
158. Printed circuit instrument panel (1275 GT)

Cable Colour Code

B	Black	P	Purple
U	Blue	G	Green
N	Brown	W	White
R	Red	Y	Yellow
	LG	Light green	

When a cable has two colour code letters, the first denotes the main colour and the second denotes the tracer colour.
This colour code applies to all of the following diagrams.

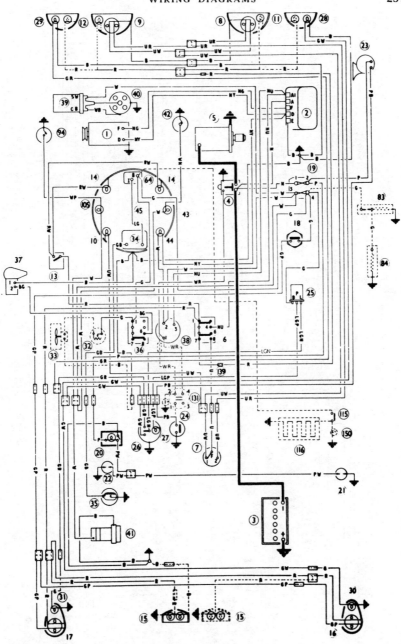

Fig. VI:1. Saloon, Van and Pick-up.

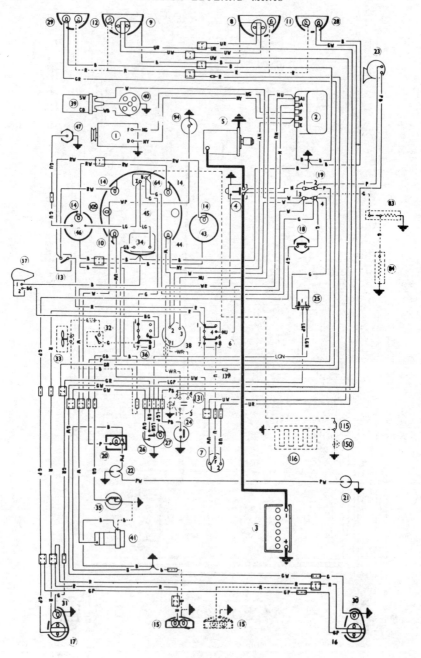

Fig. VI:2. Traveller, Countryman, Cooper and Cooper S.

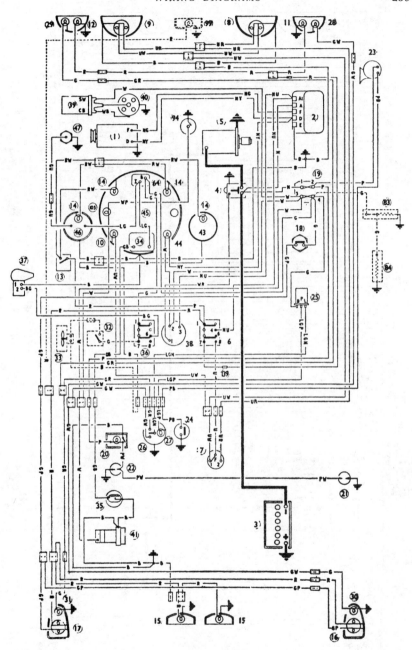

Fig. VI:3. Wolseley and Riley.

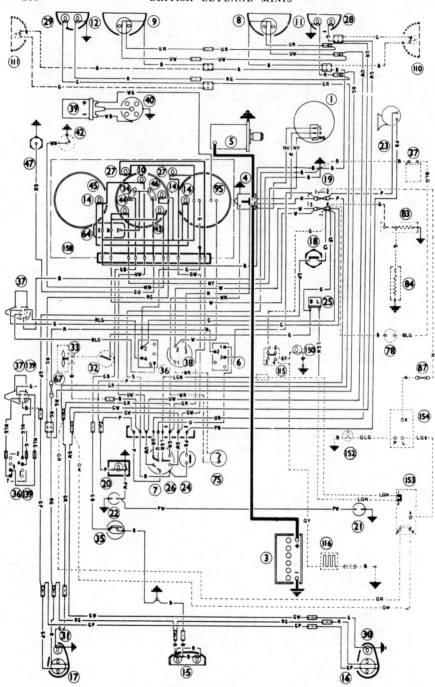

Fig. VI:4. Clubman and 1275 GT

APPENDIX VII

SOME SUPPLIERS OF SPECIALIST EQUIPMENT

Allard Motor Co. Ltd., 51 Upper Richmond Road, Putney. London.	Superchargers
British Leyland Special Tuning Department, Abingdon-on-Thames.	Tuning, Conversions and Competition parts
Chris Montague Carburetter Co., 364, Cricklewood Lane, London, N.W.2. 2QJ	Weber carburetters and service
Conversion and Tuning Centre Ltd., 45, Tulse Hill, London. S.W.2.	Carburetters, Special Manifolds and Tuning parts
Downton Engineering Works Ltd., Downton, Nr. Salisbury, Wilts.	Complete conversions Competition parts
Jack Knight Developments Ltd, Southampton Road, Salisbury, Wilts.	Special gears and transmission parts
Janspeed Engineering, Southampton Road, Salisbury, Wilts.	Engine conversions, special manifolding
Leonard Reece & Co., Beeches Avenue, Carshalton, Surrey.	Reece-Fish carburetters
Richard Longman & Co., 11, Purewell, Christchurch, Hants.	Road and Racing conversions, tuning parts

KEY TO RECOMMENDED LUBRICANTS

Component	Engine Transmission Unit, Oilcan, and Carburetter			Grease Points	Upper Cylinder Lubrication
Climatic conditions	All temperatures above − 10° C. (10° F.)	Temperatures − 15° to − 5° C. (0° to 20° F.)	All temperatures below − 15° C. (0° F.)	All conditions	All conditions
Viscosity requirement	S.A.E. 10W/50 S.A.E. 10W/40 S.A.E. 20/50 or S.A.E. 20W/40	S.A.E. 10W/50 S.A.E. 10W/40 or S.A.E. 10W/30	S.A.E. 5W/30 or S.A.E. 5W/20		
Minimum performance level	MIL-L-2104B	MIL-L-2104B	MIL-L-2104B		
FILTRATE	Filtrate Super 20W/50	Filtrate Super 10W/30	Filtrate 5W/20	Filtrate Super Lithium Grease	Filtrate Petroyle
MOBIL	Mobiloil Special 20W/50 or Super 10W/50	Mobiloil Super 10W/50	Mobiloil 5W/20	Mobilgrease MP	Mobil Upperlube
SHELL	Shell Super Motor Oil 20W/50	Shell Super Motor Oil 10W/30	Shell Super Motor Oil 5W/30 or Shell Winter Special Motor Oil	Shell Retinax A	Shell Upper Cylinder Lubricant
STERNOL	Sternol Super W.W. Motor Oil	Sternol W.W. Multigrade 10W/40	Sternol W.W. Multigrade 5W/20	Sternol Ambroline Grease LHT 2	Sternol Magikoyl
BP	BP Super Visco-Static 20W/50	BP Super Visco-Static 10W/30 or 10W/40	BP Super Visco-Static 10W/30 or 10W/40	BP Energrease L. 2	BP Upper Cylinder Lubricant
CASTROL	Castrol GTX or Castrol XL 20W/50	Castrolite or Castrol Super	Castrol CRI 5W/20	Castrol L.M. Grease	Castrollo
DUCKHAMS	Duckhams Q20-50	Duckhams Q5500	Duckhams Q5-30	Duckhams LB 10 Grease	Duckhams Adcoid Liquid
ESSO	Esso Uniflo or Esso Extra Motor Oil 20W/50	Esso Uniflo or Esso Extra Motor Oil 10W/30	Esso Extra Motor Oil 5W/20	Esso Multipurpose Grease H	Esso Upper Cylinder Lubricant

In no circumstances must any additive be introduced into the lubricants recommended for the automatic transmission.

Steering rack: Use s.a.e. 90 hypoid oil when temperatures are above — 18°C. (0°F.).
Use s.a.e. 80 hypoid oil when temperatures are below — 18°C. (0°F.).

INDEX